Wood engraving of Flamingos by William T. Rawlinson

THE BIRDS OF CYPRUS

An annotated check-list

by

PETER R. FLINT

and

PETER F. STEWART

B.O.U. Check-list No. 6 (Second Edition)

British Ornithologists' Union, 1992
c/o Zoological Museum, Tring, Herts HP23 6AP, UK

First edition 1983
Second edition 1992

ISBN 0 907446 14 0

Printed in Great Britain by Henry Ling Ltd., at the Dorset Press, Dorchester, Dorset

CONTENTS

EDITOR'S FOREWORD

First edition

Of the six publications by the British Ornithologists' Union in this series, this is the second comprehending birds of the western Palaearctic, the first having been that of Libya. Cyprus is a geographical entity, an island set in the path of migration across the eastern end of the Mediterranean, with a remarkably high proportion of its birds visiting it only on passage. It is a temporary haven for millions of migrants annually, particularly night flying small passerines, which often arrive tired to exhaustion, ready victims of almost unrestrained liming, trapping and shooting – a total of some 5,000,000 birds are estimated to be killed annually. In a country where these millions of birds are killed, and mostly bottled as 'delicacies' each year for commercial profit, it is important to have reliable data on which to base policies for conservation. It is hoped that this comprehensive and meticulous account of the Cyprus avifauna will serve as a reliable source for future assessment of the bird population and will encourage a more discerning and enlightened approach to the slaughter of birds which breed and winter elsewhere than in Cyprus and for which the authorities and Cypriots themselves should be conscientious in providing safe passage, rather than perpetuating anachronistic traditions.

For carrying out the double checking of the text and of the sequence and scientific names I am indebted to the authors, who will be glad to be informed at any time of errors and omissions.

J. F. Monk

Second edition

This is the second of the successful check-list series to be revised and published by the British Ornithologists' Union. The authors have once again been meticulous in their presentation and in up-dating the information, and many of their accounts, particularly those covering resident species, are impressive in their depth and coverage. They have added large scale maps of areas of ornithological interest and the details given confirm their first hand knowledge. Although there are specific hunting restrictions and protection laws, many of these are not being applied, but local conservation groups are actively applying pressure on authorities and this is welcome news. The inclusion of colour and black and white plates to illustrate both the wide variety of birds and habitats found on the island will add to the usefulness of the check-list. It will continue to be the authoritative source of information on the island's avifauna for current and future workers.

L. G. Grimes

PREFACE TO THE SECOND EDITION

The first edition of this check-list was originally conceived as an annotated and enlarged revision of the 1971 list (Stewart & Christensen 1971). However, it quickly became evident that, with so much new material to add, very little would remain of the original text, and we found it simpler to write a completely new text. In doing so we retained the style of the 1971 list in giving detailed breakdowns of passage and wintering dates. In this second edition the Introductory Chapters, Systematic List and Appendices have been revised and updated as necessary.

The list was undertaken with the co-operation of both the existing Cyprus Ornithological Societies (C.O.S. 1957 and C.O.S. 1970), though that of the later society was subsequently withdrawn. Although the list relies considerably on the published reports of the two societies it has been produced independently of both and decisions to include or omit records are the authors own and may not necessarily reflect the views of the societies.

In researching the earlier literature it has become apparent that many of the original records have been misquoted by subsequent authors, and in some cases the same errors have been repeated in several publications. Our search of the literature was made much easier by the detailed Annotated Bibliography in the 1957 C.O.S.'s *Bulletin* 15 (Bourne 1964).

In compiling the list we have obtained details of the collections of Cyprus skins held at: the Zoological Gardens, Limassol; the Department of Agriculture, Nicosia; Tel Aviv University; the Zoological Museum of Berlin; Naturhistoriska Riksmuseum, Stockholm; the Royal Scottish Museum, Edinburgh; the British Museum (Natural History), Tring; and the Museum of Comparative Zoology, Harvard. Our searches of the Tring collection located several important skins not previously mentioned in the literature. A collection of Cyprus skins is also held at the American Museum of Natural History, New York, but we were only able to obtain incomplete details of this collection.

In 1971 the Bannermans urged that much more attention be paid to the island's breeding birds. There have been some studies since then but our knowledge of numbers, distribution, habitat and breeding biology is still very sketchy, and, as can be seen from the systematic list, often relies heavily on the studies of Ashton-Johnson over 30 years ago. During our work on the list it has also become apparent that much more systematic and organised study is needed of migration through the island and around its coasts.

Some 8 million birds are killed in Cyprus each year by shooting, netting and liming. In addition, the few remaining natural wetlands and wilderness areas are increasingly threatened by development. We urge those in authority in Cyprus to prevent this destruction of the island's wildlife and habitats, and we encourage all our readers to support the emerging conservation organisations in the south and north of the island.

Peter R. Flint
Cliff Cottage,
Hoswick,
Sandwick,
Shetland ZE2 9HL
UK

Peter F. Stewart
10 Digby Road,
Evesham,
Worcs WR11 6BW
UK

LIST OF FIGURES

Cover: Cyprus Pied Wheatear ♀, April. (D. Frost)

Frontispiece: Wood engraving of Flamingos by William T. Rawlinson

LIST OF PLATES

BLACK AND WHITE PLATES

(13) Flooded Tamarisk scrub at Akrotiri reed beds, nesting habitat of Dead Sea Sparrow. (R. Frost)
(14) Flooded salt flats behind Ladies Mile beach near Limassol, important for migrant and wintering waders. (T. A. Box)
(15) Winter gull roosts on groynes and reef at Larnaca sea front. (R. Frost)
(16) Akhna reservoir, a new shallow reservoir in the southeast which has proved very attractive to birds. (P. M. Bullock)
(17) Broken rocky ground at Cape Pyla in the southeast, typical wintering habitat of Finsch's Wheatear. (R. Frost)
(18) Cape Kormakiti, looking east towards Kornos Peak at the western end of the Kyrenia range. (P. R. Flint)
(19) Pentadaktylos Mountain in the Kyrenia range, former nesting site of Griffon Vulture. (P. R. Flint)
(20) Dense scrub and woodland on the north coast, with the eastern Kyrenia range beyond. (P. R. Flint)
(21) Geunyeli reservoir, now the most important wetland in the north, and a haven to thousands of waterbirds every year. (P. R. Flint)
(22) Stone Pines at Salamis Forest, an area very attractive to migrants and which has been a breeding site of Long-eared Owl. (H. Sigg)
(23) Arable fields north of Boghaz, towards the end of another very dry year. (P. R. Flint)
(24) Wind stunted Juniper scrub at Cape Andreas, with the tip of the cape and the Klidhes Islands beyond. (P. R. Flint)

COLOUR PLATES

(25) Greater Flamingos at Akrotiri Salt Lake, with the reed beds beyond. (P. R. Flint)
(26) Griffon Vulture at Quarry beach, Episkopi. (T. A. Box)
(27) Baillon's Crake at Phasouri reed beds. (T. A. Box)
(28) Black-winged Stilt, a common spring migrant and a regular breeder when water levels are suitable. (T. A. Box)
(29) Spur-winged Plover, a fairly common migrant in spring. A pair bred at Phasouri reed beds in 1988. (T. A. Box)
(30) The first White-tailed Plover recorded from Cyprus, Akrotiri Salt Lake, March 1970. A hunter later shot this beautiful bird. (P. R. Flint)
(31) Audouin's Gulls at evening roost at Peristeria on the north coast, c. 48 km east of Kyrenia. (P. R. Flint)
(32) Wryneck at a garden pond during the spring migration. (D. Frost)
(33) Cyprus Pied Wheatear ♂, April. The most distinctive and interesting species of all the endemic birds. (D. Frost)
(34) Cyprus Pied Wheatear ♀, April. (D. Frost)
(35) Blue Rock Thrush, a breeding species along the upper ridge of the Kyrenia range. (M. E. J. Gore)
(36) Great Reed Warbler at Phasouri reed beds, July 1982. (T. A. Box)
(37) Cyprus Warbler ♂, a common and widespread endemic species. (M. E. J. Gore)
(38) Cyprus Warbler breeding pair, ♂ left and ♀ right. (D. Frost)
(39) Coal Tit of the distinctive endemic race. (G. van Duin)
(40) Cretzschmar's Bunting bathing in a garden pond during the spring migration. (D. Frost)

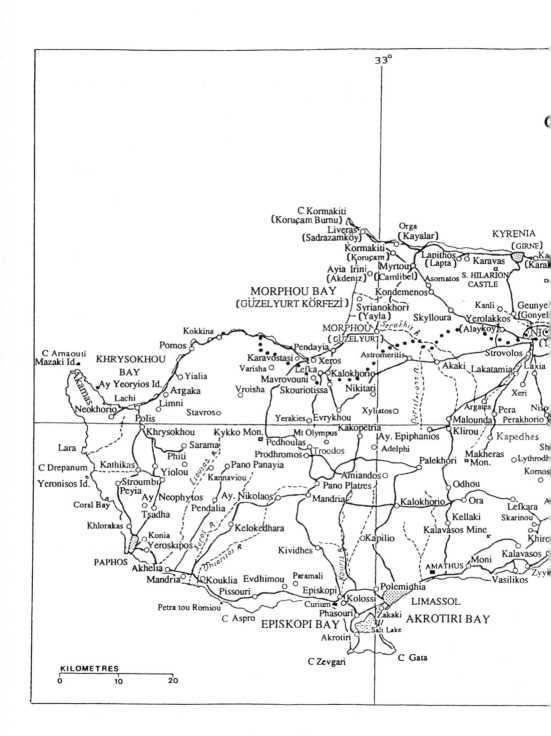

Figure 1. The main towns and villages of Cyprus mentioned

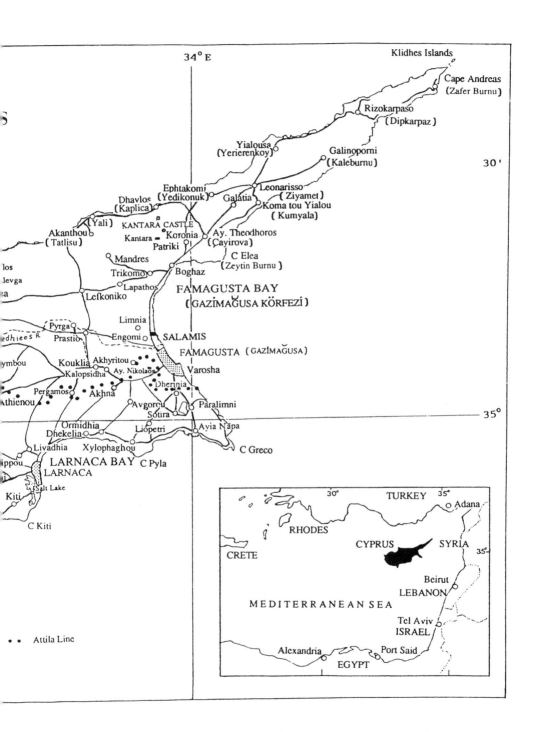

together with its major rivers. Turkish names are in brackets.

INTRODUCTION

HISTORY

Throughout most of its long history Cyprus has been subject to the domination of a succession of foreign powers, the most recent being the British, who took over the administration from Turkey in 1878 and ruled until 1960, when the island finally achieved its independence as the Republic of Cyprus. The British retain military bases within 2 Sovereign Base Areas at Episkopi/Akrotiri and Dhekelia. In December 1963 serious intercommunal fighting broke out between the Greek-Cypriots and the Turkish-Cypriot minority, and in 1964, to help prevent a recurrence of fighting, a United Nations force was despatched to Cyprus, where it still remains. In July 1974, a coup engineered by the military junta in Greece over-threw the government of Cyprus; in response to this, Turkish forces invaded and subsequently occupied the island north of a line from Famagusta through Nicosia to the south of Morphou Bay, some 37% of the island's area, and this division still prevails. North Cyprus has declared itself to be an independent state, but amongst the international community it is recognised only by Turkey.

HISTORY OF CYPRUS ORNITHOLOGY

Cobham's *Excerpta Cypria, Materials for a History of Cyprus* (1908) contains extracts and translations from books relating to Cyprus from 23 A.D. onwards. Amongst the authors mentioned in Cobham, many are pre-Linnean visitors who make references to wild birds – notable, and including the dates of their visits, are d'Anglure, 1396; Baumgarten, 1508; Locke, 1553; Elias of Pesaro, 1563; de Villamont, 1589; Moryson, 1596; Cotovicus, 1598–9; Stochove, 1631; Heyman, early 18th century; and Pococke, 1738. Abbé Mariti (1769) lived in Cyprus 1760–67 and mentions the commonest species.

The first scientific writer to visit Cyprus was Dr J. Sibthorp, who, with his artist, Ferdinand Bauer, made a fairly complete tour from 8 April to *c.* 14 May 1787, collecting, painting and studying the flora and fauna. From his journal, Sibthorp appears to have been a sound and experienced naturalist. He makes many references to birds, and comments on the migratory nature of many of them. In an appendix he lists the species he saw; some of his nomenclature is now obscure but *c.* 74 species are still recognisable. His journal was published in parts by Walpole (1818, 1820) and complete by Cobham (1908). Sclater (1904) gives an account of Sibthorp's activities and mentions a folio of 114 bird drawings by Ferdinand Bauer "which is held in the library of the Botanical Gardens at Oxford"; the drawings are without data but Sclater suspected that many were made in Cyprus.

Baron von Sack collected in Cyprus from February to early May 1820; his collection – in the Zoological Museum of Berlin – remained unknown until listed by Stresemann (1953). Baikie (1850) gives a table of his observations of the migration of water birds on the north coast from 25 August to 8 September 1849. Unger & Kotschy's list (1865) is based on that of Sibthorp, but was considered by Bucknill (1909–10) to be less accurate and complete. In fact it includes all but one of the species (Little Tern *Sterna albifrons*) reliably identified by Sibthorp, plus 8 new species identified by Dr Kotschy, the apparent errors and omissions listed by Bucknill being due to changes in nomenclature.

Lord Lilford, "the first competent modern ornithologist to study the birds of the island" (Bucknill 1909–10), visited the southern and eastern coastal areas from 14

April to 12 May 1875. In August 1878, shortly after the British occupation, Lilford sent out the collector W. Pearse, who collected throughout the winter, but died in the island in 1879. Dr F. H. H. Guillemard collected for Lilford from February to June 1887 and from November 1887 to May 1888. The 2 detailed accounts of his journeys (Guillemard 1888, 1889) give a good idea of conditions at the time. Lilford's own observations, the results of the collections by Pearse and Guillemard, and a survey of the earlier literature, were incorporated into the first detailed systematic list (Lilford 1889). Skins collected by Lilford, Pearse and Guillemard are held in the Royal Scottish Museum (RSM) and in the British Museum (Natural History) (BMNH).

G. Schrader collected in the island from October 1876 to April 1878, and sent consignments of skins and eggs to W. Schlüter of Halle on the Saale, Germany, where they were examined by A. Müller, who's list (1879), although rather brief, seems reliable. Schrader's own list (1891) is less so. His detailed records (some confirmed by Müller) are probably sound, but some of his general comments have proved to be incorrect.

In 1901, C. Glaszner, an Austrian subject resident at Larnaca, began sending to the Hungarian National Museum, Budapest (HNMB), consignments of specimens collected by him, and in 1904 Dr J. von Madarász published a lengthy and detailed list based on the results of his examination of these skin collections. Unfortunately the entire Hungarian collection was destroyed in a fire in 1956, along with many type specimens (L. Horváth). Glaszner remained in Cyprus until at least 1908 and sent a considerable number of skins to other institutions, including the BMNH and to Lord Rothschild at Tring. The palaeontologist Miss D. M. A. Bate visited the island from May 1901 to November 1902, her short paper on the birds (1903a) including details of breeding, distribution and habitat. She also contributed a skin collection to the BMNH.

In July 1907, J. A. (later Sir John) Bucknill arrived in Cyprus. He gathered around him a group of people (mainly British Colonial officials) with an interest in birds, who, in June 1908, founded the Cyprus Natural History Society. During its brief life the Society was very active, holding field meetings and exhibitions, and giving lectures. The Society obtained a room at the Education Office to use as a Museum to house its reference library and collection of specimens, which by 1911 included over 250 skins and over 850 eggs. (This collection still exists in the Department of Agriculture, Nicosia.) The Society's publications relating to birds are Annals I–IV (1908–1913), and Bulletin 2 (Bucknill 1910). C. B. Horsbrugh went out to Cyprus in 1909 at Bucknill's invitation, remaining until 1913, and made a considerable collection of skins, some of which are in the BMNH. Bucknill's *On the Ornithology of Cyprus* (1909–10) incorporates the results of the Society's work into a most valuable, detailed and generally accurate check-list. The introduction includes a detailed summary of the literature. Bucknill published 2 supplements (1911, 1913a) and a final list (1913b) based on the work of the Society. After Bucknill's departure in July 1912, and the onset of the Great War, the Society seems to have faded away. F. R. S. Baxendale (1915), mainly from his own observations, published a follow-on to Bucknill's series of papers, but there was nothing further. The publications of the Cyprus Natural History Society, Bucknill and Baxendale are of particular value because they relate to a time when the reservoirs on the Mesaoria were full of water and there was relatively little shooting.

G. F. Wilson's articles in the Cyprus Agricultural Journal (1925a,b,c, 1928) are somewhat anecdotal and often concerned with shooting, but contain some useful records. Occasional 'Natural History Notes' in the Journal (1910, 1925, 1926, 1927) contain a few records of migration. W. H. Riddell (1927) gives an excellent account of his visit from 8 March to 20 April 1927.

Sir Charles Belcher was in Cyprus 1928–30; he studied the breeding birds and made a collection of eggs, but his only publication (1929) was a brief summary of the breeding birds of low ground. F. C. R. Jourdain, who's earlier publications (1910a,b, 1913) cover minor points mainly relating to eggs, visited the island under Belcher's guidance from 8 April to 6 May 1929. His diary (Jourdain 1929a) includes many valuable breeding records, and also opinions on the egg collections made by the Cyprus Natural History Society. A later diary (Jourdain 1931) includes details of a brief visit to Larnaca Salt Lake. Jourdain's list of the breeding birds (1929b) is mainly a not entirely accurate recapitulation of Bucknill. Bucknill's 1913 list was updated by Belcher and Jourdain in 1930, though Belcher suppressed his name.

J. M. Ferrier (1936) gives an account of a brief visit, including some breeding records. W. A. Payn (1939) gives details of species and subspecies identified from a skin collection (now in the BMNH) made by him from February to May 1938, and also gives a table of migrants. Skin collections made c. 1940–1962 by the entomologist G. A. Mavromoustakis of Limassol went to Harvard, Stockholm, Tel Aviv and Limassol. In 1945–46 several 'Middle East Biological Scheme Special Bulletins' dealt with the birds of the island. Those of G. F. Wilson (1945, 1946a,b,c) mainly summarise earlier publications, but that of H. M. Morris (1946b), the Government Entomologist, contains a useful table of migration at Nicosia 1930–45. G. F. Wilson also compiled a skin collection from 1909 to 1943, now housed in the RSM.

J. H. McNeile visited the island during the breeding seasons of 1948, 1952, 1954 and 1955 to study the breeding birds, particularly Cyprus Warbler *Sylvia melanothorax*, Cretzschmar's Bunting *Emberiza caesia* and Masked Shrike *Lanius nubicus*. He never published his results and, although extracts were published by the Bannermans (1958), his detailed notes (now in the RSM) still contain much valuable unpublished material.

In 1954, in preparation for their book *Birds of Cyprus* (1958), D. A. and W. M. Bannerman spent 4 months in the island. They also circulated questionnaires to some past and present residents with an interest in birds. The questionnaires completed by D. F. Davidson (resident 1938–1956), H. M. Morris (resident 1927–1951), R. R. Waterer (resident 1928–1950) and G. F. Wilson (resident 1903–1946) are held in the BMNH and contain some important records not published by the Bannermans. Their book has a number of valuable introductory chapters, (one on 'Topography and Vegetation' by D. F. Davidson) and includes much previously unpublished material. The systematic list contains some errors and also some doubtful breeding records (see Hollom 1959). The Bannermans' *Handbook of the Birds of Cyprus and Migrants of the Middle East* (1971) is a well illustrated condensed update of their earlier book, though not always reliable regarding status (see Perrins 1973, Flint & Cole 1973).

The 'Suez Crisis' in 1956, and the development of internal political strife in the island, led to the stationing of large numbers of British military personnel in Cyprus, among them many with a keen and active interest in birds and their conservation. A network of observers was soon established, and in June 1957 P. C. T. Wildash, Dr W. R. P. Bourne and R. S. Dove founded the first Cyprus Ornithological Society (C.O.S.). The continuous observations and publications by the Society since then are largely responsible for our present knowledge of the island's birds. The Society also undertook bird ringing with British Trust for Ornithology rings 1957–1970.

The Society's main publications are its Annual Reports (Reports 4–8 were bi-annual), which consist mainly of a systematic list of birds seen and trapped, often with appendices on ringing and weather. They carry no publication date, and thus the dates given in the references refer only to the year dealt with by the Report. The Society also formerly produced a bi-annual Bulletin (Numbers 1–20, 1957–1966), and since April 1970 a monthly Newsletter. Some Reports and Bulletins (and occasionally Newsletters) contain short papers, articles or notes on migration, breeding, status, habitat, identification, etc., those we have used are listed in the References.

Two important papers published elsewhere by members of the Society are J. F. R. Ashton-Johnson's comprehensive study of 52 breeding species (1961), and D. W. H. Adams thorough and detailed radar observations of bird migration (1962), the latter perhaps the single most important contribution to ornithology from Cyprus. In 1964 the first 6 recorders of the Society produced a detailed and accurate check-list (Bourne *et al.*), the first reliable modern guide to the status of birds in Cyprus. Migration through the island was summarised by Bourne (1960a).

It was the intention of the founders that the society should promote local interest in birds and eventually develop into an indigenous ornithological society, objectives which were embodied in the constitution. With the aid of publicity campaigns the society achieved, by the late 1960s, a substantial Greek Cypriot membership. However, in 1969 a split developed in the society, and in 1970 Dr A. Artemiou, E. Michaelides, P. Neophytou, P. Theodosiou and others formed a new Greek Cypriot based society, which adopted the same name as the original society. To reduce confusion it is conventional to follow mention of one of these societies by its year of founding, namely Cyprus Ornithological Society (1957) or Cyprus Ornithological Society (1970). The later society also produces an Annual Report, again mainly a systematic list with occasional appendices, articles or short notes. Their fifteen Reports so far (1970–1984) are a valuable contribution to the ornithology of the island, the earlier ones being compiled largely by the British members; but the Cypriot contribution has increased regularly, and the 1974 and subsequent Reports were entirely Cypriot compiled. In 1972 a simple check-list was produced to be used in conjunction with the Peterson *et al.* (1965) field-guide, and since 1970 bird ringing has been carried out using Cyprus rings. The 1970 Reports of the 2 societies were compiled by the same authors and are almost identical, but their subsequent Reports are completely different. Today both societies have Cypriot and British memberships, but the first formed C.O.S. remains mainly British (expatriates and military personnel), and the later one mainly Greek Cypriot. So far Turkish Cypriots have not become greatly involved in ornithology, though in 1984 Mehmet Edhem contributed a record of migration to the Report of C.O.S. (1970).

S. J. Christensen was stationed in Cyprus with the Danish United Nations forces from November 1964 to May 1965 (returning 1968–1970); his observations (1967) include a report on the discovery of a passage of birds of prey over the east of the island in spring. In autumn 1967 and spring 1968 a team from the Smithsonian Institution, Washington, undertook bird ringing, biomedical research and a study of bird liming (Hubbard 1967a,b, 1968). Their final paper (Horner & Hubbard 1982) contains much valuable and previously unpublished data, though some of its general comments are not valid when one looks at the overall picture of migration through the island. In 1971, P. F. Stewart and S. J. Christensen published a comprehensive check-list (see Perrins 1973, Flint & Cole 1973). Royal Air Force Ornithological Society expeditions carried out systematic observations of spring migration at Cape Andreas in 1972 and 1973 (Stagg 1973, 1974, Rivers & Walker 1974), the results adding substantially to the knowledge of visible migration through the cape. R. L. Mason (1980) conducted a census in the Troodos/Mt. Olympus area from April 1975 to January 1976.

The bibliography of the avifauna of the Middle East compiled by Griffiths (1975) contains much that is relevant to Cyprus, especially regarding migration through the eastern Mediterranean and the Levant.

The authors of the present check-list were members of the British Forces in Cyprus 1959–61, 1967–70 (PFS), and 1969–72 (PRF). Our observations are included in the Reports of the 2 societies, and PFS also contributed a skin collection to the RSM.

The publication of the first edition of this check-list in 1983 stimulated considerable interest in Cyprus as a birdwatching holiday destination, and the island is now visited by many birdwatchers every year, particularly during April and early May. This has resulted in an increase in the number of rarities seen during the spring migration. The 2 C.O.S.s play a valuable role in collecting and publishing the records of these many visitors to the island, in addition to the records of their own members.

A Greek Cypriot, Andreas Kephalas, has privately published details of his own observations in southeast Cyprus; his 2 publications (1979, 1989) contain several important and previously unpublished records.

Since 1983 several visitors to the island have published surveys worthy of note. In 1985 J. D. Summers-Smith carried out a survey of the Dead Sea Sparrow *Passer moabiticus* colonies at Akrotiri Salt Lake. Bacon & Bacon (1986) studied the density of breeding Cyprus Warbler territories in relation to vegetation. A survey of breeding birds in different habitats corresponding to stages in the ecological succession of an evergreen oak forest was carried out in 1986 by Massa & Catalisano, the results confirming the general impoverishment of the Cyprian avifauna in comparison with that of other Mediterranean islands.

Unlike other Mediterrranean islands, such as Sicily and Malta, Cyprus has not yet developed an indigenous society with sufficient membership or resources to organise any systematic surveys of either migration or the breeding birds. Of migration studies the most pressing need is for a regular annual count of the apparently decreasing Demoiselle Crane *Anthropoides virgo* passage through Akrotiri in autumn. Regarding the breeding birds, an Atlas of their distribution would be of particular value, as without one it is not possible to accurately monitor the inevitable changes which are occurring as a result of the island's rapid development, or as a result of other factors, such as possible climatic change. The text of this check-list suggests many other surveys which would be of value.

GEOGRAPHY

Cyprus (9250 km^2 in area) is the third largest island in the Mediterranean, after Sicily and Sardinia. It has a maximum length of 226 km from west to east, and a maximum width of 96 km from north to south. It lies in the northeast of the east Mediterranean basin, at 34°33′–35°42′N and 32°16′–34°36′E. The north coast lies roughly parallel to the Turkish coast and at a distance of *c*. 80–110 km, the narrowest distance, between Cape Kormakiti and Cape Anamur in Turkey, being 72 km. Most of the east coast is *c*. 160–180 km from Syria, though the shortest distance, from Cape Andreas to near Latakia in Syria, is only 105 km. From Cape Greco in the southeast, Beirut, on the coast of Lebanon, is *c*. 175 km southeast. From Cape Gata on the south coast, Tel Aviv, on the coast of Israel, is *c*. 320 km south–southeast, and the north coast of Sinai and the Nile Delta are *c*. 370 km to the south and south–southwest respectively. The Taurus mountains in Turkey are easily visible to the north of Cyprus, and on a clear day the Jebel Ansariya in Syria may be seen to the east.

The island (Fig. 2) is occupied by 2 mountain ranges of a general east–west trend, with a broad east–west plain between them. Almost the whole of the south and west of the island is occupied by the Troodos mountains and their surrounding foothills, their highest peaks being Olympus (1961 m), Adelphi (1612 m), Papoutsa (1554 m) and Makheras (1423 m), with many others over 1200 m. The contours of the Troodos range are generally well rounded by erosion, though some of its river valleys possess cliffs and rock faces. A narrow coastal plain comes between the foothills and the sea, but there are also some extensive coastal cliffs, notably between Kouklia (Paphos) and Curium, which reach a height of 200 m at Cape Aspro. At its eastern end the range terminates in the isolated peak of Stavrovouni (672 m), and in the west in the Akamas promontory and Cape Arnaouti, which form the western side of Khrysokhou Bay. To the south, bounded by Akrotiri Bay and Episkopi Bay, is the Akrotiri peninsula with cliffs of up to 60 m along its southern edge between Cape Gata and Cape Zevgari.

The northern or Kyrenia range of mountains runs as a narrow unbroken ridge along the north coast, rising abruptly in the west at Kornos Peak, near Cape Kormakiti and in the east extending as a range of hills along the Karpas peninsula to Cape Andreas. Most of the ridge has a height of *c*. 600–800 m, the highest points being Kyparissovouno (1024 m) and Buffavento (955 m). The centre of the ridge is only 4–6 km from the north coast, and the width of the ridge above 400 m is nowhere more than 3 km. Although much lower and less extensive than the Troodos range, the steep slopes and rocky and rugged aspect of the Kyrenia range make it considerably more spectacular. Its slopes descend abruptly in the north to a very narrow coastal plain, and in the south to the central plain.

The central plain, or Mesaoria, extends across the island from Morphou Bay in the west to Famagusta Bay in the east, a distance of 92 km, and southeast to the promontory of Cape Greco and to Larnaca Bay. Its greatest breadth north/south, in the east, is 38 km. Most of the plain is below 100 m, though it is somewhat higher and more hilly around and west of Nicosia.

There are a few small rocky islands close offshore, but the only ones of any significance are the Klidhes Islands, off Cape Andreas, the largest of which is *c*. 700 × 200 m and lies *c*. 1·5 km offshore. The coasts of Cyprus are rocky with occasional sandy beaches; with the small tidal range and relative infertility of the surrounding sea they are generally not attractive to sea and shore birds.

The island has no perennial rivers and only in the higher Troodos are there perennial streams. Seasonal rivers flow during the winter months, often becoming very swollen and rapid after heavy rain in the mountains. The longest river, the Pedhieos (length 95 km), which flows across the Mesaoria into Famagusta Bay, only exceptionally flows for as long as 6 weeks in the year. Some of the shorter, steeper rivers, like the Kouris, which flow south or southwest from the Troodos mountains, are more constant, but usually none reach the sea during the summer months. Their wide, boulder strewn and often waterless river beds are striking features of the landscape. When in flood the rivers bring down large quantities of material from the mountains. In some depressions near the Pedhieos river bed, the alluvium is 5–6 m thick, and the present rate of deposition on the flood plain of the lower Pedhieos is *c*. 60 cm per century. Material brought down by rivers flowing south from Troodos has been moved eastward by longshore drift to form the tombolo of sand and shingle which joins what was once the island of Akrotiri to the mainland to form the present Akrotiri peninsula.

There is a shallow salt lake on the Akrotiri peninsula and another south of Larnaca; depending on rainfall the former may or may not contain water throughout the year, but the latter is always dry in summer (Fig. 2). Of the 2 lakes, Akrotiri is

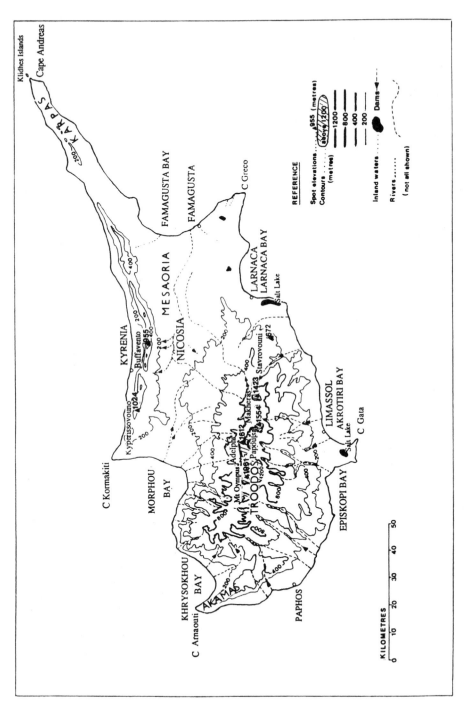

Figure 2. The topography of Cyprus and its main inland waters, dams and rivers.

much less saline than Larnaca, and therefore the ecology of the 2 is quite different (Johnson 1990), which probably explains their often very different bird populations. Depending on winter rainfall, several shallow fresh water lakes or marshes may form, notably near Syrianokhori, Paralimni, Famagusta/Salamis and Galatia, but most are now greatly reduced by drainage. The Mesaoria irrigation project of 1898–1901 involved the construction of several large reservoirs, the main ones being Syngrasis, Kouklia, and Akhyritou (Ayios Nikolaos on recent maps). They have now fallen into disuse, but Kouklia in particular may still hold water after wet winters. Since 1944 many small modern dams have been built and an extensive dam building programme continues.

The population in mid 1978 was estimated at c. 650,000. The population percentages in 1960, when the last official census was held, were 77% Greek Cypriot, 18·3% Turkish Cypriot and 4·7% other minorities (Maronites, Armenians, Latins, others). The largest town and capital of the island is Nicosia, on the central plain (Fig. 1). The five other major towns (all coastal) are Limassol, Famagusta, Larnaca, Paphos and Kyrenia. The majority of the population live in nucleated villages, which on fairly uniform low ground are spaced c. 3–5 km apart. A variety of slope and lithology results in dense spacing of villages at irregular intervals, as on the Paphos plateau. Strings of villages mark the main valleys like the Solea and Middle Pedhieos valleys.

GEOLOGY

Although only a small island, Cyprus presents unusually interesting geological structures, the dominant and most interesting being the vast igneous dome of the Troodos massif in the southwest, which has become famous as the best documented example of an ophiolite complex, that is land-based fragments of oceanic crust and upper mantle forced up at tectonic plate margins. The Troodos massif is formed almost entirely of upper Cretaceous basic and ultra-basic igneous rocks which are exposed in a broad band from the shores of Khrysokhou and Morphou Bays to within 10 km of Larnaca; but gravity and borehole data suggest that the igneous rocks which form the massif underlie the whole of Cyprus as a northerly inclined rectangular slab whose boundaries roughly coincide with the extremities of the island (Gass 1980).

The Kyrenia range in the north of the island is an Alpine fold mountain system, formed by the oldest rocks in the island, mainly hard compact limestones of Cretaceous age, which have been tilted so that their beds are now in a vertical position. Here and there along the range the limestones are pierced by masses of igneous rock. The Kyrenia range is flanked by Eocene sandstones and shales, and similar rocks occur locally on the southern and western slopes of the Troodos range.

Miocene deposits of white chalky marls and limestones extend over nearly half the island, and their glaring whiteness forms a striking feature of the landscape. The deposits underlie the whole plain of the Mesaoria, outcropping northward around the Kyrenia range and onto the Karpas, southward toward Larnaca, and extending eastward beneath the Pliocene beds to rise again in the southeast from Dherinia and Sotira to Cape Greco. The greatest surface area of these deposits, however, is on the southern and western slopes of the Troodos massif, where the beds form a broad tract of hilly country from near Kophinou and Lefkara to the Akamas in the extreme west.

In the lowlands, Pliocene and more recent strata have a considerable distribution. Pliocene deposits of the Athalassa formation are made up of sandy marls, calcareous sands and conglomerates, capped by a hard secondary limestone crust (Kafkalla), a by-product of the summer drought. Kafkalla capped plateaux have their main development in the central and southeastern Mesaoria, where the capping is continuous over many miles or may be limited to widely distributed mesas and buttes.

Today Cyprus shows much evidence of recent uplift. Raised beaches are common and river terraces are an ever present feature, while surfaces in the old land, especially in the 2 mountain systems, can be seen. Earthquake epicentres grouped offshore along the southern coast demonstrate continuing major tectonic upheavals. Gravity measurements coupled with the compiled distribution of recent earthquake foci suggest there is at the present underthrusting of Mediterranean crust beneath Cyprus, and this could be largely responsible for the continuing uplift of the island (Searle & Panayiotou 1980).

CLIMATE

The climate in Cyprus is generally of an extreme Mediterranean or Warm Temperate Western Marginal type, characterised by long, very hot, dry summers and cool, wet winters, separated by short autumn and spring seasons of rapid change, with long periods at all seasons of sunshine and cloudless skies.

In summer the island is mainly under the influence of a shallow trough of low pressure extending from the great continental depression centred over southwest Asia. In winter Cyprus is near the track of fairly frequent small depressions which cross the Mediterranean from west to east between the continental anticyclone of Eurasia and the generally low pressure belt of North Africa. These depressions give periods of disturbed weather usually lasting for a day or so and produce most of the annual precipitation.

Over the eastern Mediterranean, surface winds are usually of light or moderate strength and mostly westerly or southwesterly in winter and northwesterly or northerly in summer. Over the island itself, however, winds are quite variable in direction owing to topography and local heating effects, and during the summer months considerable sea and land breezes occur. Gales are infrequent but may occur especially on exposed coasts during winter depressions.

Within the island there are considerable variations of climate. The moisture bearing winds are predominantly those from the southwest; thus precipitation is high in the west and southwest, with maximum precipitation on Mt. Troodos, and a consequent partial rain shadow to the northeast over the Mesaoria. In the north, the Kyrenia mountains also largely confine moisture to their northern slopes and a narrow coastal strip. Average annual precipitation (Fig. 3) over the whole island is 489 mm, but on Troodos is as much as 1190 mm, and on the Mesaoria as low as 290–315 mm (data covers 30 years of records, 1941–1970). The incidence of precipitation is very unreliable and often varies greatly from year to year. Both very wet and severe drought years occur, some droughts being extreme enough to have caused crop failure, famine and emigration in the past. Recent annual (October to September) totals of rainfall for the whole island have varied from as high as 759 mm in 1968–69 to as low as 182 mm in 1972–73. Rainfall is often very heavy but of brief duration, and a month's rainfall figure may represent only 3 or 4 rainstorms. November to March are the wettest months, and during July to September precipitation is usually negligible. The large relict river valleys now occupied by small seasonal rivers suggest that the island's climate was once much wetter than it is now, and statistical analysis of the rainfall reveals a decreasing trend in the last 30 years. Snow falls frequently every winter in the Troodos range above 1000 m, usually occurring from December to mid April. Snow cover is not continuous in winter but it may lie to

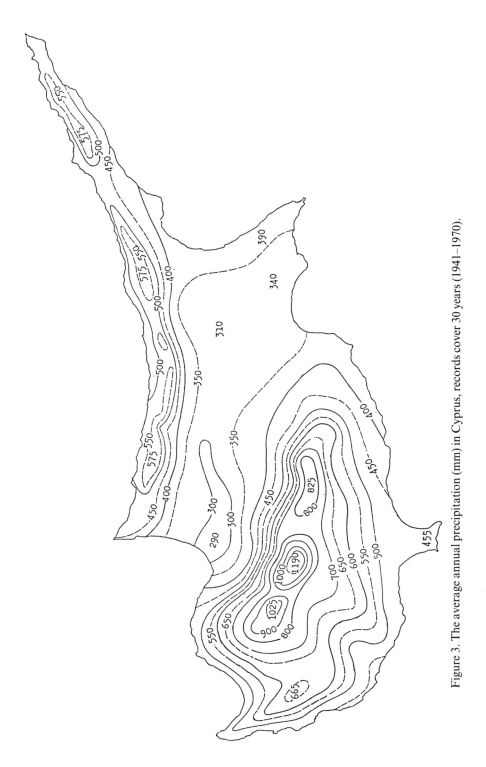

Figure 3. The average annual precipitation (mm) in Cyprus, records cover 30 years (1941–1970).

considerable depths for several weeks especially on the northern slopes of the high Troodos.

Sea temperatures rise to 27°C in August and are above 22°C from June to November. During January to March, sea temperatures fall to 16–17°C. The average annual air temperature is 20·6°C, relatively high for the latitude, due to the warming effect of the surrounding sea. Over the island as a whole the average annual maximum temperature is 25·6°C and the average annual minimum 13·9°C, but, as with precipitation, temperatures also vary considerably within the island. The central Mesaoria has more of a continental climate than coastal areas and is very hot in summer; in Nicosia the average temperature in July, the hottest month, is 29°C, hotter than either Beirut or Cairo, and the maximum temperature frequently exceeds 38°C. In winter the Mesaoria is relatively cold for low ground, the average temperature of Nicosia in January, the coldest month, being only 10°C. Marine influences give cooler summers and warmer winters near most of the coastline, especially the west coast. At Paphos the average temperature in the hottest month (August) is 26°C, and the average temperature in the coldest month (February) is 13°C. In the mountains, air temperatures drop by c. 5°C per 1000 m altitude.

Elevation and distance from the coast have considerable effects on relative humidity. Over the whole island during winter days, and at night throughout the year, humidity varies between 65% and 95%. Near midday in summer it is much lower, with values on the central plain usually a little over 30% and occasionally as low as 15%. Fog is infrequent and visibility is generally very good or excellent. Day-length varies from 14·5 hours in June to 9·8 hours in December.

VEGETATION

From the earliest records it is clear that the island was once covered with forest not only in the mountains but also extensively on low ground (Unwin 1925, Holmboe 1914); a map of hypothetical climax vegetation (Christodoulou 1959) shows forest covering the whole island, with the exception of some low-lying coastal areas of soil salinity or high water-table, which bear edaphic sub-climax vegetation. Christodoulou has, however, pointed out that the high summer temperatures and low rainfall of the central lowlands give them a semi-arid climate, and has questioned whether their climax vegetation is dense forest. Forests still existed in many parts of the island in Ptolemaic times though the plains were cleared prior to 275–194 BC (Strabo, in Cobham). Many centuries of clearance, and the unrestricted grazing of goats, have destroyed almost all the original forests, the remnants of which are now largely confined to the higher Troodos. Scattered trees such as Aleppo Pine *Pinus halepensis,* wild Olive *Olea europaea* and Carob *Ceratonia siliqua* often occur on the maquis-covered hillsides (see below) and in many cases must be regarded as last remnants of the ancient forests (Holmboe). The loss of forest cover and consequent rapid water run-off have resulted in extensive and severe soil erosion, especially on the slopes, and have also aggravated the annual flood/drought cycle of the rivers. Erosion by wind is also common on the now largely bare Mesaoria.

After the British occupation, a start was made on re-afforestation, and the State Forests now occupy 18% of the island's surface area, mainly in the 2 mountain ranges, though not all of the designated State Forest areas yet carry forest. The Paphos Forest in the western Troodos range contains about two-thirds of the island's forest trees, mainly Aleppo Pine (the principal forest tree) and the endemic

Golden Oak *Quercus alnifolia*. The Cyprus Cedar *Cedrus libanotica brevifolia* now occurs naturally only in a restricted area of the Paphos Forest. On Troodos itself, the Aleppo Pine is replaced by the Troodos Pine *Pinus nigra caramanica*, which forms pure forest above *c.* 1600 m. River valley bottoms in the Troodos range carry deciduous trees such as Oriental Plane *Platanus orientalis* and Oriental Alder *Alnus orientalis*, with a thick understorey of shrubs and Bramble *Rubus ulmifolius*. In lower riverbeds and gullies Oleander *Nerium oleander* is common. The forests of the Kyrenia range, mainly Aleppo Pine and Mediterranean Cypress *Cupressus sempervirens*, tend to be much more open and less well developed than those of the southern range, mainly because of the very porous nature of the limestone there. The humidity resulting from proximity to the sea, and a lower degree of insolation, result in a thicker growth of vegetation on the north side of the Kyrenia range than on the south.

High maquis, composed largely of dense Juniper *Juniperus phoenicia*, occurs mainly in the east of the island or on coastal promontories, notably on the Karpas, at Cape Greco and Akrotiri, and on the Akamas.

Extensive areas of uncultivated low ground and hills are covered with xerophytic shrubs forming low maquis or, in drier areas, a very open garigue. The commonest shrub, especially in garigue, is the low Prickly Burnet *Poterium spinosum*, which forms such a prominent part of the landscape. Other common shrubs are Lentisk *Pistacia lentiscus*, Rockrose *Cistus villosus*, Thorny Gorse *Genista sphacelata* and Thorny Broom *Calycotome villosa*, which may occur together or on their own. *Cistus villosus* maquis, in particular, covers extensive areas of the dry slopes and hillsides of the lower regions as well as mountain slopes up to 1600–1700 m.

Where soils are very shallow and dry, and grazing pressure heaviest, the garigue is reduced to almost barren steppe, carrying only a few scattered dwarf shrubs and a brief annual flush of xerophytic grasses and herbs. Of the grasses the most characteristic is *Stipa tortilis* but *Triticum ovatum*, *Avena barbata*, *Hordeum murinum* and *Langurus ovatus* are also numerous. The herbs include *Medicago*, *Trifolium*, *Plantago* and *Valerianella*. The tall white-flowered *Asphodelus ramosus* is also common. Steppe is mainly a lowland vegetation and is particularly developed on the Kafkalla limestone plateaux, but is also found on sloping land and on bare hillsides. In both steppe and garigue the plants do not cover the ground, but grow apart from each other with much bare ground between them.

Salicornia fruticosa occurs commonly on salt flats around the Akrotiri and Larnaca Salt Lakes, and also on saline pans in the eastern Mesaoria, e.g. near Kouklia and Dhekelia. Several of the offshore rocks (such as Yeronisos I. and Ayios Yeoryios I.) carry an annual flush of grasses and herbs, and the largest of the Klidhes Islands also has a sparse and windblown covering of Sea Purslane *Atriplex halimus*, Lentisk and Prickly Burnet, with a couple of stunted Junipers.

In spite of severe difficulties with water, Cyprus is the most thoroughly cultivated land in the east Mediterranean; about 46% of the island is now classed as farmland, though much of it is of indifferent quality. The area of land under perennial irrigation continues to increase, and of the total area of cultivated land, some 10% is now perennially irrigated (compared with 3·5% in 1946), while in a normal year a further 13% can be watered from spate floods. Much of the arable land, especially on the Mesaoria, is used to grow barley and wheat, with the barley on the poorer soils. Vegetables, particularly early potatoes, are also widely grown. Citrus growing is an important industry and the number of trees is increasing rapidly, this expansion being encouraged by the demand for export and made possible by the increase in perennial irrigation. The main citrus plantations are near Morphou and Famagusta and at Phasouri near Limassol. Grape vines are extensively grown, particularly on the white chalky marls and limestones of the south and west Troodos massif, where they form a mono-culture over large areas.

The cultivated olive is the most numerous non-forest tree, and is widespread below c. 800 m. Olives are grown in groves and also in open cultivation. A usually very open cultivation of Carobs covers much poor land in coastal areas and lower hillsides within 20 km of the sea, the highest density occurring in the southern Troodos foothills. Almond is increasingly planted, especially on poor, sloping or rocky soils, and is now the most numerous deciduous tree. On the largely treeless Mesaoria the dominant tree is Hawthorn *Crataegus azarolus,* though other species like *Eucalyptus* and *Acacia* are increasingly planted. Fruit trees, mainly apple, fig, apricot, cherry and peach, may be grown where there is perennial irrigation, especially within the Troodos massif.

The long hot dry summers are inimical to plant growth and for most plants the growing seasons are in winter and spring. Trees in Cyprus take longer to mature than those in regions where heat and moisture coincide, and many have a gnarled and stunted appearance. During winter and early spring the island is green, and the low ground and lower hills are transformed, especially during February, March and April, by a bright and colourful carpet of wild flowers. These vanish in the rapidly increasing heat of May, when the island regains its characteristic brown and parched appearance.

MIGRATION AND MOVEMENTS

The island's geographical location relative to the western Palaearctic and Africa and its paucity of breeding species ensure that the most prominent feature of Cyprus ornithology is migration. Almost 200 species occur as regular passage migrants, while another 20 or so occur irregularly (Appendix 6). In general the migrants are species which breed in Europe, pass south through the island in autumn to winter in Africa or the Middle East, and return northward in spring. The main exceptions to this are Cory's Shearwater *Calonectris diomedea* and the Manx Shearwater *Puffinus puffinus,* which occur offshore, and the Black-headed Bunting *Emberiza melanocephala,* which winters in India. There is also some east-west movement of wildfowl from Iran and the Caspian area.

Recoveries of ringed birds (Appendix 2) show that passage migrants and winter visitors originate mainly from Scandinavia, central and eastern Europe and the western U.S.S.R. to c. 48°E. However, recoveries of 127 Palaearctic-African passerine migrants, mainly Sylviidae, ringed or recovered in Europe and the U.S.S.R., reveal a distinctly northwestern origin; only 8 originate east of 25°E and the average longitude of origin of the remainder is only 15°E at an average latitude of 53°N. As their ultimate destination is Africa, it follows that many of these birds must make a definite detour around the east Mediterranean, avoiding the Mediterranean – Sahara crossing by passing through the Middle East. It also follows that birds, having migrated southeast to the Middle East, must then make a turn southwards to their winter quarters in Africa, and, therefore, fly a dogleg migration route. This change in direction is exaggerated on conventional projection maps, but is still valid, though less marked, on a gnomonic projection; a great circle route from 53°N, 15°E over Cyprus passes through the Gulf of Aden and the Horn of Africa, east of most Sylviidae wintering areas in Africa. Ringing recoveries indicate that many use a similar route in spring, though there is much variation between, and perhaps within, species, and some use this route in one season only. The change in migration direction of German Lesser Whitethroats was graphically illustrated by experiments in a planetarium, the birds re-orientating from southeast to south in autumn when shown the night skies over Cyprus (Sauer *in* Ricard 1969).

Ringing recoveries are undoubtedly influenced by both ringing and recovery bias. Thus of the 127 recoveries mentioned above only 2 are Willow Warblers *Phylloscopus trochilus,* an abundant migrant of which millions breed in Finland (Merikallio *in* Moreau 1972) and surely millions more in the western U.S.S.R. It is of interest, and probably significant, that the 2 recoveries are from these countries. The recoveries of these trans-Saharan passerine migrants also include only 3 diurnal migrants, namely 2 Sand Martins *Riparia riparia* and a Swallow *Hirundo rustica,* both abundant migrants of which relatively few are killed in Cyprus. However, the origins of these 3 diurnal migrants (31°E, 39°E and 35°E respectively) are much further east than those of the nocturnal migrants recovered, and indicate a generally north–south migration route. The recoveries of other abundant diurnal migrants, such as Turtle Dove *Streptopelia turtur* and Bee-eater *Merops apiaster,* also indicate a generally northern origin. Presumably these diurnal migrants undertake a more direct north–south migration route than the nocturnal migrants. Few recoveries of long distance migrants are from the northeast, which must indicate that few migrants from there pass through Cyprus.

The important radar observations of Adams (1962), and visual observations, show that the direction of migration from Cyprus in autumn is mainly south to southeast, with some movement west of south in late autumn. In spring most migrants fly tracks between north–northeast and northeast, though about 10% fly northwest (Adams 1962). These directions of migration support the evidence of the ringing recoveries in showing a detour around the east Mediterranean for many birds.

Further west in the east Mediterranean, south of Crete, Casement's (1966) radar observations at sea agree with those of Adams in showing the dominant direction of autumn migration as south–southeast, though Casement's brief observations in spring revealed tracks west of north. It is also clear from Casement's radar observations elsewhere in the Mediterranean, and from the mass of data listed by Moreau (1953, 1961), that there is a broad front migration across much of the Mediterranean, and the evidence from Cyprus of a detour around the east Mediterranean for some species should be seen as one part of an overall movement, and not viewed in isolation.

The number of birds in Europe which winter south of the Sahara has been estimated by Moreau (1953, 1961, 1972). His final estimate (Moreau 1972:48) of nearly 5000 million birds (not including water-birds) for the west and central Palaearctic gives a density of *c.* 200 birds to the km^2. Using these data, and adopting the method used by Moreau (1972:45), it is possible to estimate the numbers of birds which pass through Cyprus in autumn. Excluding Turkey north of Cyprus, which is largely mountainous and liable to possess a low density of migrants, a front of *c.* 2500 km of land lies to the north of Cyprus, and the frontage of the island, east to west, is 210 km; if the trans-Saharan migrants from only the area of land directly to the north pass through the island in autumn then their total would be 105 million birds.

In fact migrants are drawn from a much wider area, ringing recoveries showing a concentration from Scandinavian and central and eastern European countries. Also to be included are the millions of birds which pass through the island to winter in the Middle East and Africa north of the Sahara. Allowing for these 2 factors, and for the unknown numbers of water-birds, it seems not unreasonable to increase the original total to 150 million birds passing through Cyprus in autumn, with a smaller number returning in spring. As emphasised by Moreau (1972) such estimates should not be taken as 'hard' or quoted as such, though it is probable that at least the order of magnitude is correct.

From the radar observations of Adams it is clear that the great majority of migrants pass unnoticed, either because they fly at night or because they overfly high and out of sight by day. Adams found that by night most migrants flew at altitudes between 900 m and 1800 m, and by day between 300 m and 1200 m, though many flew at much greater heights. The many records from the higher Troodos and Mt. Olympus of both visible migration and grounded migrants are also evidence of the heights at which some migrants fly.

Adams observations also revealed that migration in Cyprus is a phenomenon of almost clockwork regularity, the weather in both autumn and spring being characterised by light winds, good visibility and minimal cloud, which generally have little effect on the almost routine daily pattern of migration. In autumn 1958 and spring 1959 the only serious adverse weather influence on the amount of migration seen on radar was a cold northerly airstream for a "few weeks" in February 1959, and on one evening in May migrants were grounded by local storms. Adams also found that a combination in spring of easterly winds and anticyclonic conditions caused a dramatic increase in the number of birds reaching the island from the Levant (see later), a phenomenon that was also noticed by Christensen (1967).

Autumn migration
Most autumn migrants pass through Cyprus during August, September, October and November, though for some species, particularly waders, such as Wood and Green Sandpipers, *Tringa glareola* and *ochropus,* passage begins as early as late June, and in July many species of wader are on the move, along with terns (*Chlidonias* species) and Slender-billed Gulls *Larus genei.*

A very substantial westward passage of flocks of ducks (*Anas* species), herons and egrets, gulls (*Larus* species) and other water-birds occurs along the north coast during August, September and October. The duck are the most numerous and have shown daily totals of up to 7000 or more from late August to mid September. Some fly south through the passes of the Kyrenia range, but most coast west into Morphou and Khrysokhou Bays. From there some round the Akamas, but many rest offshore and fly south through the Troodos passes at dusk. This westward passage of water-birds on the north coast appears to be very similar to that which occurs on the north coast of Sinai in autumn (Paran & Paz 1978), and probably has a similar origin. Flocks approaching Cyprus from the north clearly avoid crossing the island by day, and the geography of the north coast tends to deflect them to the west, the coast presumably acting as a leading line and causing the westerly passage to develop. So far observations of this passage have been relatively brief, and organised observations at several points along the north coast are needed to determine fully the nature of the passage and the total numbers of birds involved. Bourne (1960a), from autumn radar observations, also mentions a flyway of water-birds originating from the Gulf of Alexandretta (northeast of Cyprus), moving along the south Cyprus coast and then south to the Nile Delta; but from the few visible observations so far this appears to involve mainly Greater Flamingos *Phoenicopterus ruber.*

A brief but concentrated passage of Demoiselle Cranes *Anthropoides virgo* crosses the island from mid August to early September, with flocks of 100s seen daily, some roosting overnight near Morphou or at Akrotiri. Mason (1980 and *in litt.*) mentions radar echoes in the third week of August 1975 of small flocks of large birds leaving the Turkish central south coast at *c.* 1730 hours and flying almost due south towards the Nile Delta, passing the island *c.* 36 km west of Paphos. This movement was observed for about a week. Most birds flew at a speed of *c.* 64 km per hour and at altitudes ranging from *c.* 1800 m to *c.* 3350 m. The date and details of the observations suggest that the species involved may have been Demoiselle Crane. Flocks of

Common Cranes *Grus grus* cross the island mainly from mid October to early November, also usually in 100s, though flocks of 1000s have occurred in some recent years. A passage, totalling in excess of 6000 birds, over Episkopi, 25 October 1987, is graphically described by Murray (1987a and *in litt.*). The flocks passed at a height of *c.* 1200 m on a broad front (*c.* 1·2 km wide) and took 45 minutes to pass; some 25–30 flocks were seen, the flock sizes varying between 36 and 300 birds. In addition many other flocks passed heard but unseen above the clouds. A fascinating range of species was seen in association with this movement, including Great White Egrets *Egretta alba* and several species of falcons, including a Saker *Falco cherrug,* all moving south in the same northerly airstream.

Large soaring birds normally avoid the island on migration. Up to a third of a million White Storks *Ciconia ciconia* may cross the Bosporus in autumn (Cramp & Simmons 1977), yet only a few singles or 10s are usually seen in Cyprus, presumably because White Storks avoid long sea crossings owing to the lack of thermals. Similarly large soaring birds of prey also avoid Cyprus on migration, e.g. many 1000s of eagles, mainly Lesser Spotted *Aquila pomarina,* cross the Bosporus in autumn, but relatively few occur in Cyprus.

Many medium sized and smaller birds of prey do migrate through Cyprus in autumn, the main species involved being Honey Buzzard *Pernis apivorus,* Common Buzzard *Buteo buteo* and Red-footed Falcon *Falco vespertinus,* with smaller numbers of other falcons, Black Kite *Milvus migrans,* Osprey *Pandion haliaetus* and harriers *Circus* spp. A few eagles, mainly Lesser Spotted, Booted *Hieraaetus pennatus* or Short-toed *Circaetus gallicus,* also occur each autumn, usually singly. These birds of prey cross the island on a broad front, but concentrate at and depart from the capes, particularly Cape Gata. The main passage there is from September to early October, when daily totals of buzzards (*Pernis/Buteo*) have occasionally exceeded 1000. There has been some confusion over the identity of these buzzard flocks, and the passage dates of *Pernis* and *Buteo* are not yet correctly established. Occasional observations at Cape Andreas, Cape Greco and Cape Kiti have shown a migration of birds of prey through the east of the island. Although the extent of this passage needs to be investigated, it does not seem to be so large as that at Akrotiri. The maximum number of raptors counted on autumn passage in one year (1969) was 3151 (17 species), but the observer coverage has always been very incomplete and this figure is undoubtedly much too low.

Of the smaller diurnal migrants, Bee-eaters are the most obvious; they cross high over the island on a broad front, and at times during their peak migration, mid to late September, may be heard calling almost continuously overhead. Were it not for their far-carrying calls they would pass largely unnoticed, as do most other high flying migrants. Sand Martins and Swallows are also very common, especially at capes on the south coast, where departure rates frequently exceed 1000 per hour and for Sand Martins have reached 7500 per hour at Cape Gata in mid September.

Many species of small passerines occur as nocturnal migrants, among them many warblers (Sylviidae), the most numerous of which are Willow Warbler and Blackcap *Sylvia atricapilla*. Grounded night migrants occur throughout the island, wherever there is cover, and form dense concentrations in scrub behind the departure coast, where millions are killed annually in mistnets or on limesticks. At Cape Greco alone *c.* 3600–9000 were killed each morning in late September 1957, and equally high numbers were said to be taken from August into October (C.O.S.(1957) Bulletin 3). The arrival of nocturnal migrants on the south coast in autumn was witnessed by Bourne (1959b and *in litt.*) who saw "or more often heard small birds drop like stones from the sky at first light and immediately dive into cover". Retraps of ringed birds, mainly Willow Warblers, at Akrotiri, show that individuals occasionally remain for several days, and usually show a weight increase when retrapped. Willow Warbler and Lesser Grey Shrike *Lanius minor* are unusual in being very much more numerous in autumn than in spring, when the reverse is more usually the case for many species. Marsh Warbler *Acrocephalus palustris* and Red-breasted Flycatcher *Ficedula parva* occurrences are almost entirely in autumn, though neither is very common.

Until October almost all birds on passage are long distance migrants which will winter south of the Sahara. In October and November, however, there occur many shorter distance migrants, species which winter in the Middle East or North Africa. Those seen moving by day include Lapwing *Vanellus vanellus*, Skylark *Alauda arvensis*, Corn Bunting *Miliaria calandra*, Meadow Pipit *Anthus pratensis*, White Wagtail *Motacilla alba*, Spanish Sparrow *Passer hispaniolensis*, Starling *Sturnus vulgaris* and many finches (Fringillidae) and thrushes (Turdidae), though apparently both Song Thrush *Turdus philomelos* and Redwing *Turdus iliacus* move mainly by night. The direction of migration for most of these species, though not the thrushes, is predominantly south within the island, mainly south to southeast at Cape Gata, and east at Cape Andreas. Many thrushes, mainly Mistle Thrush *Turdus viscivorus*, also fly east from Cape Andreas, but within the island the few records of thrush passage where direction is mentioned are west of south.

Also part of this late autumn passage are nocturnal migrants like Chiffchaff *Phylloscopus collybita* and Robin *Erithacus rubecula*, both very common; up to 500 Robins a day have been killed on limesticks at Paralimni in early November. On Troodos 1957–58, R. S. Dove found that many late migrants, especially finches and thrushes, occurred in numbers in late autumn (when the low ground is dry and unsuitable), but moved on later and were not seen again in spring, when there is water and a flush of vegetation on the low ground (C.O.S.(1957) 2nd Report).

In late autumn 1958, Adams (1962) watched diurnal migrants on radar between dawn and midday on 19 and 26 October, and on 16 November. On each occasion there was a steady passage of scattered echoes moving south to southeast on a broad front crossing the whole length of the south coast. The direction of migration agrees with that obtained by visual observation; but a broad front departure is not obvious from the ground, probably because the visible low flying birds tend to coast and concentrate at the capes, while the high flying birds fly straight out to sea without deviating (Bourne 1960a).

Adams also made observations between dusk and midnight on 15 dates during late October and early November 1958. On each night a dense haze of fine echoes developed along the south coast as night migrants took off in a concentrated departure in the half hour after sunset, and flew in a generally southerly direction out to sea. None of the individual echoes making up the haze was large and in October all were very fine. The initial waves of migrants moved at ground speeds between 27·5 and 55 km per hour. The number of birds migrating decreased sharply after the first 1–2 hours, probably because most of the migrants present in the island that day had by then crossed the coast.

During October the dense waves of small birds flew average tracks between southeast and south-southeast by south, this movement continuing on a reduced scale during November. However on 4, 8, 9 and 10 November the major direction of migration was south-southwest or southwest with a coarser appearance of the radar mist display, probably due to a predominance of birds of thrush rather than warbler size. Such a southwesterly thrush migration would be in agreement with the few records of visible migration. The altered direction of migration was probably due to a change from trans-Saharan migrants flying round the eastern end of the Mediterranean to birds of Russian origin going to winter on the shores of the

Mediterranean (W. R. P. Bourne *in* Adams 1962). On all his observation dates in November, Adams also saw bird echoes off the south coast moving in a southwesterly direction, but these birds had clearly set out from the coasts of Syria and the Lebanon without overflying Cyprus. These observations suggest that the southwest passage of winter visitors is on a broad front across much of the east Mediterranean.

On 10 November Adams saw a different movement in the form of a distinct wave of birds flying south-southeast passing over the south coast of Cyprus at *c*. 2130 hours. The circumstances of the observation suggest that the birds had left Turkey at dusk and had overflown the island. No other late waves from Turkey were recorded on other nights, possibly because they would have arrived after observations ceased.

Winter visitors

The island in winter, with its mild temperature, rainfall and new growth, is very attractive to birds, and some 90 species occur as regular winter visitors, with another 29 or so as irregular visitors. Many of them are species which also occur as late autumn passage migrants. Both Robin and Chiffchaff are common and widespread in wooded areas and scrub, where also occur smaller numbers of Sardinian Warblers *Sylvia melanocephala*. Song Thrushes are also common and widespread, both in wooded and in more open areas, and smaller numbers of other thrushes also occur. In garigue and open low scrub the most conspicuous bird is the Stonechat *Saxicola torquata*. Starling, Skylark, Meadow Pipit and White Wagtail are common in open areas, the wagtails being particularly obvious along the roadsides. Large numbers of finches also overwinter, notably Chaffinch *Fringilla coelebs*, Serin *Serinus serinus*, Greenfinch *Carduelis chloris*, Goldfinch *Carduelis carduelis* and Linnet *Carduelis cannabina*.

Winter visitors with more specialised habitat preferences are Finsch's Wheatear *Oenanthe finschii*, in open rocky areas, and Wallcreeper *Tichodroma muraria*, on rock faces, whilst in reed beds occur Reed Bunting *Emberiza schoeniclus*, Penduline Tit *Remiz pendulinus* and Moustached Warbler *Acrocephalus melanopogon*.

Up to 10,000 Greater Flamingos winter on the salt lakes, mainly at Akrotiri, with several 1000 Teal *Anas crecca* and Pintail *Anas acuta* and smaller numbers of other ducks. Smaller wetlands and reservoirs also often hold some duck, grebes (Podicipedidae) and gulls, especially Black-headed Gull *Larus ridibundus*, which is also numerous around the coasts and harbours. Few species of plovers (Charadriidae) or waders (Scolopacidae) winter regularly in any numbers, the most numerous being Lapwings, which occur commonly on cultivated areas of the plains.

In general the main wintering period is December to February, with arrival in November and departure in March, and for many species, especially the smaller passerines, the wintering numbers and periods are remarkably consistent from year to year. Retraps of ringed birds in subsequent winters also show a remarkable fidelity to the original wintering site, most obviously in species ringed in large numbers such as Robin and Chiffchaff. Hard weather further north may, however, cause considerable influxes of species which are not normally common or do not usually occur in winter. Among these variable or irruptive species are White-fronted Goose *Anser albifrons*, Great Bustard *Otis tarda*, several thrushes – Ring Ouzel *Turdus torquatus*, Fieldfare *Turdus pilaris*, Redwing and Mistle Thrush – and Bearded Tit *Panurus biarmicus*, Siskin *Carduelis spinus* and Hawfinch *Coccothraustes coccothraustes*. Changes in numbers of birds within the island, and records of day and night passage, indicate that there is some movement to, from or through the island throughout the winter, the extent no doubt depending greatly on the weather. Mason (1980) mentions radar observations in December 1975 of large numbers of birds heading south from Turkey with almost equally large numbers departing due east from Cyprus at the same time.

Ringing recoveries show the areas of origin of winter visitors to be rather similar to those of passage migrants, mainly eastern Europe, Scandinavia and the western U.S.S.R.; but although most small passerine winter visitors show origins to the west of north, this is much less marked than with some trans-Saharan migrants. The number of recoveries is too small to draw any firm conclusions, but so far the areas of origin of small passerines like Woodlark *Lullula arborea*, White Wagtail, Blackcap, Chiffchaff, Black Redstart *Phoenicurus ochruros* and Robin have been mainly eastern Europe and Scandinavia, whilst those of finches are from eastern Europe and the western U.S.S.R., and those of larger passerines like thrushes and Starlings mainly from the western U.S.S.R.

Spring migration
The passage of birds through the island in spring is generally more obvious than in autumn. This can be partly accounted for by the spring passage being briefer, less protracted and more concentrated than the autumn one and by the island in spring, after the winter rain, being much more attractive to birds than in autumn, so that many species, especially water or wading birds, remain for several days or weeks. Some 25 species, mainly Scolopacidae, Sylviidae and Muscicapidae are much more numerous in spring than in autumn, and for several spring migrants there are few or no autumn records, notably Great Spotted Cuckoo *Clamator glandarius*, Subalpine Warbler *Sylvia cantillans*, Black-eared Wheatear *Oenanthe hispanica*, Rüppell's Warbler *Sylvia rueppelli*, Bonelli's Warbler *Phylloscopus bonelli*, Pied and Collared Flycatcher *Ficedula hypoleuca* and *albicollis* and Woodchat Shrike *Lanius senator*.

Nevertheless, the total number of birds which pass in spring is less than in autumn. Bee-eater, hirundines, Blackcap and Willow Warbler are among the most abundant migrants, passing in vast numbers in autumn, but all are less numerous in spring, indeed Willow Warbler is usually scarce then. The radar observations of Adams (1962) also reveal a generally smaller volume of migration in spring than in autumn. Winter mortality undoubtedly has some effect in reducing numbers returning in spring, and as pointed out by Bourne (1960a), the configuration of the coast of Asia Minor to the north tends to guide diurnal migrants into the island in autumn, but in spring the inclination of the coast of Sinai and the Levant deflects northward flying birds to the east and away from Cyprus.

However for those species, mainly nocturnal migrants, where there are striking differences between the spring and autumn numbers, the discrepancy appears to be due either to some birds overflying the island without stopping in autumn, as may be the case with, for example, Rüppell's Warbler and Collared Flycatcher (Moreau 1961); or due to birds following a loop migration path, spring migrants returning by a different route from that used in autumn, as is known to be the case with Lesser Whitethroat (Mead 1974) and is probably the case with a number of other species including Subalpine Warbler, Willow Warbler, Pied Flycatcher and Lesser Grey Shrike (Moreau 1961, 1972).

The first few obvious spring migrants, such as Swallow and House Martin *Delichon urbica*, begin to appear in early or mid February, occasionally in late January, but no passage of any scale occurs until the second half of February. In spring 1959, Adams saw virtually no passage by radar until 21 February, though the weather was previously adverse. Radar observations in 1964 revealed passage on 20 February with distinct movements northeast and northwest from the island, and on 21 February a movement in from the southwest all along the south coast. Visual observations at the time suggest that finches, especially Greenfinch and Chaffinch,

Plate 1. Rocky hillside with scattered trees and scrub in Paphos District, breeding
habitat of Cretzschmar's Bunting. (R. Frost)

Plate 2. Vineyards with scattered trees in Paphos District, a breeding habitat of
Black-headed Bunting. (P. R. Flint)

Plate 3. Paphos Forest, a large forest containing two-thirds of the island's forest trees, mainly Aleppo Pine and, in the foreground, the endemic Golden Oak. (P. R. Flint)

Plate 4. Stream with Plane and Alder in the Paphos Forest, the culverts are a nesting site of Red-rumped Swallow. (D. Frost)

Plate 5. Ridge top in the higher western Troodos between Stavros and Kykko Monastery, breeding habitat of Woodlark. (D. Frost)

Plate 6. Cedar Valley, the endemic Cyprus Cedar now occurs only in a restricted area of the higher western Troodos. (D. Frost)

Plate 7. Forest of Troodos Pine on Mt. Troodos, habitat of the endemic Crossbill. (R. Frost)

Plate 8. Asprokremmos reservoir, a large new reservoir in the southwestern Troodos foothills. (R. Frost)

Plate 9. Dhiarizos valley, a wide partly cultivated valley in the southwestern Troodos foothills. (T. A. Box)

Plate 10. Sparsely vegetated chalky hills in the southwestern Troodos, such glaringly white landscapes form striking features of the island in summer. (P. R. Flint)

Plate 11. Kensington cliffs and Quarry beach at Episkopi, breeding site of Griffon Vulture, Eleonora's Falcon and Alpine Swift, and winter habitat of Wall-creeper. (R. Frost)

Plate 12. Phasouri reed beds and water meadows in the left foreground, with Phasouri citrus plantations beyond, and part of Akrotiri Salt Lake in the distance to the right. (P. Olesen)

Plate 13. Flooded Tamarisk scrub at Akrotiri reed beds, nesting habitat of Dead Sea
Sparrow. (R. Frost)

Plate 14. Flooded salt flats behind Ladies Mile beach near Limassol, important for
migrant and wintering waders. (T. A. Box)

Plate 15. Winter gull roosts on groynes and reef at Larnaca sea front. (R. Frost)

Plate 16. Akhna reservoir, a new shallow reservoir in the southeast which has proved very attractive to birds. (P. M. Bullock)

Plate 17. Broken rocky ground at Cape Pyla in the southeast, typical wintering
habitat of Finsch's Wheatear. (R. Frost)

Plate 18. Cape Kormakiti, looking east towards Kornos Peak at the western end of
the Kyrenia range. (P. R. Flint)

Plate 19. Pentadaktylos Mountain in the Kyrenia range, former nesting site of the Griffon Vulture. (P. R. Flint)

Plate 20. Dense scrub and woodland on the north coast, with the eastern Kyrenia range beyond. (P. R. Flint)

Plate 21. Geunyeli reservoir, now the most important wetland in the north, and a haven to thousands of waterbirds every year. (P. R. Flint)

Plate 22. Stone Pines at Salamis Forest, an area very attractive to migrants and which has been a breeding site of Long-eared Owl. (H. Sigg)

Plate 23. Arable fields north of Boghaz, towards the end of another very dry year. (P. R. Flint)

Plate 24. Wind stunted Juniper scrub at Cape Andreas, with the tip of the cape and the Klidhes Islands beyond. (P. R. Flint)

may have been involved (C.O.S.(1957) 11th Report). There is also a marked diurnal westward passage of Chaffinches at Akrotiri from mid February to mid March, with rates of up to 2000 per hour.

A mainly eastward passage of water and wading birds occurs along the south coast in spring (a reciprocal of that on the north coast in autumn), with a smaller passage up the west coast. This coasting passage also has had relatively little study, though it is known that some duck raft in Curium Bay (20,000 there once mid March) and fly northwest across the island at dusk. It seems likely that large flocks, flying very fast, at air speeds of *c.* 90–100 km per hour, which were seen by radar to reach the island from the southwest on the nights of 21 and 22 February 1959 were part of this duck passage (Adams 1962).

The number of cranes which pass in spring is less than in autumn, and the flocks are also less obvious, often passing by night and generally overflying the island without landing, so that few are identified as to species.

The numbers of migrants increase until by early or mid March a steady passage is in progress, continuing until mid May, after which it rapidly tails off. Visible migration is most obvious at the northern capes, from where a stream of diurnal migrants pass out to sea – in early spring mainly finches and other species which have wintered in the Mediterranean region, and later long distance migrants such as Swift *Apus apus,* Bee-eater and hirundines. Behind the capes, especially in the juniper scrub at Cape Andreas, many grounded nocturnal migrants congregate, sometimes in spectacular concentrations. A departure after sunset from the north of the island was often seen by Adams from 9 April until late in May.

The species composition of these nocturnal migrants changes as the spring migration progresses, and even over a period of a week it is possible to notice the changes as earlier migrants become less numerous and later migrants become more so. Typical early migrants are Rüppell's and Subalpine Warblers, Orphean Warbler *Sylvia hortensis,* Isabelline Wheatear *Oenanthe isabellina* and Redstarts of the race *Phoenicurus phoenicurus samamisicus;* and typical late migrants are Whinchat *Saxicola rubetra,* Barred Warbler *Sylvia nisoria,* Garden Warbler *Sylvia borin,* Wood Warbler *Phylloscopus sibilatrix,* Flycatchers and Golden Oriole *Oriolus oriolus.*

As might be expected, the earlier migrants are those with a southerly breeding distribution (often in Turkey), and the later migrants generally those which breed further to the north in Europe and the U.S.S.R. The same general rule applies to many other spring migrants, Greater Sand Plover *Charadrius leschenaultii* for example, which breeds in Turkey, being a particularly early migrant wader, and Sanderling *Calidris alba,* which breeds in the Arctic, being a late one.

Adams found that most birds arriving in the island had flown tracks east of north and must have departed from the vicinity of the Nile Delta. He also found that the first bird echoes reached Cyprus between 2100 and 0100 hours, remained at a fairly constant level until between 0500 and 0800 hours, after which they gradually diminished, fading away between midday and dusk. (This timetable does not include low flying diurnal migrants like Swallows, which are unlikely to be recorded by radar.) Allowing for the varying flying speeds of the different species, Adams considered this arrival timetable to be consistent with a strong departure from the Nile coast after dusk, moderating after midnight and diminishing suddenly at dawn. He found that birds arriving at the south coast of Cyprus during the night flew on across the island, while migrants arriving after dawn probably landed.

Adams found that on many occasions by day, and once by night (in bright moonlight), birds crossing the south coast west of the main bulk of the Troodos range on tracks between 000° and 040° either followed the west coast of the island round to the northeast, flying across Khrysokhou and Morphou Bays, or (the majority) turned gradually eastward between the mountains and the sea, passing west of and avoiding the higher Troodos. At 1100 hours on 27 March 1959 he also tracked a very large bird echo, which must have represented a large flock of large birds, coasting from Pomos Point, across Morphou Bay and along the Kyrenia range. The minimum possible altitude was c.4000 m and the speed c.110–145 km per hour. The high speed of the flock suggests that wildfowl may have been involved.

The average direction of almost all radar-detected spring migration seen by Adams was north-northeast, with an average track of 030°–035°, and although an irregular northwesterly passage was seen it accounted for less than one tenth of the total volume of migration, and more than half the northwest-bound migrants passed over Cyprus during the three nights of 9–11 April. The northwesterly movement seen on the night of 10 April was exceptionally large, and the number of birds involved was much greater than the number recorded by Adams on any other date in either season. The movement appeared as a dense mass of echoes in the form of a wave approaching the island from the direction of Israel and the Lebanon, the leading birds crossing the south coast of Cyprus at 2200 hours. The depth of the initial wave was c.112 km, the length of the wave apparently limited only by the performance of the radar equipment. At midnight, when the radar watch ended, immense numbers of birds were streaming across the island, many of them flying straight over the peak of Mt. Olympus. The average track of the movement was 320°, its calculated heading 345°.

The birds must have crossed the coasts of the Lebanon and Israel between Beirut and Tel Aviv, but the continuous density of the wave along the whole length detected by radar suggests that the movement probably extended further north and south along the eastern coast of the Mediterranean. The wind was light northeasterly, with clear skies and exceptionally good visibility. Such weather was encountered at no other night watch in either April or May, the wind being westerly throughout most of April and all of May. It seems possible that birds which normally pass up the Levant coast were influenced in some way by the unusual weather so as to follow a route cutting across the corner of the Mediterranean instead of probably continuing up through the Levant as they are presumed to do normally.

The weather in any particular spring will clearly affect the numbers of birds passing through the island, and may explain why some species, particularly some warblers, flycatchers and shrikes, are scarce in some springs but common in others, and why they occasionally occur in huge influxes in different areas; a northwestward movement from the Levant coast, for instance, would bring birds to eastern rather than western Cyprus. The results of a study of liming at Paralimni in spring 1968 (Hubbard 1968) suggest that this may be the case, the species occurring there being rather different from those seen and trapped at Akrotiri in the same spring; Lesser Whitethroat, for example, was the most numerous species at Paralimni but not at Akrotiri, and both Barred Warbler and Savi's Warbler *Locustella luscinioides* were limed in 10s at Paralimni, but neither occurred at Akrotiri. Also during simultaneous observations and ringing at Akrotiri and Cape Andreas 4–7 April 1969, Lesser Whitethroat were rather scarce at Akrotiri (only 4 out of 90 ringed birds) but abundant at Cape Andreas (64 out of 116 ringed birds) (P. F. Stewart). These differences in migration patterns across the island are worthy of further study, and further simultaneous observations at points in the east and in the west of the island would be of value.

A combination of easterly winds and anticyclonic weather was also considered by Christensen (1967) to be responsible for a small but important passage of birds of prey, including eagles, over eastern Cyprus in spring. In the period 8–12 April 1965 he saw 5 *Aquila* eagles and several other birds of prey around Famagusta, and on 11 April saw raptors arriving over the sea with a strong southeasterly wind; they included a Short-toed Eagle, 4 *Accipiter* sp, 2 falcons and a buzzard, which all went north along the east coast. Subsequent observations at Cape Andreas in 1972, 1973 (Stagg 1973, 1974) and 1974 (P. R. Flint) confirmed the regularity of this passage, small numbers of raptors, including buzzards and eagles, occurring each spring. The maximum daily totals of buzzards at Cape Andreas are only in 10s, as opposed to the large scale passage through the island in autumn, perhaps because, as with other diurnal migrants, the inclination of the coast to the south may deflect the birds to the east and away from Cyprus. Away from the east coast most records of raptors tend to be of species less dependent on soaring flight – falcons, harriers (especially Pallid Harrier *Circus macrourus*) and Osprey. These are more widespread in the island presumably because they make a broad front crossing of the east Mediterranean.

At the end of May a few diurnal migrants, mainly Bee-eaters, Swifts and hirundines may still be seen leaving the northern capes, and passage has occasionally been observed into June (once 200 Sand Martins were seen at Akrotiri in early June). It is interesting to note that individual Swallows have been seen leaving northern capes as early as mid February and that some are still passing in late May. The radar observations of Adams showed that small numbers of night migrants also are still passing at the end of May. If the salt lakes hold water, some waders, particularly Little Stint *Calidris minuta* and Ruff *Philomachus pugnax,* may remain, exceptionally in 100s, into early June.

Changes in status

Since the first edition several species of migrants and winter visitors have become more numerous or more regular. Flocks of Cormorants *Phalacrocorax carbo* are now probably regular on spring passage, and small numbers also now winter regularly, some of them at inland waters. The Sandwich Tern *Sterna sandvicensis* has apparently become more numerous in winter in recent years, though some will have been overlooked in the past. The White-breasted Kingfisher *Halcyon smyrnensis,* first reliably recorded in 1977, is becoming more regular, overwintering in 3 winters since 1985. The Citrine Wagtail *Motacilla citreola,* first recorded in 1971, has been a regular spring migrant since 1985, at least 7 birds occurring in spring 1990. There have been 7 records of the Pygmy Cormorant *Phalacrocorax pygmeus* since the first record in 1982, and 5 records of the Caspian Plover *Charadrius asiaticus* since the first record in 1984.

The only migrant which appears to be declining is the Demoiselle Crane. The few observations made of the autumn migration in recent years suggesting that both the size of the flocks and the total number of birds passing are less than they were 20 years ago.

BREEDING

In summer the dry and often glaring landscape of Cyprus can seem almost devoid of birds, apart from the occasional Magpies *Pica pica* or Hooded Crows *Corvus corone*; nevertheless, some 46 resident and 27 migratory species breed regularly, while another 25 species breed occasionally or have bred in the past.

The richest bird habitats are the forests of the Troodos range, to which are confined several species, among them Coal Tit *Parus ater*, Short-toed Treecreeper *Certhia brachydactyla*, Jay *Garrulus glandarius*, Chaffinch *Fringilla coelebs*, Crossbill *Loxia curvirostra* (confined to the *Pinus nigra* forest of the higher Troodos) and the migratory Spotted Flycatcher *Muscicapa striata*. Along open ridge tops Woodlarks *Lullula arborea* may be heard and valley bottoms echo with the song of Wren *Troglodytes troglodytes*, Cetti's Warbler *Cettia cetti* (also occurring to sea level) and the migratory Nightingale *Luscinia megarhynchos*. The Serin *Serinus serinus* has its main distribution in wooded areas of the Troodos range.

Migrant breeders particularly numerous in the Troodos range, though also occurring elsewhere, include Red-rumped Swallow *Hirundo daurica*, with a nest seemingly under every roadside culvert, Masked Shrike *Lanius nubicus* in wooded areas, and Black-headed Bunting *Emberiza melanocephala* in the vine-growing areas of the southwest. The migratory Cyprus Pied Wheatear *Oenanthe cypriaca*, common and widespread throughout the island, is particularly numerous in the more rocky and open wooded areas of the Troodos range, where it reaches very high breeding densities.

The forests of the Kyrenia range are less extensive, drier, more open and mostly at a lower altitude than those of the Troodos range and contain none of the 'montane' species of the Troodos forests. The much more rugged nature of the Kyrenia range does provide ample nest sites for cliff and crag nesters like Griffon Vulture *Gyps fulvus*, and the migratory Alpine Swift *Apus melba*, whilst Blue Rock Thrush *Monticola solitarius* nest along the ridge tops. Other species to occur in both mountain ranges and surrounding areas include Rock Dove *Columba livia*, Woodpigeon *Columba palumbus*, Crag Martin *Ptyonoprogne rupestris*, Jackdaw *Corvus monedula*, Raven *Corvus corax* and the migratory Cretzschmar's Bunting *Emberiza caesia*.

Resident species with a wide distribution in the island include Kestrel *Falco tinnunculus*, Chukar *Alectoris chukar*, Scops Owl *Otus scops*, Little Owl *Athene noctua*, Crested Lark *Galerida cristata*, Great Tit *Parus major*, House Sparrow *Passer domesticus*, Greenfinch *Carduelis chloris*, Goldfinch *Carduelis carduelis*, Linnet *Carduelis cannabina* and Corn Bunting *Miliaria calandra*. The Barn Owl *Tyto alba* is not uncommon on low ground. The Spanish Sparrow *Passer hispaniolensis* has a patchy but widespread distribution, often sharing its tree colonies with House Sparrows. Fan-tailed Warbler *Cisticola juncidis* occurs wherever cereals are grown and is more often heard than seen in its song flight over the standing crops. The attractive Black Francolin *Francolinus francolinus* is now mainly confined to the coastal southwest and to the Karpas peninsula.

Among the more numerous and widespread migrant breeders are Swift *Apus apus*, Swallow *Hirundo rustica*, House Martin *Delichon urbica* and Olivaceous Warbler *Hippolais pallida*. Less numerous migrant breeders include Turtle Dove *Streptopelia turtur*, Great Spotted Cuckoo *Clamator glandarius*, Nightjar *Caprimulgus europaeus*, Pallid Swift *Apus pallidus*, the colourful Bee-eater *Merops apiaster*, Roller *Coracias garrulus* and Hoopoe *Upupa epops*, and (a few pairs of) Yellow Wagtail *Motacilla flava* and Golden Oriole *Oriolus oriolus*. Some 110–120 pairs of the migratory Eleonora's Falcon *Falco eleonorae* breed on sea cliffs in the south, from Cape Gata westward towards Petra tou Romiou.

Confined to the hot, dry and rather treeless central lowlands are Calandra Lark *Melanocorypha calandra*, the migratory Short-toed Lark *Calandrella brachydactyla* and a few surviving Black-bellied Sandgrouse *Pterocles orientalis*. Stone Curlew *Burhinus oedicnemus* also breed there as well as elsewhere on low ground.

The 2 resident or partly migratory *Sylvia* warblers, the Cyprus Warbler *S. melanothorax* and Spectacled Warbler *S. conspicillata*, have limits of distribution closely corresponding with annual rainfall. In general, *melanothorax* occurs in the wetter southwest and north, and *conspicillata* on the dry central lowlands. Their breeding distributions overlap along the southern slopes of the Kyrenia range and in the northern and eastern foothills of the Troodos range.

The only 2 wetland species to breed regularly are the migratory Reed Warbler *Acrocephalus scirpaceus* and the Kentish Plover *Charadrius alexandrinus*, which is also apparently not resident. In the not infrequent years with high water levels, Moorhen *Gallinula chloropus*, Coot *Fulica atra* and Black-winged Stilt *Himantopus himantopus* also usually breed at Akrotiri and occasionally elsewhere. Many other wetland species have also bred in favourable years, both recently and in the past, including 20 of the 25 species of occasional or former breeders, an indication of the breeding potential of wetland habitat. Many of these species bred in the early years of this century, when the Mesaoria reservoirs were newly constructed and full of water and when there was also much less disturbance and shooting than nowadays. The wetlands of Cyprus are also all relatively small, and even in wet years their size must restrict the number of species which breed.

Only 3 species of seabird breed and none of them are numerous, a reflection of the relative infertility of the surrounding sea. Shag *Phalacrocorax aristotelis* and Herring Gull *Larus argentatus* occur in small numbers around the coasts, the largest colonies being at the Klidhes Islands, where some 15 pairs of Audouin's Gull *Larus audouinii* also breed.

In addition to the regular, occasional and former breeders, another 23 species have been doubtfully described as breeding at one time or another. Investigation suggests that the breeding records of 19 of these species are either erroneous or probably so, the remaining 4 being at best unsubstantiated. One source of confusion has been the misinterpretation of the statement by Belcher (1929) that "Towards Famagusta, and at the other end of the plain at Morphou, are marshes of a fair extent where Ducks (Garganey, Marbled, Shoveler and Tufted) and the three species of Grebe (Great Crested, Eared and Little) have nested in years of abundant water, *at all events at the former locality*" (our italics). This has resulted in statements in the subsequent literature that these species have nested at Famagusta and at Morphou. In fact there are no records of breeding at either location, and it is clear that Belcher was simply summarising the earlier breeding records (not all reliable) from the Mesaoria reservoirs, which, from Troodos, where he was writing, certainly are "towards Famagusta".

Changes in status

Prior to its human settlement the island was probably almost entirely covered in woodland and must have presented a richer and much more extensive habitat for woodland birds than it does today. There is no evidence to say whether any woodland species have been lost as a result of deforestation, but in view of the greatly reduced habitat the loss of species seems very probable. It also seems likely that the distribution of some woodland species, now confined to the forests of the Troodos range, was more widespread in the past. For instance, species apparently confined to the mountains (such as Wren *Troglodytes troglodytes* and Coal Tit *Parus ater*) in fact occur to the lowest tree line level of the Paphos Forest and probably had a much wider distribution when the forests covered the low ground.

The island's now extensive areas of garigue and steppe carry few breeding species, though the increase in these habitats has been clearly advantageous to open country species such as Stone Curlew *Burhinus oedicnemus*, Black-bellied Sandgrouse *Pterocles orientalis*, Calandra Lark *Melanocorypha calandra*, Short-toed Lark *Calandrella brachydactyla*, Crested Lark *Galerida cristata* and Corn Bunting *Miliaria calandra*.

During this century the status of several species has changed considerably and there have been both extinctions and colonisations. At least 2 species, Dipper *Cinclus cinclus* and Lesser Kestrel *Falco naumanni*, have become extinct as breeding birds. Marbled Teal *Marmaronetta angustirostris* was probably a not uncommon regular breeder, but also no longer breeds. Griffon Vulture *Gyps fulvus*, Black Vulture *Aegypius monachus*, Imperial Eagle *Aquila heliaca*, Bonelli's Eagle *Hieraaetus fasciatus*, Chukar *Alectoris chukar* and Black-bellied Sandgrouse have all declined in numbers and the extinction of the Black Vulture as a breeding species may have already occurred, and that of the Imperial Eagle seems inevitable. The main reason for all these declines and extinctions is probably shooting, though changes in agricultural practice which result in less availability of carrion have also probably adversely affected the large birds of prey. The effects of agricultural insecticides such as DDT on birds of prey in Cyprus are not known; however, the egg of a Herring Gull *Larus argentatus* taken at the Klidhes Islands in 1974 contained 29 parts per million wet weight DDE (the principal metabolite of DDT). This level of DDE is high and in bird-eating birds of prey is known to cause reduced reproductive success (Leontiades 1977).

The Black Francolin *Francolinus francolinus*, which was greatly reduced in numbers by excessive shooting, has shown a welcome increase in the last decade as a result of protection, and has recolonised some of its former breeding range.

Two species, Greenfinch *Carduelis chloris* and Dead Sea Sparrow *Passer moabiticus*, have recently colonised the island: the Greenfinch is now common and widespread; the sparrow is known only from one location (Akrotiri Salt Lake), but it is apparently increasing in numbers and showing signs of dispersion away from the breeding site. The Blackbird *Turdus merula* and Woodchat Shrike *Lanius senator* also appear to be extending their breeding ranges to the island. Goshawks *Accipiter gentilis* probably now breed within the Paphos Forest, though unless shooting can be controlled there seems little chance of their long term survival. The Collared Dove *Streptopelia decaocto* and House Martin have both considerably increased their distribution in the island in recent years. The Cetti's Warbler also is apparently becoming more numerous and widespread in the island, and the Serin *Serinus serinus*, which was formerly confined to wooded areas of the Troodos range, has recently extended its breeding range onto low ground. This is apparently as a result of the steady increase in perennial irrigation and tree planting, particularly of plantations, on low ground, factors which are probably at least partly responsible for the colonisation by the Greenfinch. Much suitable habitat for the latter, however, existed prior to its colonisation and it is difficult to see why it did not breed previously considering it is such a numerous passage migrant and winter visitor. The colonisation by the Dead Sea Sparrow is probably concomitant with its continuing range expansion in the Middle East.

Breeding seasons

In general most resident birds breed within the period March or April to July or August, the main exceptions being the Shag and Griffon Vulture, which start breeding early, in January or even late December, and the Crossbill, which, from the few available records, appears to breed throughout much of the year. As might be expected, the breeding season of the migrant breeders begins later than that of the residents, almost all the migrants breeding within the period from April or May to July or August. The one main exception is Eleonora's Falcon *Falco eleonorae*, which, because it feeds its young on autumn migrants, breeds from late July to October. Species which nest at all altitudes on the island, such as Cyprus Pied Wheatear and Olivaceous Warbler *Hippolais pallida*, begin breeding at low elevations some 2–4 weeks earlier than their populations at higher elevations (e.g. Troodos).

Altitudinal movement
During the winter months some birds which breed on Troodos move to lower ground or migrate, the main species involved being Serin, Greenfinch, Goldfinch and Linnet. In contrast, it has been stated in the literature that several species, notably Cetti's Warbler, Cyprus Warbler and Cyprus Pied Wheatear, move from low ground to high ground in late summer or early autumn, subsequently migrating or returning to low ground in winter. However, there is no published evidence to support this and it seems unlikely that any significant movement occurs. The Cyprus Pied Wheatear does become less numerous or unobtrusive in hotter areas of low ground late May to early August, and similarly the Corn Bunting is also less obvious July to September; but for neither species is there any evidence of a corresponding increase on high ground.

Endemism
Considering its large migrant and wintering avifauna and the proximity of Cyprus to the mainland, the degree of endemism is high. Vaurie (1959, 1965) recognised 7 endemic subspecies: Scops Owl *Otus scops cyprius* (Madarász 1901), Cyprus Pied Wheatear *Oenanthe pleschanka cypriaca* (Homeyer 1884), Cyprus Warbler *Sylvia (melanocephala?) melanothorax* (Tristram 1872) (accorded specific status by Williamson 1968 and Voous 1977), Coal Tit *Parus ater cypriotes* (Dresser 1887), Short-toed Treecreeper *Certhia brachydactyla dorotheae* (Hartert 1904), Jay *Garrulus glandarius glaszneri* (Madarász 1902) and Crossbill *Loxia curvirostra guillemardi* (Madarász 1903). These 7 endemic subspecies comprise 9·5% of the total number of breeding species.

The following endemic races, all discarded by Vaurie, have also been described: Crested Lark *Galerida cristata cypriaca* (Bianchi 1907), Dipper *Cinclus cinclus olympicus* (Madarász 1903), Hooded Crow *Corvus corone pallescens* (Madarász 1904a), Raven *Corvus corax cyprius* (Orlando 1939) and Chaffinch *Fringilla coelebs cypriotis* (Harrison 1945). Vaurie did state, however, that the local populations of both Dipper (now extinct) and Raven require further study.

Endemic races of Wren *Troglodytes troglodytes cypriotes* (Bate 1903b) and Great Tit *Parus major aphrodite* (Madarász 1901) have also been described, but neither is now considered to be restricted to Cyprus, both occurring elsewhere in the east Mediterranean area. The east Mediterranean race of Chukar *Alectoris chukar cypriotes* (Hartert 1917) is often erroneously listed as an endemic, but was in fact never considered to be restricted to Cyprus. A Middle Eastern race of Jackdaw *Corvus monedula pontocaspicus* (Kleiner 1939), discarded by Vaurie, was also never considered an endemic, though sometimes wrongly listed as such.

Of the 7 endemic subspecies recognised by Vaurie, none has other races which occur as winter visitors to the island, and only one, the Scops Owl, has another race occurring on passage in the island, indicating a fairly long reproductive isolation. That species such as Wren, Great Tit and Crested Lark have not evolved distinct island forms suggests either that they have colonised the island relatively recently, that immigration has prevented reproductive isolation, or that for these species the island conditions are not that different.

Five of the 7 endemics are sedentary and 2 are migratory or partly so. It is noteworthy that the 2 migratory endemics are also the 2 which are the most markedly different from their closely related species or subspecies on the mainland.

This is particularly so for the Cyprus Pied Wheatear, which is entirely migratory, and only slightly less so for the Cyprus Warbler, which is partly migratory.

The Cyprus Pied Wheatear was listed by Vaurie as a race of the Pied Wheatear *Oenanthe pleschanka*, but subsequent field studies have shown it to differ considerably and there is probably adequate evidence to consider it an endemic species.

The Cyprus Warbler was treated as a race of the Sardinian Warbler *Sylvia melanocephala* by Vaurie, but Williamson (1968) considered the Cyprus Warbler to be much closer to Rüppell's Warbler *S. rueppelli*. Williamson based his decision on the striking similarities in plumage pattern, though at the same time considering the 2 to be sufficiently distinct to stand as good species. Williamson did not in fact specify any distinctions, but presumably had in mind morphological differences and the less migratory nature of the Cyprus Warbler. McNeile, who studied the breeding of all 3 species, considered the Cyprus Warbler "in all its habits and characteristics in the field to have very much more affinity with Rüppell's Warbler than Sardinian". As Rüppell's Warbler is a widespread and fairly common breeding bird in the adjacent southern coastlands of Turkey (Beaman 1978) and does not breed in Cyprus, *melanothorax* could be a geographical race of *rueppelli* in Cyprus. The relationship of the 2 might be better understood after a detailed comparison of their behaviour, breeding biology and vocalisations.

The endemic Crossbill *L.c. guillemardi* differs from nominate *curvirostra* in that red males are very rare, females are grey on the crown and mantle and the bill is much larger and thicker, similar to that of *L.c. scotica* (Vaurie), which has been designated a separate monotypic species by Knox (1975). As *guillemardi* is sedentary, isolated and morphologically distinct it seems worthy of further study; at the moment almost nothing is known of its behaviour, breeding biology and vocalisations, and even its nest and eggs are undescribed.

In general the plumage of endemic island birds tends to be more drab and less distinctive than that of their mainland counterparts (Grant 1965). Of the 7 Cyprus endemics, 5 of them, Scops Owl, Coal Tit, Short-toed Treecreeper, Jay and Crossbill, are indeed more drab, darker or greyer than their mainland counterparts. However the Cyprus Warbler and the Cyprus Pied Wheatear, although they do have more black in their plumage, are at least as distinctive as their mainland counterparts, and in fact the female Cyprus Pied Wheatear is much *more* distinctive, acquiring in summer the striking plumage of the male (Christensen 1974). The reasons for these differences are not clear, but it may be significant that the former 5 species are sedentary, and the latter 2 migratory or partly so.

There is some evidence that island birds are vocally, as well as morphologically, less distinctive than their mainland counterparts, and perhaps for the same reason, that the smaller number of birds on islands reduces the need for specific distinctiveness (Grant 1965). The songs of only 2 Cyprus endemic birds, Short-toed Treecreeper and Cyprus Pied Wheatear, have been compared in any detail with their mainland counterparts, and both are much simpler (Bergmann 1983). It is interesting to note that although the local race of Short-toed Treecreeper is only moderately well differentiated morphologically (Vaurie 1959), its song is remarkably short and simple when compared with mainland populations.

Numbers of birds

The number of species present in summer, some 73, is considerably less than in winter when, with residents and regular winter visitors (some fall into both categories), some 124 species are present. Not only are fewer species present in summer, but as even casual observation shows, the actual total number of birds present in summer is also much smaller than in winter, one reason being that the hot dry summers are inclement to many species. Even species adapted to the island's summer may have difficulties in the not infrequent drought years, as was shown by J. M. E. Took's study of breeding Calandra Larks *Melanocorypha calandra* at Prastio in 1973 (C.O.S. (1957) 20th Report).

It is noteworthy that Turkey, though only 72 km away from Cyprus, has 251 breeding species (Vittery *et al.* 1971), over 3 times as many as Cyprus. This difference is not unexpected for far fewer species of land birds reside on islands than the adjoining mainland (Lack 1969). Lack concluded that the small numbers of bird species on islands is due to ecological limitations, and not to difficulties of bird dispersal, and this is clearly the case in Cyprus, where well over 200 species occur as regular passage migrants or winter visitors but do not remain to breed.

Apart from the harsh summer climate, the most obvious ecological limitations in Cyprus are the absence of perennial wetlands and the deforestation of most of the island. However such obvious habitat deficiencies do not account for most bird absentees, and it has to be presumed that many ecological restrictions are not obvious, as is the case with other islands (Lack 1969). Why, for example, should regular breeders in Cyprus include only one *Oenanthe* species, 6 Sylviidae and no Picidae, when the corresponding figures for Turkey are (at least) 4 *Oenanthe* species, 25 Sylviidae and 7 Picidae (Vittery *et al.* 1971)? As woodpeckers are not migratory and have never been recorded from Cyprus, even as vagrants, their absence as breeding birds might be thought to be due to their failure to reach the island at all. This is at best only a partial explanation however, for one of the Picidae, the Wryneck *Jynx torquilla*, occurs both as a regular passage migrant and as a winter visitor, wintering birds spending at least 4 months in the island; but it has never been known to breed.

Lack (1969) concluded that island birds are often specially adapted to the reduced ecological diversity on islands, enabling fewer species with broader niches to exclude a greater number of specialists. This is certainly the case with the Cyprus Pied Wheatear *Oenanthe cypriaca*, which occupies the habitats (described by Beaman 1978) which in Turkey are occupied by 4 *Oenanthe* species, *oenanthe, hispanica, isabellina* and *finschii*, and which also occurs in pine forest, a habitat apparently not utilised in Turkey. The latter 4 wheatears all occur in Cyprus as either common passage migrants or in the case of the last as a winter visitor, but none has ever been known to breed. *O. finschii* winters in apparently ideal breeding habitat, but all leave at the end of winter, and in summer the same habitat is occupied by breeding Cyprus Pied Wheatears.

Aerial feeders are apparently less effected by the ecological limitations of Cyprus, and 9 species (one *Caprimulgus*, 3 Apus, one *Merops* and 4 hirundines) breed regularly, compared with 12 in Turkey.

It is interesting to compare the number of breeding species on Cyprus with those on other Mediterranean islands. MacArthur & Wilson (1967) state that there exists within a given region of relatively uniform climate an orderly relation between the size of a sample area and the number of species found in that area. A double logarithmic plot of breeding bird species (excluding sea birds) against island area for 12 Mediterranean islands (Fig. 4) gives a linear relationship between the log-species and log-area with a slope of 0·270, which means that an increase of island area *c.* 13 fold is necessary to double the number of bird species. A more detailed analysis by Massa using data from 37 islands gives a slope of 0·271. The required increase in island area is again *c.* 13 (12·906) not 40 as listed by Iapichino & Massa (1989: 29). The graph indicates that the avifauna of Cyprus (along with those of the Maltese Islands, Crete and Sardinia) is impoverished in comparison with those of Kos,

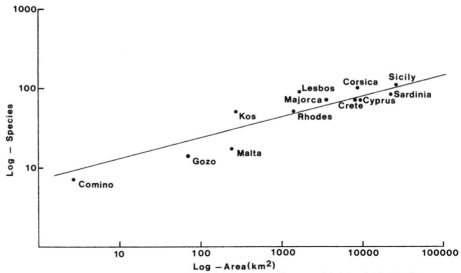

Figure 4. Species/area plot for breeding birds (excluding sea birds) of 12 Mediterranean islands. Maltese Islands (J. Sultana), Aegean Islands (G. Müller), Majorca (Parrack 1973), Crete (J. Parrott *per* J. F. Monk), Corsica (J. C. Thibault), Sicily (Iapichino & Massa 1989, Systematic List), and Sardinia (Iapichino & Massa 1989, Fig. 8).

Rhodes, Lesbos, Majorca, Corsica and Sicily. (The low position of Sardinia on the graph is perhaps due to it having had less ornithological coverage than the other islands mentioned). The Maltese Islands are known to have an impoverished avifauna due to extinctions from excessive shooting (Sultana & Gauci 1982), but most of the scatter away from the graph is probably due to varying habitat diversity between islands, which was shown by Watson (*in* Williamson 1981) to be more important than area in determining the number of bird species on an island, and Cyprus, in particular, is much poorer in woodland and wetland habitat than, for instance, Lesbos and Majorca (G. Müller, Parrack 1973). The impoverishment of the Cyprian avifauna (and that of Crete) in comparison with those of Corsica and Sicily, was also shown by Massa & Catalisano (1986), who surveyed the species occurring in an ecological succession of evergreen oak forest on these 4 islands. They believed the general impoverishment of Cyprus to depend upon its eastern Mediterranean location, where it is influenced by the Asiatic steppe climate.

BIRD KILLING AND CONSERVATION

Bird killing in Cyprus remains on a heavy and sustained scale throughout much of the year. In the Greek Cypriot south of the island there have been both improvements and set backs, but the overall situation has probably not improved in the last 10 years. Reports from the Turkish controlled north of the island indicate that bird killing has greatly increased there. Because of the growing international concern over the extent of bird killing in Cyprus, the International Council for Bird Preservation commissioned Gernant Magnin to investigate the situation in the Republic of Cyprus during spring and autumn 1986. This study was funded by The World Wide Fund for Nature, Friends of the Earth (Cyprus) and the Cyprus

Ornithological Society (1957); it was given the co-operation of all conservation groups in the Republic. Magnin's detailed and thorough report describes in graphic, and often disturbing detail, the extent of bird killing in the Republic. The 3 main methods of bird killing in Cyprus – Shooting, Liming and Netting – are discussed below, the text on the latter 2 being largely based on Magnin's findings (Magnin 1987). Except where stated otherwise, all statements in this chapter refer to the Republic of Cyprus (excluding the Turkish controlled north).

Shooting (called 'hunting' in Cyprus)
This is immensely popular and unfortunately the number of hunters is increasing. There are now over 40,000 licensed hunters, compared with 35,000 in 1982. In addition, the use of air guns is increasingly popular and there are now 28,000 registered. The hunters represent a very serious threat to the birdlife of Cyprus as they now kill more birds than are killed by liming and netting, and they also kill many more of the larger species which have much smaller populations and lower reproductive rates. In the past the peasant with his shotgun who shot an occasional bird for the pot may have been considered a traditional hunter, but the large scale and organised hunting of today is in no way traditional. The present day combination of affluence, greatly increased leisure time, a modern road system and often four-wheel drive vehicles means that very large numbers of hunters now frequently get to formerly inaccessible areas of the island. For instance the Akamas peninsula, site of a proposed National Park and a major concentration point for migrant birds, is packed with up to 2000 hunters on a typical shooting day, an intolerable pressure on such an environmentally important area.

Notwithstanding the above, the game and wild bird laws are quite good (see Appendix 5). Although hunting dates vary from year to year, in general, hunting is permitted in defined areas on Wednesdays and Sundays throughout January and February, from mid April to mid May, from mid or late August to the end of September, and from mid November to the end of December. In addition, however, daily shooting is permitted until the end of March and again in autumn in many coastal areas where migrants are known to concentrate. There are extensive areas of Game Reserve in the island, where shooting is prohibited all year (e.g. the Paphos Forest which is a very large Permanent Game Reserve). Although these reserves are mainly for Chukar and Black Francolin, they are a haven to all birds in them.

In general, the great majority of hunters abide by most, though not all, of the game laws. Evasion of the hunting permit is believed to be rare, there is virtually no shooting outside the permitted seasons, and there is little shooting within Game Reserves. Unfortunately very few hunters abide by the law concerning the protected birds, the majority shooting at any bird which comes within range. This shooting of protected birds, especially raptors and large water birds, is a very serious problem. All of the island's breeding raptors have been greatly reduced by shooting, and in autumn large numbers of migrant raptors are shot, especially at Akrotiri. The large water birds and raptors are usually shot for fun and left where they fall, their discarded corpses often being found. As Magnin observed, *control of the illegal shooting of protected species seems hardly to exist.* The shooting of small songbirds with shotguns is illegal but occurs quite widely. Shooting from cars is also illegal, but is practiced by a minority, especially at Akrotiri in autumn. The recent ban on the shooting of Black Francolin seems however to have been well observed.

There are few reliable figures of numbers of individual species shot. Report 19 of the Cyprus Ornithological Society (1970) states that *c.* 375,000 Song Thrush were shot on 10 January 1988, giving a winter total of perhaps 2 million. Bee-eaters are heavily shot in autumn, almost every flock being fired at as they pass down the valleys, and they are unfortunately very easy targets. From enquiries among hunters in autumn 1989 the average daily bag of Bee-eaters per hunter was *c*. 20, giving an autumn total into the 10s of 1000s at least – an appalling slaughter of one of Europe's most colourful and best loved birds. The Turtle Dove is a favourite prey species in both spring and autumn – in spring 1990 hunters were reporting shooting 15–20 Turtle Dove each on a 'good' day. In October 1987 up to 30 hunters gathered daily in the Kouris riverbed to fire into the dense flocks of migrating Spanish Sparrows passing overhead (Cyprus Ornithological Society (1957), Report 34).

There has been no detailed survey of shooting in the Republic. Magnin's educated guess of 2 million birds shot each year is believed to be too low by conservation groups in the Republic. Extrapolation from the results of the detailed survey of shooting carried out in north Cyprus (see Postscript) gives a figure of over 3 million birds shot each year by licenced hunters in the Republic. In addition to this are the birds shot with air guns, a *very* conservative estimate of 10 birds per gun per year would mean over a quarter of a million birds shot.

To improve the situation Magnin recommended that spring shooting should be banned, as it has been in Turkey since 1937 and in Greece since 1986. Clearly the killing of spring migrants is especially harmful, as these are the birds which have survived the autumn migration and the winter in Africa and are returning north to form that years breeding stock. We are delighted to report that Magnin's recommendation has been implemented and in 1991 spring shooting has been banned; we congratulate President Vassiliou on this courageous and far-sighted decision. Magnin also recommended that autumn shooting should not begin until the end of August, as many birds are still breeding earlier in the month. Also, and most importantly, *the law concerning the protected birds should be enforced.* The Cyprus Hunters Federation has also recommended that before the initial issue of a shooting licence, the applicant should pass a test on the recognition of the protected species.

If these measures fail to reduce the impact of the ever increasing numbers of hunters, then consideration should be given to the reduction of the shooting season, especially the very damaging daily shooting in coastal areas during the migrations. In the long term of course a real improvement will only come about through a change of attitudes, especially among the young.

Very little information is available concerning north Cyprus, however it is believed that all of the Griffon Vultures which bred in the Kyrenia range have now been shot. In May 1987 the shot and discarded corpses of Alpine Swifts were found at Galatia Lake on the Karpas. (See Postscript for north Cyprus).

Liming and Netting
The catching and killing of small migrant birds for human consumption is confined mainly to the southeast of Cyprus. The main area, especially during the autumn migration, is Paralimni to Cape Greco, with lesser areas between Limassol and Larnaca, particularly the Ayios Theodhoros and Maroni/Psematismenos valleys. The Karvounas Pass, where autumn migrants concentrate to cross the Troodos range, is another notorious area. During the winter months bird catching is more widespread, particularly in the Troodos range. In general, very little bird catching occurs in the west of the island.

Liming is the traditional and now completely illegal method of bird catching in Cyprus. Sticks covered in glue (limesticks) are placed in trees and bushes in areas known to be favoured by migrant birds, the birds alight on the sticks, become trapped by the glue and are then killed, plucked, and pickled in wine or vinegar, to be eaten later as a 'delicacy'. Limesticks may be placed and left all day; on these many birds die slowly after being trapped, since they hang upside down for hours or even days. Such birds are of course helpless and vulnerable to predators. In 1983 the remains of a Lesser Grey Shrike were found on a limestick together with a Magpie which had devoured the shrike before finding itself also ensnared (Osborn 1983). A more active form of liming is also practiced, mainly in the Paralimni area, in which the limesticks are placed only in the early mornings (before dawn) and newly arrived migrants are then chased and driven towards them. The lime is extremely sticky, the birds becoming trapped not only by their feet, but also by their wings and tail as they struggle to escape. The limers pull the birds off the sticks by the body; often tail and flight feathers and occasionally even legs remaining on the sticks. The birds are then killed by strangling or occasionally by biting the neck.

Limers are basically after fat autumn Blackcaps, the so-called 'Ambellopoullia' ('Birds of the Vineyards'), but the sticks trap any bird which alights on them. In a detailed study of liming (Hubbard 1968), 100 different species were caught at Paralimni in spring 1968, the most numerous being Lesser Whitethroat, Chiffchaff and Blackcap, but also included were such large, and now protected, species as Squacco Heron, Pallid Harrier, Stone Curlew and Barn Owl. All are of course killed by the limer, species capable of biting, such as shrikes, having their bills broken before being removed from the sticks.

A survey of autumn liming at Paralimni was carried out by Magnin in 1986, he found that up to 1000 people were occupied in liming every morning at some 300 liming sites. The average number of sticks per site was 150, which means that every morning throughout the migration, up to 45,000 limesticks were placed in the Paralimni area alone. Individual limers exceptionally caught over 2000 birds on 'good' days, a more usual daily catch per limer being 55–70 birds. Woldhek (*in* Magnin) describes standing in the midst of these limesticks at Paralimni – "all around me I heard the rustling of the wings of the dying birds that were trapped on the sticks". Magnin found the behaviour of the limers to be most blatant, liming even being practiced in the grounds of tourist hotels, notably at Protaras. Magnin also found the limers to be quite affluent, many of them arriving in brand new four-wheel drive vehicles. While the limed birds may have been an important supplement to the diet in earlier centuries, it is clear that the liming is now carried out solely for financial gain.

Although autumn is the main season for liming, it is also carried out in spring (as mentioned above), and throughout the winter for Robins and Thrushes – bunches of them often being offered for sale along the roadsides. Even in summer some liming continues – in July 1988 flocks of 100s of Corn Buntings at Akhna reservoir were decimated by heavy and persistent liming (Cyprus Ornithological Society (1957), Newsletter 88/7). The liming of Calandra Larks and Goldfinches for sale as cage birds also occurs in summer.

Mistnets were introduced into Cyprus around 1969 and became widely used during the 1970s and 1980s. Like limesticks, their use is completely illegal under Cyprus law. The fine mistnets, generally 3 m high and 12 m in length, are fixed in position against a background of trees or bushes so that they are invisible to the birds. The birds fly into the nets and become entangled, later to be removed and killed by the netter.

For the bird catchers the mistnets have many advantages over limesticks: catches are much higher and the amount of work involved is much less. Mistnets may be left up all day, every day, and need only be erected once, at the start of each migration. All the catcher has to do is check them occasionally and remove the birds caught. Because of their nature, mistnets catch a much wider variety of bird species than limesticks, including aerial species such as Swifts and Swallows, and even ground living species like Chukars and Quail. Netting is a very cruel practice. Birds trapped at dusk are generally not removed until the next morning, by which time many have died after hours of suffering. Thus on an October morning in 1986, of 6 Swallows that had been trapped in a net the night before, 2 were dead and the other 4 had bloody wounds to their wings and feet, and another net discovered on 8 November 1986 contained 3 dead Robins and a dead Chiffchaff (Magnin). In addition, it also takes time and patience to remove a bird uninjured from a mistnet, but obviously this is of no concern to the netters who simply pull the birds from the mesh, the numerous holes and many severed feet in the nets testifying to this (Magnin).

By the early 1980s it is probable that mistnets had largely replaced limesticks for bird catching in Cyprus. Although there are no accurate figures, many 10s of 1000s of nets undoubtedly were being used in the early 1980s. For example nets were erected in virtually a *continuous* 10 km line on both sides of the road from Paralimni to Cape Greco, and the whole valley at Ayios Theodhoros (*c.* 7 km in length) was full of rows of mistnets stretching right across the valley, individual catchers using as many as a 100 mistnets each. Nets were even placed in the centre of Larnaca town, and across a country road, blocking it to traffic (Magnin).

In December 1984, after many years of protest from conservation groups, the Council of Ministers decided to approve enforcement of Law No. 39 of 1974 (Appendix 5) which prohibits the use of nets and limesticks for the capture of wild birds, and at the same time they placed a ban on any further importation of mistnets. This decision was followed in 1985 by a major and very effective police campaign against mistnets which greatly reduced the number in use. As a direct result of this, Magnin found no mistnets in use at Paralimni in 1986, and only 7 well hidden nets in the valley at Ayios Theodhoros. However, he found 40 mistnets in the Maroni valley and 27 nearby in the valley near Psematismenos, and, despite repeated requests to the police, no action was taken against the latter netters, who continued their catching throughout the autumn migration. He also found nets in use in many other areas, including Phinikaria, where he found 7 nets in part of an area of many private and often fenced orchards, and where the total number in use was probably much higher. In the Kalavasos valley Magnin found 5 large nets, 2 of them less than 100 m from the Police Station.

After the police action against mistnets in 1985, the bird catchers largely reverted back to using limesticks, it being their belief that the authorities would turn a blind eye to this providing they were away from main roads and not visible to tourists. Certainly in autumn 1986, when it became clear that massive liming activity was once again taking place at Paralimni, protests by both local and international conservation groups to the President of Cyprus and to the Chief of Police failed to result in any action by the police.

In March 1988 Cyprus finally ratified the Berne Convention (Appendix 5) for the protection of wild birds, which specifically forbids both liming and mistnetting, and the Government are coming under increasing pressure to actually enforce this. An enquiry to the Chief of Police in Nicosia in March 1990 revealed that in 1989 the police in co-operation with Game Wardens destroyed *c.* 500 mistnets and *c.* 200 limesticks, and that 56 mistnets and 700 limesticks were held by the police as exhibits pending the trial of cases before the Court. This response is extremely encouraging as it shows that the authorities are at last prepared to take action against the limers, and the Police and Game Wardens are to be congratulated on their efforts.

There is no room for complacency however, the number of mistnets destroyed in 1989 is an indication of how many are still in use despite several years of police action. Indeed reports in 1990 indicate an upsurge of both liming and netting, and that nets, apparently illegally imported, are once again becoming fairly freely available.

In 1986 Magnin calculated that up to 2.2 million birds were killed by liming and netting. This figure was considered too low by conservation groups in the Republic, especially as it did not make sufficient allowance for birds killed in winter, spring and summer. If liming and netting are continuing at about the 1986 level, then the total number of birds killed annually in the Republic of Cyprus, including those shot, will be around 6 million; to which must be added the 2 million killed in the north (see Postscript), making a total of around 8 million for the whole island. This loss is not shared equally between all species, and for those species which are favourite prey, e.g. Woodcock, Turtle Dove, Bee-eater, Song Thrush, Robin, Lesser Whitethroat and Blackcap, the numbers killed probably represent a significant proportion of their breeding populations.

Project Birdsong
What can be done to stop this massive and often illegal bird killing? One of the most effective conservation groups in the Republic of Cyprus, Friends of the Earth (Cyprus), P.O. Box 3411, Limassol, are campaigning vigorously for a ban on spring shooting and for enforcement of the existing law on liming and netting. They also realise that the education and enlightenment of young people is one of the most important aspects of conservation, and to meet an urgent need for more Greek language educational materials they approached the British ornithologist and comedian Bill Oddie with a suggestion for a video on migration. With Bill's support, and assistance from the International Council for Bird Preservation, a highly pro-fessional 20 minute video, 'The Miracle of Migration', was produced. It has already been translated into 6 languages, including Greek and Turkish.

The video is available on free loan to schools and youth groups, but Friends of the Earth also intend to equip each post-graduate science teacher leaving the Pedagogical Institute in Nicosia with his or her own copy of the video, together with an accompanying leaflet and posters, all in Greek. This is Project Birdsong. In April 1990 the first batch of 100 Project Birdsong packages was delivered to the Pedagogi-cal Institute. To help fund the scheme Friends of the Earth are inviting people to sponsor a Project Birdsong package, which will be inscribed with the donor's name. They also welcome new members, both from within Cyprus and overseas.

Also active in the conservation field are the Cyprus Wildlife Society, P.O. Box 4281, Nicosia, which is run by Andreas Demetropoulas, the island's leading conservationist and the man behind the Lara Bay turtle conservation project.

The International Council for Bird Preservation are an international federation represented in over 100 countries. In 1990 they ran a 12 month campaign in north Cyprus to promote bird conservation, this included a mobile exhibition and slide shows in schools and villages, and field work to assess the methods and extent of bird killing. To support their world-wide work they welcome donations and new members; their address is 32 Cambridge Road, Girton, Cambridge, UK.

Apart from supporting the above organisations, individuals can help by reporting instances of liming and netting to the local police. Protest letters are also valuable, they should be sent to His Excellency the President of Cyprus, Presidential Palace, Nicosia, Cyprus. Overseas visitors can also write to the Cyprus High Commission or Embassy and to the office of the Cyprus Tourism Organisation in their own countries. Letters can also be very usefully sent to the Cyprus Mail, P.O. Box 1144, Nicosia, and to the Cyprus Weekly, P.O. Box 1992, Nicosia.

Conservation of Habitat
The continuing loss of the island's relatively few remaining areas of natural wetland is a serious problem. The Paralimni Lake, the marshes at Syrianokhori and the

Fresh Water Lake at Famagusta have all suffered drainage and reclamation in the past. The formerly extensive and superb Zakaki marshes, which 20 years ago were full of 100s of water and wading birds, have now almost completely vanished beneath the ever expanding Limassol New Port. The reed beds at Phasouri continue to suffer burning and clearance to provide more grazing land for cattle, and the reed beds at Akrotiri Salt Lake have also been considerably reduced over the last 20 years.

The reservoirs of the many dams constructed in recent years are used by migrant and wintering water birds, but their fluctuating water levels mean that they generally can not be used for breeding. The existence of the dams also means that little or no water now flows in the river valleys below them, and consequently many of the reed beds in the lower valleys and around the river mouths are drying out and dying. In particular, the new and very large Kouris Dam poses a threat to the existence of the Phasouri and Akrotiri reed beds. These reed beds at Phasouri and Akrotiri are the best remaining areas of marshland left in Cyprus, and an effort should be made to preserve them by ensuring an adequate water supply and by prohibiting further clearance and encroachment. This could be best done by making both areas, and the adjoining salt lake, into a National Nature Reserve. As suggested by Magnin, the provision of an information centre at Akrotiri (as well as elsewhere) would also be of great value in educating and enlightening the local population about wildlife and conservation. Such a centre would display information on habitats, vegetation and birds, would provide the opportunity for the observation of birds at close range, and would highlight the national heritage and beauty of Cyprus. A positive side effect for the Cyprus economy would be the consequential encouragement of wildlife tourism, especially outside the summer season.

Postscript North Cyprus

Details of the situation in north Cyprus have recently been made available to us by the North Cyprus Society for the Protection of Birds.

Several years ago a Swiss ornithologist, Harry Sigg, and his wife, who were living in Turkey, visited north Cyprus on a birdwatching holiday. They were appalled at what they found – the widespread liming and netting of migrant birds; the shooting of birds on a very large scale, often just for target practice; the killing of birds of prey, and the destruction of habitats. Harry Sigg created a support group in Switzerland and Germany, who sponsored him to carry out conservation work in north Cyprus. Then in 1990 the International Council for Bird Preservation provided further sponsorship, enabling him to spend a whole year conducting research and conservation education in north Cyprus. The results of this survey reveal extensive bird killing.

The law relating to wild birds is Chapter 65 (1959), an old British hunting law, but law enforcement is very poor. There are 3 hunting seasons in each year. In 1989/90 they were: *General Hunting*, mainly for Chukar, Francolin and waterfowl, November and December 1989 (Sundays only); *Thrush Hunting*, 15 January to 25 February 1990 (11 hunting days); and *Turtle Dove Hunting*, 25 April to 20 May 1990 (7 hunting days).

There are c. 12,000 hunters in north Cyprus. The total number of birds shot per year is around one and a quarter million, of which nearly one million are Song Thrush, with smaller numbers of Turtle Doves and other species. Many Song Thrush are killed during illegal night hunting with lights and air rifles. During the survey 100s of hunters were interviewed and their bags monitored. The average number of birds shot per hunter per day in winter (by midday) was 11. Many of the species shot were endangered species in Europe. Of the hunters interviewed 34% admitted shooting birds of prey.

Netting and/or liming are common and widespread practices in the Kyrenia range and on the Karpas peninsula; the main centres being Rizokarpaso (Dipkarpaz), Ayios Seryios (Yeniboğaziçi), and villages around Famagusta (Gazimağusa) and Kyrenia (Girne). The number of birds killed by netting and liming is around three quarters of a million per year. Including those shot, the total number of birds killed each year in north Cyprus is *c*. 2 million. These figures are provisional and may differ slightly from the final results to be published by the International Council for Bird Preservation.

Limers and netters sell large parts of their catches to the Republic of Cyprus, where prices are double those of the north. There is also some illegal export to England and Australia. Birds are also sold to restaurants in the north, especially those in Ayios Seryios. The illegal sale of shot wild birds is also common in the markets of Nicosia.

In 1989 Harry Sigg founded a Bird Protection Group in north Cyprus, which in June 1990 was expanded to become the North Cyprus Society for the Protection of Birds. The society is organising conservation and educational programmes for adults and school-children, these involve mobile exhibitions, slide and video presentations, poster, leaflet and sticker campaigns, and birdwatching expeditions. The society is also campaigning to get the existing very inadequate hunting laws enforced, and for the introduction of new more humane hunting and bird protection laws based on the Berne Convention.

The natural wetlands in north Cyprus have been largely drained and reclaimed during this century, and Gonyeli Reservoir is now the most important wetland, being used by 10s of 1000s of birds each year. The society are very concerned by the threat of leisure and recreational developments to the reservoir, and have put forward a detailed plan to ensure the reservoir remains a haven for birds. The plan includes fencing, extensive tree planting (in conjunction with the Forestry Commission), the erection of a birdwatching hide and the provision of educational and informational material. The society also monitors the remaining seasonal wetlands north and south of Salamis, which are now seriously threatened by tourist development.

In September 1990 Dr Tobias Salathé of the International Council for Bird Preservation visited north Cyprus as a guest of the society. The highlight of his visit was a field trip to Gonyeli Reservoir, which was also attended by many members of the public. Dr Salathé was also taken to the Karpas peninsula to see the catching and killing of birds by limers and netters. During this visit 2 members of the society made complaints to the local police, as a result of which 4 mistnets and 40 limesticks were confiscated. A subsequent result of this incident was that the 2 members of the society had their lives threatened.

In spring 1991 the North Cyprus Society for the Protection of Birds had a membership of well over 300, of whom more than 260 live in north Cyprus. Of its committee of 11, 10 are Turkish Cypriots.

Other conservation groups working in the field of bird protection are: the Green Peace movement, and the National Trust of Northern Cyprus.

ACKNOWLEDGEMENTS

First Edition

We should firstly like to express our gratitude to the editor, Dr J. F. Monk, who has greatly improved the text and who's advice, encouragement and patient help over a long period have been invaluable. To Dr W. R. P. Bourne we are in debt for most helpful detailed criticism of the Systematic List and the Breeding, Migration and Ornithological History chapters. We should also like to thank the committee of the Cyprus Ornithological Society (1957) for their co-operation; Charles Bennett, Secretary of the Society, for providing descriptions of rarities from the societies files for the years 1971–76 and for promptly and helpfully answering many queries over a long period; and Linda and Owen Sweeney, Mike Betts, Jill Whiter and Mick Lobb, recent Recorders of the society, for a constant supply of the records submitted to them and for also answering many queries.

Our thanks to the following who at some time provided unpublished records or material used here; Stuart Allen, E. Asplund, T. Attorps, A. H. Banks, I. Beames (per Dr D. W. Yalden), P. T. Bell, Charles Bennett, Dr H. H. Bergmann, Dr W. R. P. Bourne, Terry Box, M. Calvert, B. Carlsson, Brigadier T. Caulfeild, Wilf Corris, Vic Cozens, Dennis Crassweller, J. Eaton, Sqn Ldr R. Foers, Bob Frost, S. Fulford, M. E. J. Gore, Major T. T. Hallchurch, the late Dr J. M. Harrison, T. Hedley Bell, D. Herdson, A. Hill, B. Hill, Sqn Ldr P. G. Jenkins and Sqn Ldr M. Jourle (RAFOS Expedition 1982), S. C. Joyner, M. Komulainen, Mick Lobb, R. L. Mason, C. Mayhead, T. R. Mitchell, S. Mumford, Lt Col J. R. Neighbour, D. Noakes, A. S. Norris, A. Palmer, J. Petersson, P. H. Rathbone, Gordon Rayner, Miss L. A. Robertson, A. Seymour, Mrs H. R. Shepherd, Arthur Stagg, A. N. Stephens, Dr P. O. Swanberg, J. Veale, Frank Walker, Jill Whiter and Dr D. W. Yalden.

We are grateful to I. C. J. Galbraith, Peter Colston and D. K. Read of the British Museum (Natural History) at Tring for assistance and facilities afforded during our visits there; to Peter Colston also for information and opinions on some Cyprus skins and to Michael Walters for information and opinions on some Cyprus eggs held at Tring; to Dr W. R. P. Bourne for a list of some of the important skins there; to Steen Christensen for lists of the skin collections at Limassol and Nicosia; to Haim Hovel for a list of the Tel Aviv skin collection; to C. Edelstan (per Steen Christensen) for opinions of skins in the Naturhistoriska Riksmuseum; to I.C.T. Nisbet (per Dr W. R. P. Bourne) for a list of the Harvard skin collection; to Ian Lyster for a list of skins at the Royal Scottish Museum, for opinions of some of them and for loan of material from the museum; to Mary LeCroy for information on the New York skin collection; and to Dr L. Horváth for information on the fate of the Budapest skin collection.

For access to the papers of the late Dr D. A. Bannerman our thanks to M. J. Rowlands, Head of Library Services, British Museum (Natural History), South Kensington. For photocopies of many essential references our thanks to Anthony Cheke and Dr A. S. Richford of the Alexander Library, at the Edward Grey Institute, Oxford, to Anthony Cheke also for his assistance during our visit there; to J. C. Eames and G. S. Rance of the British Trust for Ornithology (BTO) Library; and to Mrs Anne Vale as Librarian of the Sub-Department of Ornithology at Tring, and also for her assistance during our visits there. For photocopies or originals of references we would also like to thank the staff of the library of the British Museum (Natural History), South Kensington; the librarians of the RAF Ornithological Society Library; the staff of the library of the Royal Botanic Gardens at Kew; Charles Bennett; Dr W. R. P. Bourne; Sqn Ldr R. Foers; Major T. T. Hallchurch; the Director of Public Information, Nicosia; Dr A. Panayiotou of the Geological Survey Department, Nicosia; the staff of the Meteorological Service, Nicosia; L. I. Leontiades, Conservator of Forests, Nicosia; and Dr G. C. Brown of the Department of Earth Sciences, The Open University. For their assistance in locating several obscure references our thanks to the staff of the Bibliographical Information Service and the Official Publications Library of the British Library. Our thanks also to the staff of the Alton and Lerwick Public Libraries for their assistance in obtaining reference material on inter-library loan from the British Library Lending Division.

We would also like to thank Bob Spencer and Mrs Molly Benson of the B.T.O. Ringing Office, Tring, for access to the ringing and recovery files and for assistance and facilities afforded during our visits there; Stuart Allen, Wilf Corris, Vic Cozens and Mick Lobb for biometric data of birds ringed by them; Steen Christensen for his comments on several records; Charles Bennett, Mick Lobb, Lt Col J. R. Neighbour and Dr D. W. Yalden for their contributions to the section 'Sites of Ornithological Interest in Cyprus'; Ernst Warstat for translations of German references; Eric Hardy for information on the publications of the Middle East Biological Scheme, the Jerusalem Naturalists Club and the Haifa Naturalists Club; the Head of the Game and Wild Life Service, Nicosia (*per* Charles Bennett) for information on hunting dates; J. D. Summers-Smith for his opinion of a *Passer* photograph; Chris Mead for his opinion of a *Sylvia* skin; and Adrian Akers-Douglas of Friends of the Earth (Cyprus) for his contribution to the Conservation Section.

For details of the numbers of breeding species on other Mediterranean islands our thanks to Joe Sultana (Maltese Islands); J. C. Thibault (Corsica); Günther Müller (Aegean Islands); and John Parrott (*per* Dr J. F. Monk) (Crete). For publishing requests for records our thanks to the editors of *British Birds* and *Var Fagelvarld*; and to the editors of the COS, OSME and RAFOS Newsletters.

Our particular thanks to our wives Karen and Julie for their patience and their assistance in many ways over a long period, to Karen also for checking and typing the manuscript. Finally our apologies to anyone who we may have inadvertently omitted to thank for their assistance.

Second Edition

We should firstly like to express our gratitude to the new editor, Dr Llewellyn Grimes, for his advice and assistance during the production of this second edition. We should also like to thank the committee of the Cyprus Ornithological Society (1957) for their co-operation, and particularly Charles Bennett, Secretary of the Society, for his extensive and unfailingly prompt and helpful assistance.

Our thanks to the following who provided unpublished records for this edition: Charles Bennett, Neil & Angie Bowman, Terry Box, Peter Boye, Fred Butler, Vic Cozens, M. Curtis, John Diley, Guus van Duin, M. H. Fallon, C. F. Fenn, Richard Foers, J. E. Francis, Bob Frost, Darren Frost, David & Mandy Hawkins, Barbara Hay, T. Hedley Bell, Klaus Hein, Peter Hellyer, Ken Heron, I. Hillery, I. Hunter, Dr A. R. Johnson, John Le Gassick, S. M. Lister, Dr Stefan Lunk, E. Möller, Bill Oddie, D. J. Odell, G. J. Oreel, N. Petrou, A. Ranner, D. Raw, Gordon Rayner, M. Roberts (*per* Bob Frost), S. A. Rothery, U. Schroeter, G. Smith, Arthur Stagg, K. Steiof, Denis Summers-Smith, Peter Tate, M. H. Thurston, M. Ullman, J. A. van der Ven (*per* C. Mitchell), S. P. & J. C. Warwick, David Whaley and M. Whorley; also to Jeremy Bullock, M. S. Cooper, M. Fairer, P. J. Langston, Bob Murray, W. Pompert, M. Sainsbury and R. A. Streatfeild (all *per* Charles Bennett); and to L. Batt, G. Etherington, T. Fountain, M. I. Hayes, D. Massey, Al Roberts, T. Russell and N. A. Smith, members of the Royal Air Force Ornithological Society 1990 expedition (all *per* Chris Sparks) and particularly to Chris Sparks for his most helpful assistance.

For their assistance with queries our thanks to Mark Beaman, Wilf Corris, Haim Hovel, D. & L. Hutton (*per* Charles Bennett), Reg Kersley, Mick Lobb and Bob Murray. For their opinions of various records our thanks to Peter Britton, Peter Colston, Steve Madge and Richard Porter. For biometric data of birds ringed by them our thanks to Vic Cozens, A. J. Crease, B. Hancock and

N. A. Smith (all *per* Vic Cozens). For information on a ringing recovery our thanks to G. Backhurst.

We are grateful to Charles Bennett, Adrian Akers-Douglas of Friends of the Earth (Cyprus), and to Peter Cant and Harry Sigg of the North Cyprus Society for the Protection of Birds, for their considerable contributions to the Bird Killing and Conservation chapter; to A. Haviaras, Chief Superintendent of Police, Nicosia, for information on the use of air guns, mist nets and limesticks; to the Head of the Game and Fauna Service, Nicosia, for details of the bird protection legislation (both *per* Adrian Akers-Douglas); and to Miriam Langeveld and Dr Tobias Salathé of the International Council for Bird Preservation for information on North Cyprus and for a copy of the Berne Convention.

For their most valuable contributions to the appendix on Ornithological Sites our thanks to Charles Bennett, Bob Frost, Mal Gault, Peter Hellyer and Gordon Rayner. For copies of reference material our thanks to Peter Boye; A. K. Christodoulou of the Department of Forests, Nicosia; M. Georgiades of the Cyprus Tourism Organisation; Mrs M. Hadjipaschali of the Press and Information Office, Nicosia; C. Hjort; Andreas Kephalas (*per* Ken Heron); G. Nikolaus; L. Telemachou of the Department of Land and Surveys, Nicosia; and our particular thanks to Bob Frost, Librarian of the Royal Air Force Ornithological Society, for his considerable assistance. For information and maps on North Cyprus our thanks to Tansel Fikri, their London representative. For provision of photocopying facilities and materials we thank John and Betty Green of Sealite Optical Labs Ltd and Mike Taylor of Mint Print, Evesham.

We are very grateful to Terry Box, P. M. Bullock, Guus van Duin, Bob Frost, Darren Frost, Michael Gore F.R.P.S., Pete Olesen and Harry Sigg for contributing their photographs to this edition; and particularly to Bob Frost and Darren Frost for also taking many specific habitat photographs for us. Our thanks also to the many other photographers who contributed photographs which we were unable to include. Our thanks also to William T. Rawlinson A.T.D., F.R.S.A., S.W.E. for contributing the Frontispiece. For publishing requests for records our thanks to the editors of *British Birds, Birding World, Journal für Ornithologie* and *Var Fagelvarld.*

Finally our thanks to our wives Karen and Julie for their patience and support, and our particular thanks to Karen for her extensive assistance throughout the production of this second edition, especially for her sound advice and for her meticulous checking of the manuscript at every stage, without which the final text would not have the accuracy which we hope it now has.

SYSTEMATIC LIST

In the Systematic List, sequence and nomenclature follow those adopted by Cramp & Simmons (1977), that is the sequence and scientific nomenclature of Voous (1977) *List of Recent Holarctic Bird Species* (with the exception of *Oenanthe cypriaca* for the reasons given) and English names those in common usage as listed by Peterson *et al.* (1974). English names of the few species not listed in the latter are taken from the '*British Birds*' *List of Birds of the Western Palearctic* (1978). Trinomials are taken directly from Vaurie (1959, 1965) except where otherwise stated. Alternative scientific names (from Vaurie 1959, 1965) are given in brackets, as are some long established alternative English names. Cypriot names have been omitted because no comprehensive lists are available. The Greek Cypriot names for some common species were collected by Sibthorp (1787), Cobham (1908) and Took (1973). There has apparently been no attempt to collect and publish Turkish Cypriot names of birds. The Bannermans (1958) provide Greek and Turkish mainland names for almost every species on the Cyprus list, but the Greek names (at least) are frequently different from those used in Cyprus. Names of woody plants follow Chapman (1949) and of herbaceous plants Polunin & Huxley (1978).

Since the bulk of the information is based on the Reports of the 2 Cyprus Ornithological Societies, we have not thought it necessary constantly to mention those Reports, and where dated records are not annotated they are taken from the Report of the year mentioned. For more important records the Report numbers are cited, those of the original Society (founded in 1957) being simply abbreviated to R1 (= First Report), R2 (= Second Report) and so on. Reports of the later Society (founded in 1970) are prefixed by NR (for New C.O.S. Report), thus NR1, NR2 and so on. The Bulletins of the original Society are abbreviated to B1 (= First Bulletin), B2 (= Second Bulletin) and so on, and its Newsletters to NL. The Cyprus Natural History Society is abbreviated to C.N.H.S. The information in the Systematic List is correct to Report 35 and Newsletter 1991/Jan of C.O.S. (1957), and to Report 15 of C.O.S. (1970). Some data from Report 19 of C.O.S. (1970), which was received just before the typescript was sent to the printers, have been included; Reports 16–18 have not yet been published.

Authors are quoted without dates if their names occur only once in the list of references. Personal communications are indicated by giving the initials of the individual in front of his name.

Where breeding details are given, 'young' means unfledged young (still in the nest if a nidicolous species), and 'fledged young' means young which have only flown within the last few days. The number of eggs in a clutch is preceded by C/.

The following status abbreviations are used:

RB	Resident Breeder	**PM**	Passage Migrant
MB	Migrant Breeder	**WV**	Winter Visitor
OB	Occasional Breeder	**AV**	Accidental or Occasional
FB	Former Breeder		Visitor, up to 5 records.

Degrees of abundance used are 'very scarce', 'scarce', 'fairly common', 'common', 'very common' and 'abundant'. Where the degree of abundance of a species lies between 2 of these terms, then both are given, e.g. 'scarce to fairly common'.

The term 'recent' in the text refers to the period of continuous observation and regular publication of records since the formation of the original Cyprus Ornithological Society (in fact since July 1956, as the Society's first Report dealt with the year prior to its founding). The term 'in the past' refers to the period prior to this.

Museums are abbreviated as follows: Royal Scottish Museum (RSM); British Museum, Natural History (BMNH); Naturhistoriska Riksmuseum, Stockholm (NRS); Museum of Comparative Zoology, Harvard (MCZ).

Unsubstantiated records of breeding, rarities, and migrants seen out of season have been omitted from the Systematic List, generally without comment, though in a few cases they are mentioned within square brackets.

NON-PASSERINES

PODICIPEDIDAE

1.   TACHYBAPTUS RUFICOLLIS   WV PM OB

Little Grebe

T.r. ruficollis. Passage migrant and winter visitor in variable numbers, Aug–Apr, to reservoirs and harbours; sometimes common from early Aug, more usually from Oct or Nov to Feb. In some years numbers may peak in Nov and then decline, few remaining over winter. Maximum flocks usually in 10s, occasionally over 100, maximum 300 + Asprokremmos Dam, 21 Nov 1982.

Breeding. Usually scarce or absent May–Jul, but some remain and breed when water levels favourable. In recent times 1–6 pairs have bred at Akrotiri reed beds, and on reservoirs or dams at Akhelia, Akhna, Akhyritou, Asprokremmos, Athalassa, Kandou, Kouklia, Lythrodhonda, Phasouri and Mia Milea; broods of 2–5 small young seen mid Mar and May to early Sep. In the past, attempted breeding Akhyritou reservoir, Apr 1901 (Bucknill 1909–10) and bred in large numbers Kouklia reservoir 1910, fresh eggs mid May (Bucknill 1911). There are no 19th century breeding records. [Birds shot 1887, 1888 by Guillemard erroneously recorded as breeding records by the Bannermans (1958) and Stewart & Christensen.]

2.   PODICEPS CRISTATUS   WV PM OB

Great Crested Grebe

P.c. cristatus. Winter visitor and passage migrant in small numbers Nov–Apr to coastal waters, harbours, reservoirs and salt lakes; only frequent Dec–Mar when sometimes fairly common, maximum 29 on the sea at Evdhimou, 15 Mar 1985; in some winters very few. Occasional May–Oct.

Breeding. One recent record: a pair bred northwestern edge of Akrotiri Salt Lake 1982, C/5 found 28 Apr and 2 young there 22 May (Jenkins 1986b, R29). Stated to have bred frequently at Kouklia reservoir in the past (Jourdain 1929b), but breeding documented only once: 8–10 pairs there 1910, remaining until at least Sep, some successfully raising young; eggs 6 May (C.N.H.S.Ann.II).

3.   PODICEPS GRISEGENA   AV

Red-necked Grebe

Accidental visitor, 4 records: 2 Akrotiri Salt Lake, 10 Dec 1981 (R28); one Pedhieos River at Strovolos, 22 Nov 1984 (NR15); one Paphos harbour, 27 Dec 1986 (R33); one Phasouri reservoir, 3–9 Sep 1989 (NL89/9).

4.   PODICEPS AURITUS   AV

Slavonian Grebe

Accidental visitor (*P.a. auritus*), 2 records: one offshore Syrianokhori, 23 and 26 Dec 1957 and 2 in summer plumage Curium gravel pits, 23 Mar 1958 and one there 28 Mar (R2, B6). [2 in Oct–Nov 1963, one Oct–Nov 1966, one Dec 1967 and one Mar–Apr 1974, all with insufficient detail. 1–2 Bishops Pool, late Nov–Dec 1976 and one Larnaca harbour, 8 Dec 1976, now thought to have been Black-necked Grebe *P. nigricollis* (R. Foers). Sibthorp listed *Colymbus auritus*, but may have been referring to *nigricollis* which he did not mention. Also mentioned by Horsbrugh, apparently in error for *nigricollis*.]

5.   PODICEPS NIGRICOLLIS   WV OB PM?

Black-necked Grebe

P.n. nigricollis. Usually a fairly common winter visitor to harbours, salt lakes and reservoirs. Has occurred Jul-May, but only numerous Dec-Mar, with peak numbers late Dec to Feb. Usually 1–6 together, but sometimes a flock of 10s, maximum 87 Larnaca Salt Lake, 14 Feb 1971. Some early autumn records probably refer to passage.

Breeding. 2 recent records: a pair bred Athalassa 1979 and 1980, 4–6 juveniles seen late Jul (NR10 & 11). One in breeding plumage Akhna Dam, early-mid Jun 1990. In the past, a colony of 18 nests with eggs at Kouklia reservoir, 1 Jun 1913 and 12 nests with eggs there, "summer" 1914 (Baxendale 1913, 1915). [None bred 1909 (Bucknill 1909–10, *pace* the Bannermans 1958), and no evidence for breeding at Morphou (*pace* the Bannermans 1958 and see **Breeding** chapter).]

PROCELLARIIDAE

6.   CALONECTRIS DIOMEDEA   PM

Cory's Shearwater

Scarce passage migrant (*C.d. diomedea*). Spring passage, mainly off the south and east coasts, late Mar to mid May; autumn passage, mostly off the north coast Jul–Oct. Usually singly, though 1–2 Cape Andreas on 6 dates, 14–25 Apr 1973 (Stagg 1974) and 71 west off Cape Kormakiti in 4 hours, 25 Oct 1990 (NL90/10). The species is probably greatly overlooked offshore.

7.   PUFFINUS PUFFINUS   PM

Manx Shearwater

P.p. yelkouan. Recorded every month (scarce Dec–Mar); mostly Aug–Sep, when probably fairly common offshore. Usually 1–3 together, but "several" flocks of 4–6 off Paphos, 23 Jun 1977; 23 northeast off Cape Andreas, 21 Nov 1971 and 25 off Cape Greco, 4 Nov 1972. 11 records of beached birds, Mar and Aug–Oct (10), at least one immature. Several sight records mention *P.p. puffinus*, though all beached birds, where race determined in the hand, were *P.p. yelkouan*.

HYDROBATIDAE

8.   HYDROBATES PELAGICUS   AV

Storm Petrel

Accidental visitor, 2 records: one collected Larnaca, 13 Mar 1903 (Madarász 1904b) and seen "occasionally" in Cyprus waters, Jul 1956 (B2). [A petrel, probably this species, between Cape Andreas and the Klidhes Islands, 21 Apr 1973 (NR4).]

SULIDAE

9.   SULA BASSANA   PM

Gannet

Very scarce and irregular visitor offshore (*S.b. bassana*), mainly in winter, probably often overlooked. 6 records: a flock of over 40 (11 adults) west off Cape Greco, 18 Jan 1958 (D. Noakes); an immature off Salamis, 2 May 1965 (R12); 6 adults over Curium, 27 Feb 1969 (R16); one off Spiro's Beach, Larnaca, 11 Dec 1983 (R30); 2 off Paphos lighthouse, 28 Dec 1987 and an immature there 31 Dec 1987 (both R34).

PHALACROCORACIDAE

10.   PHALACROCORAX CARBO   WV PM

Cormorant

P.c. sinensis. Formerly a scarce and irregular winter visitor not reliably recorded for 20 years prior to 1980, since then has become a regular visitor to coastal and inland waters from Sep or Oct to mid May, mainly Dec–Mar, usually in small numbers, occasionally in 10s. Most frequent at Asprokremmos and Akhna dams, where now usually regular in winter. Spring passage first recorded 1985 with a flock of 23 north at Dhekelia, 14 Mar. Subsequent records (all flocks) are: 75 at Akrotiri Salt Lake, 25 Mar 1987; 31 north at Cape Drepanum, 5 April 1988; 35 twice off Paphos, 24 and 28 Mar 1989; 26 and 24 over Akrotiri on 20 and 26 Mar 1990 respectively; 50 and 70 northwest off Paphos airport (D. Whaley) and 80 east off Ayia Thekla (R. Frost), all on 26 Feb 1991. These records suggest regular coastal/offshore passage in spring. Only one autumn passage record, a flock of 18 east off Kyrenia, 30 Oct 1990. Prior to 1980 the only recent records were of a few offshore Jan to mid Apr 1958 and Feb 1960. In the past, one collected Larnaca, 16 Nov 1902 (Madarász 1904b); one shot Famagusta, 22 Dec 1910 (Bucknill 1911) and several obtained winter 1911–12 (C.N.H.S.Ann.IV). Although a few birds may have been overlooked offshore in winter prior to 1980, the wintering at inland waters and the passage of flocks in spring appear to be new phenomena.

11.   PHALACROCORAX ARISTOTELIS   RB

Shag

Locally common resident (*P.a. desmarestii*).
   Breeding distribution. Colonies at the Klidhes Islands, Akrotiri and Episkopi cliffs. Colonies with breeding unconfirmed at Cape Aspro, Cape Kormakiti and Ayios Yeoryios Island (Khrysokhou Bay). May also breed at Orga and Mazaki

Island. Formerly bred on an islet close to Kyrenia: *c*. 15 pairs, 25 Apr 1909 (Bucknill 1909–10). Breeding population possibly 40–50 pairs. The Klidhes hold the largest colony: maximum 70 birds, about half of them flightless juveniles, on 20 May 1973. Present at or near colonies all the year, but may also be seen anywhere around the coasts.

Breeding data. Breeds very early: at Akrotiri, where breeding most studied, eggs found late Dec to Jan, once early Apr; young from late Jan; fledging mid Mar to May.

12.   PHALACROCORAX PYGMEUS   WV?

Pygmy Cormorant

Very scarce and irregular visitor since 1982, once overwintering. At least 7 records: 2 Phasouri/Akrotiri reed beds, 22–29 Aug 1982 until one bird shot (R29); 2 or 3 wintered Polemidhia Dam/Yermasoyia Dam/Akrotiri from 25 Dec 1982 to 6 Mar 1983 (R29, R30); one Asprokremmos Dam, 27–28 Jul and one Akrounda Creek, 26 Sep, both in 1985 (R32); 1–3 Akhna Dam, 12 Nov to 3 Dec 1989 (NL89/11&12); one Akhna Dam, 14 Nov 1990 and 4 there, 4 Jan 1991 (both K. Heron *per* C. J. L. Bennett).

PELECANIDAE

13.   PELECANUS ONOCROTALUS   PM

White Pelican

Scarce passage migrant, mainly in autumn on the south coast, especially at Akrotiri; in recent years *c*. 3–5 records per year. Occurs Sep–Jan, mainly Oct–Nov and (less frequently) Dec; occasional Mar–Aug, not recorded Feb. Birds usually overfly or remain only 1–2 days, but some occasionally remain for several weeks at salt lakes or dams. Usually singly or less than 10 together, but sometimes in large flocks in autumn, mainly Nov: 58 (34 adults, 24 juveniles) roosting Akrotiri Salt Lake, 24–25 Nov 1964; 45 juveniles roosting Akrotiri Salt Lake, later flew south, 9 Nov 1972; 36 over Akrotiri, 9 Nov 1978; 40 over Dhekelia, 25 Aug 1980; 80 (50 adults, 30 immatures) at Larnaca Salt Lake, 11 Nov 1983; *c*. 120 Akrotiri Salt Lake, 5 Nov and *c*. 120 heading out to sea from Larnaca Salt Lake, 6 Nov, both in 1984; 56 south at Khlorakas, 21 Dec 1985; 35 Larnaca Salt Lake, 10 Nov and 35 offshore Pendayia in late Nov, both in 1986. Also a raft of *c*. 50 (3 immatures, the rest adults) on the sea east of Cape Andreas, 29 Oct 1990. (See also *Pelecanus* spp.)

14.   PELECANUS CRISPUS   PM

Dalmatian Pelican

Very scarce and irregular passage migrant, 6 recent records: Mar (4), Sep and Nov. In detail: 50 Dhekelia, 17 Sep 1957 and 5 Akrotiri, 5–6 Mar 1958 (both R2, B6); 3 Akrotiri, 28 Mar 1959 (R3); 13 Larnaca Salt Lake, 15 Mar 1967 (R14); 2 Akrotiri Salt Lake, 21 Nov 1972 (R19); 29 Cape Zevgari, *c*. Mar 1979 (R26). In the past, individuals shot Larnaca Salt Lake, 13–14 Nov and Kouklia reservoir, 23 Nov 1908 (Bucknill 1909–10). (See also *Pelecanus* spp.)

PELECANUS spp

33 recent records, overflying or at wetlands: Jan, Mar (2), Apr, Jun, Jul (3), Aug (2), Sep (2), Oct (11), Nov (8) and Dec (2). Usually singly, occasionally in flocks, maximum 70 over Akrotiri, later flying south, 13 Nov 1972 (R19). In the past, "seen in winter on a number of occasions at Limassol, Syrianokhori, Kouklia and Larnaca" (Waterer).

ARDEIDAE

15.   BOTAURUS STELLARIS   PM WV
      Bittern

Scarce passage migrant (*B.s. stellaris*) Mar–May, mainly Apr; once Jun; occasional late Aug to Dec. Usually singly, 1–3 records per year. Occasionally overwintering: one shot Koutraphas, 17 Jan 1982; one Livadhia, 12 Feb and one shot near Dhali, 19 Feb, both in 1984; one Phasouri reed beds throughout Jan 1988. Individuals at marshes twice Jan and twice Feb in the past (Bucknill 1909–10).

16.   IXOBRYCHUS MINUTUS   PM OB?
      Little Bittern

Fairly common passage migrant (*I.m. minutus*) Apr–May, mainly at south coast wetlands, usually singly or less than 10 together, maximum 20 Akrotiri reed beds, 5 May 1970; less common mid Aug to Oct, mainly singly, but 11 Limni, 24 Sep 1978 and 13 Moni, 1 Oct 1979, indicating a small coasting passage. A few singles Mar, Jun, late Jul and Nov, once mid Feb and once early Dec. Possibly bred Phasouri reed beds 1982: adult pair there Jul and fledged juvenile seen 21 Jul (R29). [Nest found Paphos District, 18 May 1909, "thought probably" of this sp (Bucknill 1909–10).]

17.   NYCTICORAX NYCTICORAX   PM OB
      Night Heron

Fairly common passage migrant (*N.n. nycticorax*) mid Mar to May, mainly Apr, usually in the south and east and often at wetlands; usually singly or in flocks of less than 20, maximum 40 Coral Bay, 8 May 1989. Occasional Jun to mid Aug, sometimes oversummering (maximum up to 21 Akrotiri reed beds Jun–Jul 1981). More numerous on autumn passage with flocks of 10s late Aug to early Oct, with some flocks moving west along the north coast; occasional to late Nov, once mid Dec. Maximum numbers from Khrysokhou Bay area with a flock of 64 heading west at Polis, 30 Aug 1978 and flocks of 40–50 at Lachi and Limni in Sep 1982. In the south a flock of 36 Akrotiri Salt Lake, 30 Aug 1981.
      Breeding. Athalassa (1980): 4 juveniles present on 19 Jun and 9 birds there 28 Jul suggesting 2 pairs bred in eucalyptus trees (NR11). Phasouri reed beds (1982): at least 9 adults there Jul–Aug and a juvenile seen 19 Aug. Unfortunately all the birds were shot on 29 Aug, the first day of the shooting season. The breeding colony site was examined on 17 Sep, 8 nests showed signs of recent occupation, and 2 eggshells typical for the species were found (Rayner 1982).
      A juvenile bird found freshly killed on a road west of Yeroskipos, 23 Apr 1984 was considered to have fledged in Africa, and more likely in tropical Africa than in

Egypt. This apparently is the first Eurasian record of an African fledged Night Heron (Oreel 1987).

5 recoveries of birds ringed in Hungary (2), Austria, Yugoslavia and Israel (Appendix 2).

18. ARDEOLA RALLOIDES   PM

Squacco Heron

Common passage migrant. Usually scarce mid-late Mar, common Apr–May with flocks of up to 50, mainly at south and east coast wetlands, where some may remain for weeks; occasional Jun–Jul, sometimes 1–3 oversummering. Common Aug–Sep with some flocks coasting west off the north coast, Kyrenia to Khrysokhou Bay. Maximum numbers from Polis: a total of 333, 30 Aug 1978 and 80 there, 14 Sep 1983. Occasional Oct, twice early Nov and once mid Dec.

19. BUBULCUS IBIS   PM

Cattle Egret

Scarce passage migrant (*B.i. ibis*), usually 2–6 records a year, mainly in spring, late Mar to May, especially Apr. Occasional in all other months. Occurs singly or in small flocks, maxima 13 Akrotiri, early-mid Apr 1975, and 12 Akhna Dam, 5 Jun 1990.

20. EGRETTA GARZETTA   PM WV OB

Little Egret

E.g. garzetta. Common passage migrant, sometimes from early Mar, common mid or late Mar to May, peak numbers Apr, mainly in the south and east; maximum flocks of 100+ at south coast sites in mid Apr 1981. Some remain for weeks at wetlands. Flocks of 10s also coast east on the south coast and north on the west coast. Occasional Jun–Jul, sometimes 10s oversummering. Return passage Aug to Oct or Nov (occasionally to mid Dec), mainly late Aug to Sep, with many flocks of up to 100 coasting west along north coast, Kyrenia to Akamas. Sometimes in 100s: 300 west off Polis, 30 Aug 1978 and 228 Aphrodites Baths, 2 Sep 1982. A few occasionally overwinter Nov–Mar, mainly at Famagusta harbour or Akrotiri Salt Lake, once 30 briefly early Jan.

Breeding. 2 records: nest and large unfledged juvenile in dead bushes in area of flooded scrub on edge of Akrotiri reed beds, 19 Jul 1981 (R28); 5 pairs attempted to breed in eucalyptus clump at Akhna Dam, Jul 1989, though all eggs were reported eaten by crows (NL89/7).

21. EGRETTA ALBA   PM WV

Great White Egret

E.a. alba. Scarce passage migrant, numbers varying considerably, usually *c.* 3–5 records a year, occasionally more, coasting or at wetlands. Most frequent in spring, mainly Mar–Apr, occasionally into May, usually singly or less than 10 together, maximum 28 Akrotiri, 23 Mar 1958. Twice early Jul. Scarcer on return passage

Aug–Nov (occasional early Dec), maxima 9 Akrotiri Salt Lake, 3 Oct 1982, and 26 there 14 Nov 1988 (T.A. Box). Scarce and irregular mid Dec to Feb, occasionally overwintering: up to 5 Famagusta harbour, mid Nov 1957 to mid Jan 1958; 3 Akrotiri Salt Lake, Oct 1981 to Feb 1982; up to 5 Akhna Dam, late Oct 1988 to Feb 1989 and up to 10 there Nov 1989. The very much more numerous Little Egret *E. garzetta* sometimes reported as this species.

22. ARDEA CINEREA	PM WV OB?

Grey Heron

A.c. cinerea. Very common passage migrant in 10s, sometimes flocks of up to 100 or more on both passages. Spring passage Mar–May, peak numbers late Mar to Apr, mainly in the south and east. Occasionally 1–13 oversummering Jun–Jul. Autumn passage Aug–Oct (exceptionally to mid Nov), peak numbers mid Aug to early Oct, many flocks coasting west on the north coast and south down the west coast, with smaller numbers at wetlands, maximum a total of 357 off Polis, 31 Aug 1982. Few flocks cross the island directly on either passage. Exceptionally occurs in small mixed flocks with other *Egretta/Ardea* spp (Stagg 1974, NR8). A few usually overwinter at reservoirs, salt lakes and marshes; maxima up to 18 at Kouklia reservoir, late Oct 1969 to mid Feb 1970, and up to 19 Akhna Dam, Dec 1989. Possibly bred Athalassa 1980, 2 adults and 2 juveniles on 17 Jun, though nest not found (NR11).

23. ARDEA PURPUREA	PM

Purple Heron

Very common passage migrant in 10s, most numerous in autumn. Occasional early–mid Mar, main spring passage late Mar to early May, with flocks coasting east on the south coast and north on the west coast and others at wetlands; maxima a total of 95 Phasouri, 7 Apr and 61 Mazotos, 11 Apr, both in 1982, and 100 overflew Akrotiri Salt Lake from the south, 13 Apr 1987; a few birds till late May. Occasional Jun to early Aug, twice 1–4 oversummering. Autumn passage mainly mid Aug to Sep, when many flocks coast west along the north coast and south down the west coast; maxima 115 off Kyrenia, 13 Sep 1961, a total of 145 west Polis/Lachi, 27 Aug 1980 and 120 at Lachi, 5 Sep 1983; occasionally a few to early Dec. In autumn some north coast flocks rest in trees in Polis Forest. Some flocks cross the island directly on both passages, maximum 70 resting in trees Nicosia, 5 Sep 1972. The large diurnal passage, especially in autumn, is at variance with Cramp & Simmons, who term it mainly a night migrant, usually singly or in small groups.

One recovery of a bird ringed in Austria (Appendix 2).

CICONIIDAE

24. CICONIA NIGRA	PM

Black Stork

Scarce passage migrant, usually singly or less than 10 together. Prior to 1972 only 2 spring records, but observations at Cape Andreas late Apr to early May 1972 and Apr 1973, revealed a small passage in both years, maximum 23 on 1 May 1972 (Stagg 1973, 1974). An immature oversummered Geunyeli reservoir late May to Jul 1972.

Occasional Aug. Probably regular on autumn passage mid Sep to Nov, most records late Sep to Oct, mainly on the south coast, maximum 14 Akrotiri Salt Lake, 6 Nov 1981. Occasional Dec, once Jan and Mar. [The 60 flying through the Kyrenia Pass, 26 Oct 1973 (R20) seem doubtful.]

25. CICONIA CICONIA   PM
  White Stork

Passage migrant (*C.c. ciconia*) in variable numbers; usually scarce, singly or in small flocks, occasionally up to 100, though 700, 2–3 Sep 1978, and 1200–1300, 25 Aug 1986, at Akrotiri and 1000 Akhna Dam, 27 Aug 1989. Spring passage Mar–May, mainly Apr to early May, mostly in the east, particularly at the Karpas and Cape Andreas. Occasional Jun–Jul, up to 18 oversummering Geunyeli reservoir, late Jun to Aug 1972. Autumn passage Aug–Oct, flocks usually in the south, particularly at Akrotiri Salt Lake, the birds evidently reluctant to face the long sea crossing south; some fly south only to turn aside and coast, others return to the salt lake, and some flocks remain in the area for several weeks. Occasional Nov, Dec, and Jan, once Feb. [An unusually large passage reported late Aug 1956 was later realised to have been cranes (Bourne 1959a). Schrader reported seeing only nests at Nicosia, sometime between Oct 1876 and Apr 1878, but since he presumably saw no birds, and breeding has not been reported by any other authors, before or since, he may have been mistaken.]
  4 recoveries of birds ringed in Germany (3) and in the U.S.S.R. (Appendix 2).

THRESKIORNITHIDAE

26. PLEGADIS FALCINELLUS   PM
  Glossy Ibis

Common passage migrant in spring: occasional Feb to mid Mar, main passage late Mar to early May, (a few till mid–late May), with flocks coasting east on the south coast and north on the west coast, with others at wetlands mainly in the south and east, where some remain for weeks; usually in 10s, sometimes flocks of 100–150, once "hundreds" early Apr. Occasional Jun–Jul, a few sometimes oversummer in Akrotiri reed beds, but no evidence of breeding. Usually only a few singles at wetlands Aug to mid Sep, but at that time flocks of 10s coast west off the north coast, and also occur off other coasts; maximum 100 west off Kyrenia, 1 Sep 1961. Occasional late Sep, once early and mid Oct.
  One recovery of a bird ringed in the U.S.S.R. (Appendix 2).

27. PLATALEA LEUCORODIA   PM
  Spoonbill

Scarce passage migrant (*P.l. leucorodia*), usually at wetlands, also with some flocks in spring coasting east on the south coast and north on the west coast. Usually singly or in small flocks, maximum 21 moving in off the sea, Paphos headland, 25 Apr 1989 (N. & A. Bowman). Up to 5 records in most recent years, mainly mid Mar to mid May, with peak numbers mid Apr to mid May; less frequently seen Aug to mid Oct.

Occasional in all other months; one overwintered Akrotiri Salt Lake, Nov 1981 to Jan 1982.

PHOENICOPTERIDAE

28. PHOENICOPTERUS RUBER   WV PM

Greater Flamingo

P.r. roseus. Common winter visitor to the salt lakes, highest numbers usually at Akrotiri, annual numbers and arrival and departure dates varying considerably, partly as a result of water levels. First birds to winter at Akrotiri usually arrive Nov (occasionally Oct); peak numbers *c.* 5000–10,000, sometimes Dec–Feb, sometimes for only a few weeks mid-winter. An unusually high water level at Akrotiri is apparently unsuitable, since most or all birds then depart. Occasionally up to 3000 remain early Mar, fewer later. Sometimes a flock of up to 100–200 non-breeders remains throughout the spring and summer, exceptionally into Aug or Sep, once 108 till early Sep. Sometimes immatures predominate after Mar (Bourne *et al.*, Foers 1979), in other years adults (P. R. Flint). Usual peak winter numbers at Larnaca are a few 100 to 2000, exceptionally up to *c.* 10,000 (probably briefly) if Akrotiri unsuitable. Occasionally a few briefly at other wetlands.

Common passage migrant Oct–Apr, though passage flocks have occurred in every month. In late autumn, mainly Nov, small flocks appear at the salt lakes usually within 1–2 days of their first holding water, strongly suggesting a regular passage overhead. Flocks have been seen off Cape Andreas at this time, with others moving west on the south coast, some stopping at the salt lakes. In late autumn and winter, flocks of up to 1000 also occur off north and northwest coasts. A flock at Famagusta area in early Dec 1957 was tracked in from the northeast by radar (R2). Some flocks depart south and southwest from Akrotiri, maximum 1000 southwest, 1 Nov 1968, also "large flocks" tracked by radar from Akrotiri "towards the Nile Delta", Jan 1969 (R16). Radar observations of birds assumed to be Greater Flamingos are mentioned also by Mason. In spring, mainly Feb–Apr, numbers at the salt lakes sometimes fluctuate markedly as flocks of up to 500 pass through. Flocks (including local wintering birds) tend to move east and northeast on south coast in spring, also 2 records of flocks moving NNE from Cape Andreas. If Akrotiri Salt Lake holds water all summer occasional flocks may pass through, sometimes remaining for a few weeks – once 40 late May, 60 mid Jun, 40 early and late Aug and 14, including a recently fledged juvenile, once mid Aug.

8 recoveries/sightings of birds ringed in Iran (2), France (5) and Spain (Appendix 2). Although only 2 of the recoveries are of Iranian birds, it seems almost certain that the great majority of birds are of Asiatic origin (mainly Iran with probably some from Turkey – Foers 1984), and that only a small proportion are from West Mediterranean countries (Johnson).

ANATIDAE

29. CYGNUS OLOR   WV

Mute Swan

Usually a scarce and irregular winter visitor, mainly to the salt lakes. Recorded in 9 recent winters, mainly Dec–Mar, usually singly or up to a few 10s, some remaining for 2–3 months, most records involving immatures. An exceptional influx occurred in Dec 1984, coinciding with extremely cold weather throughout most of Europe.

Peak numbers were 380, mainly immatures, at Larnaca Salt Lake, 19 Dec, declining to 200 there by mid Jan 1985, to 30 late Apr with the last 2 on 5 Jun; also up to 40 at Akrotiri Salt Lake till late Apr and a few birds at Ayios Nikolaos. Fortunately the authorities reacted quickly to protect the birds at Larnaca, so relatively few were shot, and many people came to see and feed these unusual visitors. In the past, 3 mid Apr 1887 (Guillemard 1888). [8 records of unidentified swans, mainly Jan, but including 16 at Akhyritou reservoir, 5 Nov 1908, probably this species (Bucknill 1909–10).]

30.   CYGNUS CYGNUS   AV
Whooper Swan

Accidental visitor, one recent record: 3 at Akrotiri, 27 Jan to 2 Feb 1963 (R10, B13). In the past, a young ♂ shot Spathariko Marsh, Famagusta district, 28 Dec 1910 (Bucknill 1911). [2, unsubstantiated, on a lake near Larnaca, sometime between Oct 1876 and Apr 1878 (Schrader).]

31.   ANSER ALBIFRONS   WV
White-fronted Goose

A.a. albifrons. Usually a scarce winter visitor, Dec–Feb (occasional late Oct to Nov and Mar–Apr, once early May), sometimes common in severe winters, usually at or near wetlands and most frequent in the east and southeast. Probably of regular occurrence or nearly so. Recent maxima: "hundreds" feeding in fields of wheat and barley near Rizokarpaso, 6–20 Feb 1974 (NR5); 3000–5000 in the island, Jan–Feb 1983, the largest flock being of up to 2500 on the Mesaoria near Ayios Nikolaos, 27 Feb (R30); and 300–350 Spiro's Beach/Pool area, Jan to mid Feb 1989 (NL89/2). In the past, "many hundreds" of geese, early Jan 1925, some of which, when shot, proved to be *albifrons* (Wilson 1925b).

32.   ANSER ANSER   WV
Greylag Goose

Scarce and irregular winter visitor Dec–Feb, with most records early–mid Jan. Recorded in 9 recent winters, usually at or near wetlands, singly or in small flocks, maximum 25 Spiro's Beach, 20 Jan 1985 (R32). Birds usually remain only a few days, but in Jan–Feb 1983 a considerable influx occurred with small flocks recorded from 7 different locations and it's likely that some remained in the island for several weeks (R30). Twice early Mar and once mid May. In the past, singles twice late Nov (Müller, Bucknill 1909–10) and once mid Apr (Riddell).

One at Akrotiri Salt Lake, 9 Jan 1979 was pink-billed but not necessarily *A.a. rubrirostris*, as pink-billed Greylags of uncertain taxonomic status breed west through south Russia to Hungary and Austria (Cramp & Simmons).

33.   BRANTA RUFICOLLIS   AV
Red-breasted Goose

Accidental visitor, one record: 2 in fields near Larnaca Salt Lake, 9 Feb 1991 (K. Heron, J. Bullock, both *per* C. J. L. Bennett). The 2 birds were amongst a large flock of White-fronted Geese *Anser albifrons*. [One seen Larnaca market 1928 was assumed to be a locally shot wild bird (G. H. Riddell *in* the Bannermans 1958).]

34.   ALOPOCHEN AEGYPTIACUS   WV
Egyptian Goose

Formerly (1906–28) a scarce winter visitor, late Nov to early Apr, mainly Dec to early Mar, to watercourses and small wetlands near Nicosia, occasionally elsewhere, usually 2–3 together, maximum 12 (Bucknill 1909–10, 1911, 1913a, C.N.H.S. Ann.IV, Wilson 1925b, 1928, 1954). Seen by D. F. Davidson (*in* the Bannermans 1958) "in some winters". Only 3 recent records: 3 at Akrotiri, 3 Jan 1958 (R2, B6); one Patriki, 27 Jan (not 27 Jun) and 20 Feb 1962 (R9, B13) and one Spiro's Pool, 14 Jan 1989 (NL89/1). Bourne *et al.* considered that recent birds might come from Tel Aviv Zoological Gardens, where *c.* 30 full-winged birds were driven away, 1955–68 (Cramp & Simmons).

35.   TADORNA FERRUGINEA   WV
Ruddy Shelduck

Scarce winter visitor to wetlands, mostly Jan–Feb, when probably almost regular, occasional Nov–Dec and Mar to mid Apr. Usually less than 10 together; a flock of 50 south over Nicosia, 29 Nov 1964 (Christensen 1967), one of 30 Paralimni Lake, Jan 1976 (Kephalas 1989) and another of 28 Larnaca Salt Lake, 22 Dec 1984 (R31) were exceptional. Perhaps more numerous in the past: "quite a number", Jan 1911 (Bucknill 1911), and "quite plentiful" in winter "in small flights", 1876–78 (Schrader).

36.   TADORNA TADORNA   WV PM
Shelduck

Common winter visitor, mainly to the salt lakes, mid Dec to mid Mar, peak numbers Jan–Feb; occasional from Oct and into May, twice early Jun, once Jul. Usually in 10s or 100s, sometimes 1000 or more, maxima 2000 Larnaca Salt Lake, early Jan 1982 and 2247 Akrotiri Salt Lake, mid-late Jan 1983. Occasional increases at the salt lakes mid Feb to early Mar and simultaneously flocks off the south coast (maximum 300 off Larnaca, 15 Feb 1976) suggest spring passage.

37.   ANAS PENELOPE   WV PM
Wigeon

Common on autumn passage and in winter. In autumn, flocks up to 350 coast west off Kyrenia, mainly late Aug to Sep, though once 150 early Nov; also 16 Akrotiri once mid Aug. D. F. Davidson and J. A. McGeoch (*in* the Bannermans 1958) report migrants flying "up the valleys of the Troodos Range and over the saddles and passes of both ranges". Occasional Oct. Winter visitors present Nov–Mar, peak numbers Dec–Feb, usually in 100s, mainly at the salt lakes and reservoirs, though 800 on the sea off Larnaca in Dec 1956. In the past, Bucknill (1909–10) considered it the most abundant wintering duck, with 5000 at Akhyritou reservoir and at Kouklia reservoir, but no such numbers in recent times. Few records of spring passage, though flocks of 5–30 coasting east at Ayia Napa, 23–30 Apr 1983, suggest spring passage offshore possibly regular and overlooked. A few at wetlands Apr, occasionally into May.

38. ANAS STREPERA   WV PM
Gadwall

A.s. strepera. Scarce passage migrant and winter visitor to wetlands, recorded every month, mostly Nov–Apr. Usually singly or a few together, usually remaining only a few days, occasionally longer. Maximum 27 Akrotiri Salt Lake, 28 Feb 1980 with 20 remaining 20 Mar. Occasional flocks of up to 40 on passage Akrotiri Salt Lake, late Jul to mid Aug.

39. ANAS CRECCA   WV PM
Teal

A.c. crecca. Very common winter visitor. Small numbers at wetlands Oct–Nov and 1000s Dec to early Mar, peak numbers usually Jan–Feb, up to 5000 Akrotiri Salt Lake and sometimes 1000–2000 at Larnaca Salt Lake, Paralimni and Galatia. Usually only a few remain into Apr (once 40–50 in early Apr). A few records of spring passage on the south coast Mar–Apr: *c.* 2500 on sea off Curium, 13 Mar 1962, which flew northwest at dusk; *c.* 20 on sea off mouth of Dhiarizos river, 24 Apr 1985 and 50 Episkopi Bay, 15 Apr 1988. Occasional May–Jul. Flocks of autumn migrants occur Aug to early Oct, mainly off the north coast, though some records perhaps refer to Garganey *A. querquedula* (*q.v.* and see *Anas* spp).
   One ringed Akrotiri, 22 Nov 1959, retrapped there late 1962. One ringed in the U.S.S.R. recovered in Cyprus, and one ringed in Cyprus recovered in Iran (Appendix 2).

40. ANAS PLATYRHYNCHOS   WV PM OB
Mallard

A.p. platyrhynchos. Common winter visitor and autumn migrant. Passage flocks occur Aug to early Oct, mainly on north coast, maximum 800 Khrysokhou Bay, 29 Aug 1978. A few at wetlands Oct–Nov, often in 100s Dec to early Mar, sometimes up to 1000 at Akrotiri Salt Lake. A few remain into Apr and occasionally all summer. (See *Anas* spp.)
   Breeding. Occasional breeder since 1970: Akrotiri 1970 and 1971; Phasouri 1987–90, and probably at both locations in 1982; Evretou and Akhna dams 1990. Broods of 4–12 young seen Apr–Jul. 1–3 pairs breed probably each year when suitable water levels exist.

41. ANAS ACUTA   WV PM
Pintail

Very common winter visitor and spring migrant (*A.a. acuta*). Occasional mid Sep to Nov, sometimes several 1000s Dec to early Mar, mainly at Akrotiri Salt Lake, peak numbers, up to 4000, Jan–Feb. Occasional peak numbers Feb to early Mar, probably migrants from south. Sometimes flocks of 1000s on spring passage off south coast late Feb to mid Mar with 10s into Apr; maximum a mixed flock of 20,000, mainly this species and Shoveler *A. clypeata*, on sea off Curium, 19 Mar 1972, which flew northwest at dusk (NR3). A few at wetlands into Apr, occasionally into May or Jun. [Breeding reported by Bourne *et al.* was an error, being transposed from Garganey *A. querquedula* (W. R. P. Bourne).] (See *Anas* spp.)

One recovery of a bird ringed in the U.S.S.R. (Appendix 2).

42.   ANAS QUERQUEDULA   PM OB
Garganey

Common passage migrant. Once mid Feb, occasional from late Feb, in 10s at wetlands mid Mar to Apr but sometimes 100–200 together, maximum 500 Larnaca Salt Lake, 9 Apr 1988. A few till late May. Flocks of 10s or 100s on eastward passage off south coast Mar–Apr, maximum numbers off Ayia Napa: *c.* 1000, 3 Apr 1982 and *c.* 1000 on sea, 29 Mar 1983. Occasional Jun–Jul. Autumn passage mainly Aug–Sep, with small numbers at wetlands and flocks of 100s or 1000s coasting west off north coast late Aug to mid Sep; maximum 5400 off Polis/Akamas Beach, 1 Sep 1982 (NR13). Usually a few Oct, sometimes into Nov; twice early Dec, 3 records early and once mid Jan. Probably greatly overlooked on autumn passage, and many Aug–Sep records of *Anas* spp (*q.v.*) probably refer to Garganey. Observations on north coast of Sinai, Sep 1974 (Paran & Paz) indicate a broad front migration of water birds, mainly *querquedula*, from north to south across entire width of eastern Mediterranean, possibly originating on south coast of Anatolia. Many of these birds must pass over or around Cyprus.

Breeding. Kouklia reservoir 1910, C/9 14 May (Bucknill 1911); 20 ducklings there, probably this species, 3 Aug 1967. No evidence for breeding at Morphou or Famagusta (*pace* the Bannermans (1958) and see **Breeding** chapter).

43.   ANAS CLYPEATA   WV PM FB
Shoveler

Common winter visitor and spring passage migrant. Only occasional in autumn, mid Aug to Oct, though possibly overlooked on passage then. A few Nov, 10s or 100s mid Dec to Mar, maximum 1700 Larnaca Salt Lake, 8 Feb 1959 (R3). Winter numbers at the salt lakes sometimes peak Feb or early Mar, probably due to migrants from the south. Usually only a few into Apr, sometimes in 10s, maximum 130 Akrotiri Salt Lake, 6 Apr 1983. Occasional May–Jul. Flocks on passage occur off the south coast late Feb to Apr: maximum a mixed flock of 20,000, mainly this species and Pintail *A. acuta*, on sea off Curium, 19 Mar 1972, which departed northwest at dusk (NR3). (See *Anas* spp.)

Breeding. One record: a few pairs nested at Kouklia reservoir 1910; C/8 taken 14 May (Bucknill 1911).

One recovery of a bird ringed in the U.S.S.R. (Appendix 2).

ANAS spp

Very large numbers of duck pass over and around Cyprus in autumn, mainly mid Aug to Sep, though some passage continues into Nov. Some flocks fly south through the passes of the Kyrenia Range but most coast west along the north coast into Morphou and Khrysokhou Bays, where they roost by day "well out to sea and usually not very visible unless one.is out at sea in a boat. At dusk they take wing to continue their migration through the night [over the island]. One main route is up the Solea valley, low through the Platania pass at treetop level and away to the south . . . Another main route from Morphou Bay is up the Xeros valley and low through the pass between Pedhoulas and Kykko and away to the south over Platys valley. From Polis Bay the route is straight over Khrysokhou and southwards following the trough of low ground between Paphos Forest and Akamas ridge" (Waterer). The species involved appear to be mainly Garganey *A. querquedula*, Wigeon *A. penelope*, Teal *A. crecca* and Mallard *A. platyrhynchos*, but most records simply refer to duck sp. Largest numbers recorded: 64 flocks, totalling *c.* 7400 birds, west off Orga, 12 Sep 1976 (R23), reported as *A. crecca* at the time but not definitely identified as such (T. Caulfeild *per* C. J. L. Bennett); *c.* 6000 duck sp in Khrysokhou Bay, 4 Sep 1978 (R25); and 8 flocks totalling *c.*7550 duck sp in Khrysokhou Bay off Lachi, 26 Aug 1980 (Mrs J. Whiter). If such daily totals are usual, then the autumn passage probably involves several 100,000 birds. Apparently smaller numbers occur on spring passage, Feb–Apr, mainly Mar; many flocks coast east and northeast on south coast, some stopping at the salt lakes, and sometimes 1000s roost in Episkopi Bay by day and fly northwest across the island at dusk, maximum *c.* 20,000, 19 Mar 1972. Large flocks, probably from Larnaca Bay, have also passed northwest over Nicosia at dusk. Species involved apparently different from those in autumn, mainly Shoveler *A. clypeata* and Pintail *A. acuta* reported, though most spring flocks unidentified.

44.   MARMARONETTA (=ANAS) ANGUSTIROSTRIS   FB
Marbled Teal

Formerly not uncommon and probably bred regularly. In 1875 a small flight was seen on the shores of Episkopi Bay, 15 Apr, and ♀ shot near Limassol early May, which "evidently had a nest" (Lilford). Guillemard (1889) obtained one, 8 Apr 1888 and afterwards a nest and eggs at Famagusta Lake. Bucknill (1909–10) bought 3 in Limassol bazaar, 9 Feb 1909. "Some numbers" appeared at the reservoirs mid Apr 1910 and a few pairs remained to nest at Kouklia, a highly incubated C/7 being taken there on 5 Jul and several young shot, 1 Sep (Bucknill 1911). Baxendale (1915) was shown a fresh C/10 at Fresh Water Lake, 24 May 1914, the down from the nest later identified by F. C. R. Jourdain. One or more at Kouklia reservoir, 11 Apr 1929 (Jourdain 1929a). Waterer described it as a sometimes fairly plentiful spring and summer visitor (prior to 1950). Only 3 recent records: 2 Akrotiri, 16 Apr 1958 (R2); one Akrotiri reed beds, 27 May 1978 (R25); 3 Larnaca Salt Lake, 2 Mar 1985 (Hjort *et al.*).

45.   NETTA RUFINA   WV
Red-crested Pochard

Scarce winter visitor mid Nov to Mar, mainly Jan–Feb. Occasional Apr, once early Aug and once mid Oct to early Nov. Now occurring more frequently, being recorded in most winters since 1970. Most widespread early 1972 with up to 23 at Akrotiri Salt Lake and smaller numbers at Kanli, Geunyeli, Pendayia, Famagusta and Athalassa. Maximum of 47 at Bishops Pool, Akrotiri, 8 Jan 1977. Only recorded twice prior to

66   Anatidae

1970: one Mar 1954 (the Bannermans 1958); common and widespread, Dec 1910 to mid Feb 1911 (Bucknill 1911).

46.   AYTHYA FERINA   WV PM
Pochard

Fairly common winter visitor to salt lakes and reservoirs; occurs Oct–Nov to Mar–Apr, peak numbers usually Dec–Feb. Usually in 10s, sometimes in 100s; 3000 Akrotiri Salt Lake, mid Jan 1968 (R15), was exceptional. Occasional May–Jul.

47.   AYTHYA NYROCA   WV PM OB?
Ferruginous Duck

Scarce passage migrant and winter visitor to wetlands, has occurred in every month, most frequently Nov–May, usually singly or less than 10 together, occasionally up to 25, twice 50 in Dec. 25 late Jul 1970 were probably early autumn migrants. "Young" shot Kouklia reservoir, 1 Sep 1910 (Bucknill 1911) may have been migrants; a pair summered Akrotiri reed beds, May–Jul 1969, but there is no evidence of breeding (see Tufted Duck *A. fuligula*).

48.   AYTHYA FULIGULA   WV PM
Tufted Duck

Scarce winter visitor Nov–Mar, sometimes into Apr, usually singly or less than 20 birds together, occasionally up to 60; the large counts of *c*. 100 Akrotiri, Jan 1975, and 400 at Larnaca Salt Lake, 26 Dec 1978, were exceptional. Very few records Jun–Oct. [Bucknill (1911) reported a few at Kouklia reservoir, summer 1910 and eggs on 1 Jul, but this breeding record is mentioned neither in the C.N.H.S. Annals for 1910 nor in Bucknill's own 1913 checklist – it may be that he was not certain of it. Bourne *et al.* suggested that Ferruginous Duck *A. nyroca* was more likely. No records of nests at Famagusta or Morphou (*pace* the Bannermans 1958 and see **Breeding** chapter).]

49.   AYTHYA MARILA   AV
Scaup

Occasional winter visitor, only 4 records: ♀ Morphou, 23 Dec 1957 and 5 Jan 1958 (R2); ♂ Athalassa reservoir, 16 Nov 1963 (R10); ♀ Bishops Pool, 17 and 23 Dec 1967 (R14); ♀ Athalassa reservoir, 29 Nov and 4 Dec 1973 (NR4). [Lichtenstein mentioned a specimen from Cyprus in 1823. It may have been in von Sack's collection of 1820, but Bourne (1964) pointed out that it was not included in Stresemann's list of the von Sack collection, and thought misidentification likely. We have attempted to trace the specimen and have it re-examined, but without success.]

50.   MELANITTA NIGRA   AV
Common Scoter

Accidental visitor (*M.n. nigra*), one record: 8 off Koma-tou-Yialou, 27 Mar 1957 (B2, B6). [*Melanitta* sp reported late Mar 1888 (Guillemard 1889), 7 Feb 1908

(Bucknill 1910) and early Apr 1912 (Bucknill 1913a). "60 black duck resembling Scoter" at Cape Andreas, 7 Apr 1973 (Stagg 1974).]

51.   BUCEPHALA CLANGULA   AV
Goldeneye

Occasional visitor in winter (*B.c. clangula*), 2 recent records: one Famagusta Floods, 9–15 Jan 1972 (R19); 1–2 Bishops Pool, 18 Jan to 13 Feb 1972 (NR3). In the past, one obtained Kouklia reservoir, 9 Apr 1909 (Bucknill 1909–10); a pair Famagusta/Salamis, 17 Mar 1927 (Riddell); 2 shot Limassol marsh, 1942 (Davidson 1954).

52.   MERGUS ALBELLUS   AV
Smew

Occasional visitor in winter, 4 recent records: one Famagusta Floods, 25 Jan 1972 (R19); up to 4 Yermasoyia reservoir, 12–26 Feb 1972 (NR3); one Larnaca Salt Lake, 15 and 29 Dec 1984 (R31, NR15) and one there, 16 Jan 1985 (R32), possibly the same bird. In the past, 2 shot Syrianokhori, winter 1942–43 (Waterer), one now in the RSM, dated 24 Jan 1943.

53.   MERGUS SERRATOR   WV
Red-breasted Merganser

Scarce winter visitor, recorded in 8 winters since 1956: 1–6 birds late Nov to Mar, occasionally into Apr, most often at Famagusta harbour, where it may be regular. Only one record away from the southeast coast; 2 Akrotiri Salt Lake, 22 Apr 1987.

54.   MERGUS MERGANSER   AV
Goosander

Occasional visitor in winter (*M.m. merganser*), 4 records: one Salamis, 9 and 11 Dec 1957 (R2, B6); 6 west Akrotiri, 21 Jan 1968 and 6 Akrotiri Salt Lake, 15 Dec 1968 (R15); one Bishops Pool, 17 Dec 1977 (R24).

55.   OXYURA LEUCOCEPHALA   WV PM?
White-headed Duck

Scarce winter visitor to the salt lakes and reservoirs, possibly becoming more regular. Recorded in 9 winters since 1967, mainly Dec–Jan, occasionally into Feb, also once early Mar. Usually singly, though 6 Larnaca Salt Lake, early Jan 1985 and 14 (9♂♂) Akrotiri, mid Jan 1968 (R15). Also 2 mid-late Oct 1972 at Bishops Pool (R19) and 8 there 8–13 Aug 1970 (R17), probably autumn migrants. Only 2 records prior to 1967: a small flock at Kouklia reservoir for *c.* 3 weeks from end of Apr 1910, and one bought Larnaca market, 12 Dec 1910 (C.N.H.S.Ann.II).

ACCIPITRIDAE

56. PERNIS APIVORUS   PM

Honey Buzzard

Probably a fairly common passage migrant in spring, mid Apr to May (once early Mar, occasional early Apr and once early Jun), mainly at Cape Andreas, daily maximum of 20 there in late Apr 1972 (Stagg 1973). More are to be expected at Cape Andreas in May, as the peak migration at Eilat, Israel, takes place in mid May (Christensen *et al.*), and *c.* 60 "buzzards" at Cape Andreas, 16 May 1972, were probably *apivorus*. Common on autumn passage at Akrotiri, exact passage dates uncertain owing to confusion with Common Buzzard *B. buteo* (see Buzzard spp), but undoubtedly *apivorus* occurs earlier. In 1969–70 the buzzard passage in mid Sep consisted only of *apivorus*, and it may well occur Aug–Oct, mainly Sep, but further investigation is needed (Stewart & Christensen). Maximum in autumn 860, Sep to mid Oct 1969, mainly mid–late Sep, with 405 on 26 Sep (R16). Many, perhaps most, Aug to mid Sep records of *B. buteo* and buzzard spp probably refer to *apivorus*, notably 1500 buzzards at Akrotiri, 5 Sep 1966. On 25 Sep 1973, 391 departed from Akrotiri and were tracked by radar for 12 miles on a steady bearing of 210° (R20), which if maintained would produce a landfall on the Nile Delta. Once early and twice mid Nov, and 8 Larnaca Salt Lake, 21 Nov 1989 (F. Butler).

One recovery of a bird marked U.S.S.R. with handwritten message (Rydzewski 1958), (Appendix 2).

57. MILVUS MIGRANS   PM

Black Kite

Fairly common passage migrant (*M.m. migrans*). Prior to 1972 only singles in spring, late Mar to May, mainly at Cape Andreas; but 110 at the Cape, 30 Apr 1972 (Stagg 1973) and 14 there, 23 Apr 1973 (Stagg 1974). Once early Jun. Autumn passage (mainly at Akrotiri) Aug–Oct, mainly late Aug to Sep, usually singly or less than 10 together, though 50 Akrotiri, 5 Aug 1966 and 40+ there, 15 Sep 1981. Occasional early and once late Nov. [A Jan record attributed to W. R. P. Bourne *in* the Bannermans (1958) was apparently transposed from Marsh Harrier *Circus aeruginosus* (W. R. P. Bourne).]

One recovery of a bird ringed in Poland (Appendix 2).

58. MILVUS MILVUS   AV

Red Kite

Accidental visitor (*M.m. milvus*), only 2 definite records: one obtained near Livadhia, 22 Sep 1901 and sent to the Ungarischen National Museum, Budapest (Madarász 1904b), but unfortunately destroyed in a fire 1956 (L. Horváth), and one Maroni (Larnaca District), 3 Sep 1986 (R33). [4 records involving 7 birds, late Sep to early Oct 1957 (R2), and 6 records involving 12 birds, Oct 1980 (Hallchurch), seem doubtful, and are perhaps a result of confusion with the fairly common Black Kite *M. migrans*. One, without description, reported shot near Yeri, 5 Oct 1974.]

59.   HALIAEETUS ALBICILLA   AV

White-tailed Eagle

Apparently a very scarce winter visitor and/or passage visitor until the 1960s, but not recorded since. 6 recent records: one Larnaca Salt Lake, 14 Jan 1956 (A. H. Banks); immature Cape Greco, 15 Oct 1961 (R8); adult Akrotiri, 15 Sep 1962 (R9); immature Akrotiri, 14 and 22 Oct 1963; adult Episkopi, 14 Nov 1963 (both R10); one Cape Andreas, May 1968 (Stewart & Christensen). In the past: adult pair Kouklia reservoir, 11 Jun 1912 and singles often there and at the Fresh Water Lake (Baxendale 1915); one shot Larnaca Salt Lake, 29 Jan 1913 (C.N.H.S.Ann.IV); an adult Akrotiri Salt Lake, 3 Apr 1927 and 2 adults Larnaca Salt Lake, mid Apr 1927 (Riddell). [In 1889 said to be "sometimes met with" (in 'The Field' 1889: 653).]

60.   GYPAETUS BARBATUS   AV

Lammergeier (Bearded Vulture)

Accidental visitor (*G.b. aureus*), 4 records: 2 in mountains above Akanthou on 13 separate dates, Dec 1957 (D. Noakes); one southeast Akrotiri, 16 Oct 1966 (R13); one near Kantara, 15 Oct 1971 (NR2); one Episkopi, 19 Sep 1982 (R29). [In the past, a pair, without description, in the Kyrenia range, early Mar 1909 (Bucknill 1909–10).]

61.   NEOPHRON PERCNOPTERUS   PM

Egyptian Vulture

Scarce and irregular passage migrant (*N.p. percnopterus*), Mar–Apr and late Sep to Oct. Once each early Sep, mid Nov, late Jan, mid-late Feb, mid May and early Jul, and once in "summer". Usually singly, though 2 Yermasoyia, 26 Apr 1982 (NR13) and 4 Bishops Pool, Akrotiri, 22 Sep 1984 (R31). [20 together, 22 Sep 1967, seem doubtful (R14).]

62.   GYPS FULVUS   RB WV

Griffon Vulture

Fairly common resident (*G.f. fulvus*), slowly declining in numbers.
Breeding distribution. In 1553, Locke (in Cobham) described an individual and stated that "there are many in this island". Mariti, who was present 1760–67, mentions that "one sees many vultures standing in the fields like flocks of sheep". Lilford found considerable numbers on Akrotiri cliffs, Apr or May 1875, and believed some bred; Guillemard (1888) also found many there, Mar 1887 and Bucknill (1909–10) listed Akrotiri as a breeding site, but none are to be seen there now. In the late 1950s and early 1960s up to 140 together at carcasses, since then only 10s. Since 1956 nests have been found in the Kyrenia range at or near Lapithos, St. Hilarion, Buffavento, Akanthou, Pentadaktylos and Kantara; in the Troodos range at Kannaviou, in the Kouris valley, Vroisha and within the Paphos Forest; on sea cliffs at Episkopi, Cape Arnaouti and Cape Aspro, also at Neokhorio (Paphos) and near Polis. It does not breed at all these sites today and, in particular, all the birds in the Kyrenia range are believed to have been shot.

Breeding data. Nests singly or in small colonies invariably on rocky cliffs or crags. At Episkopi, where breeding is regular and sites more accessible, a 1979 survey located 10 nest sites of which 6 were successful (Sweeney). 16 nests were found there in 1982: 3 at Happy Valley west side; 2 on Gibraltar Cliffs; 4 at Tunnel Beach; 4 on Kensington Cliffs west face and 3 on the east face (R29). 9 nests at Episkopi in 1984 (R31) and 3 nests (each containing a chick) at the Tunnel Beach site in Apr 1989 (NL89/4). At the Episkopi colony, eggs, C/1, seen Jan–Apr, young from late Feb, and first flights twice early Aug. Observed fledging periods – *c*. 130 days (F. Taylor *in* the Bannermans 1958), and more than 4 months (Clarke *et al*.) – are longer than those given by Cramp & Simmons.

In several years since 1970 numbers have increased sharply Oct–Jan, especially at Episkopi, suggesting a winter influx, maximum 108 Episkopi, 29 Dec 1980 (this record reconfirmed by M. G. Lobb, *pace* Charalambides *et al. in* NR11). A passage northeastward resembling migration was observed Feb–Apr 1965 over Nicosia (Christensen 1967). In 1970, 3 were migrating south over Nicosia, 13 Oct and 5 on 14 Oct (R17).

63.   AEGYPIUS MONACHUS   RB

Black Vulture

Formerly a fairly common resident, now possibly extinct, or nearly so. Encountered by most earlier observers, including Guillemard (1888), Bate (1903a), Glaszner (*in* Madarász 1904b) and Bucknill (1909–10).

Breeding distribution. Waterer stated that (prior to 1950) more than 1–2 pairs resided in both ranges, with nests on pine trees. Pairs commonly seen around Troodos, 1956–58, with occasional birds over Kyrenia range and Nicosia, and up to 10 together at carcasses with Griffon Vulture *G. fulvus* (B2, R2). Numbers had declined sharply by mid 1960s, and since 1965 only 12 substantiated records, all of singles, the last in 1982.

Breeding data. Few details: an egg, containing a live chick, taken from a nest on a large pine tree near Buffavento, 28 Apr 1909 (Bucknill 1909–10); a pair nested 1949 and 1950 at Makria Kondaria, Troodos, in Troodos Pine *Pinus nigra* (Davidson 1954).

64.   CIRCAETUS GALLICUS   PM

Short-toed Eagle

Scarce passage migrant (*C.g. gallicus*), 25 records: Apr to early May (8), Sep to mid Oct (15), once Jun and Jul; usually in ones or twos, once 5 together late Sep. The spring records, including those of Christensen (1967) and Stagg (1973, 1974) are mainly from Famagusta and Cape Andreas, suggesting a passage through the east of the island. In autumn mainly at Akrotiri. [4 over Mt. Olympus, 20 Jul 1973 seem doubtful.]

65.   CIRCUS AERUGINOSUS   PM WV

Marsh Harrier

Passage migrant and winter visitor (*C.a. aeruginosus*). Passage Mar–May and Aug–Oct, mainly Apr and Sep to early Oct when fairly common. Highest passage totals:

41 at Cape Andreas, 4–25 Apr 1973 (Stagg 1974) and 60, mainly at Akrotiri, 23 Aug to 16 Oct 1969 (R16). Usually singly at marshes Nov–Feb, maximum of 12 Akrotiri mid-winter 1957–58. Occasional Jun–Jul; in 1975 a pair summered Akrotiri reed beds till Jul. 2 melanistic adult ♀♀ collected Tolke, Aug and Dec 1905 (Clark).

One recovery of a bird ringed in Tunisia (Appendix 2).

66. CIRCUS CYANEUS   WV PM

Hen Harrier

Passage migrant and winter visitor (*C.c. cyaneus*) mid Aug to early May, most frequent Apr. Highest spring passage total, 14 at Cape Andreas, 11–25 Apr 1973 (Stagg 1974). Usually 1–2 on autumn passage, mainly Sep–Oct, but perhaps has been confused sometimes with other *circus* spp. Occurs singly or in pairs at marshes Oct–Mar.

67. CIRCUS MACROURUS   PM

Pallid Harrier

Fairly common passage migrant. Twice early Mar, fairly common mid Mar to Apr, mainly late Mar to early Apr, maximum 12 northeast Cape Andreas, 9–25 Apr 1973 (Stagg 1974), occasional May; once mid Jun and mid Aug, twice late Aug; fairly common on return passage Sep–Oct, mainly mid Sep to Oct, occasional Nov. Very scarce and irregular in winter, only 5 definite records of ♂♂, Jan to mid Feb. [Several unconfirmed ♀♀/immatures Dec–Feb.]

68. CIRCUS PYGARGUS   PM

Montagu's Harrier

Scarce passage migrant, most frequent in autumn. Occurs, usually singly, Mar to early May, mainly Apr, and Sep–Oct; occasional Aug and Nov. 'Ringtail' harriers are common on passage and are probably mostly Pallid Harrier *C. macrourus*, but some probably this species. Possibly occasional in winter (see *C. macrourus*).

69. ACCIPITER GENTILIS   RB WV? PM?

Goshawk

A.g. gentilis. Apparently a scarce resident within the Paphos Forest. The Bannermans (1958) saw birds there Jan 1958; one shot there 'spring' 1961 (skin in Dept. of Agriculture, Nicosia); individuals there 26 May, 31 May and 2 Jun 1979 (R26), 13 Apr 1980 (R27), 25 Mar and 11 Dec 1985 (R32), and Jan and 26 Oct 1986 (R33). In 1984 there were 15 records of 1–2 birds there, 1 May to 2 Oct, and on 12 May a raptor nest "proved to be of a Goshawk" (NR15). Also in Jan–Apr 1984 another observer in the same area found 3 nests typical for the species, no eggs or young were seen, but an adult was present at one nest (Rudolf). Because of the extreme vulnerability of these birds to shooting, no details are given of the nest sites or locations. Those wishing to study these birds should contact C.O.S. (1970).

In the past, one shot Troodos, 12 Aug 1910 (Bucknill 1911). 14 sight records in winter 1957–59, mainly in the hills, but only 3 winter records since. [Frequently reported on passage mid Sep to Oct, and occasionally mid Mar to early May, but no satisfactory descriptions of passage birds and possibly some confusion with other spp. In view of the status given by Cramp & Simmons, any passage through Cyprus is unlikely to involve more than a very few birds.]

70.   ACCIPITER NISUS   PM WV
Sparrowhawk

Scarce to fairly common passage migrant and winter visitor (*A.n. nisus*) late Aug–May. 24 at Cape Andreas, 24 Apr to 3 May 1972 (Stagg 1973) and 80 north-east there, 9–25 Apr 1973 (Stagg 1974). A total of 45 at Akrotiri, 3 Sep to 2 Oct 1967 (R14). In winter occurs singly, mainly in wooded areas of the hills and mountains. Once Troodos early Jun (Mason) and once late Jun (J. C. Le Gassick). [4 unconfirmed sightings, mid Jun to mid Jul.]

71.   ACCIPITER BREVIPES   PM
Levant Sparrowhawk

Scarce and irregular passage migrant, perhaps overlooked: 5 singles early Sep to early Oct 1957, and singles early and late Apr 1958 (R2); one limed Paralimni, 22 Sep 1967 (Hubbard 1967a) and one shot Orounda, 26 Apr 1975 (NR6). [3 unconfirmed sightings May and once mid-winter. Probably sometimes confused with Sparrowhawk *A. nisus*.]

72.   BUTEO BUTEO   PM WV
Common Buzzard

Common passage migrant. Few records of spring passage prior to 1972, when unspecified numbers of *B.b. vulpinus* at Cape Andreas, 24 Apr to 3 May (Stagg 1973), and 289 *B. buteo* and buzzard spp flew north and northwest from there, 4–25 Apr 1973 (Stagg 1974). Twice mid May, occasional Jun. Common on autumn passage at Akrotiri, but confusion with Honey Buzzard *Pernis apivorus* obscures passage dates (see Buzzard spp). Prior to 1969 almost all records were of *B. buteo*, but S. J. Christensen in 1969–70 observed only *P. apivorus* in mid Sep, *B. buteo* first appearing late Sep. Probably *B. buteo* occurs from mid Sep, with few before, to late Oct, with peak migration late Sep to early Oct (Stewart & Christensen), usually 10s or 100s daily, maximum c. 1250 on 22 Sep 1963. Nearly 300 *B.b. vulpinus* (intermediate type mainly) at Akrotiri, 4 Oct 1968 (S. J. Christensen); most migrants are probably of this race. Scarce winter visitor Nov–Mar, usually singly or up to 3 together, mainly over Mesaoria or at Akrotiri and some have proved to be nominate *buteo* (Stewart & Christensen).

PERNIS/BUTEO
Buzzard spp *P. apivorus/B. buteo*

Because of the confusion over the composition of the autumn buzzard flocks, the autumn migrations of the 2 species are described together. Birds occur all along the north coast, suggesting a broad front arrival from Turkey. Observations at Kyrenia have shown birds arriving singly over the sea from the north, mainly in the afternoons, and individuals have been seen to fly through the Kyrenia Pass and south across the plain. Birds cross the island singly or in small flocks of 10s or less, and although they occur widely, the higher Troodos is generally avoided, birds passing east or west around the range. Many, perhaps most, of the buzzards leave the island via the Akrotiri peninsula and Cape Gata. The first mention of this passage is that of Waterer: "I have reason to believe that heavy birds of prey migrate over Cyprus in large numbers. Once when fishing some miles off Cape Gata I observed a steady stream of heavy birds of prey heading south out to sea. They were apparently a species of eagle which I could not identify for they were high and sailed on still spread wings on a southbound air current. They were quite definitely not vultures. The migration went on for hours in a steady stream. The birds were spread out over a wide area, I recall counting 23 in sight at one time. The date was early Sep 1949". (Our present knowledge suggests buzzards were involved rather than eagles, though this does not detract from the value of the observation.) Waterer's observation was never published and the buzzard passage at Akrotiri was re-discovered by M. D. Backhouse in 1957, since when it has been observed many times. Birds begin to arrive at Akrotiri in the early morning, approaching from Episkopi to the northwest and Polemidhia and Limassol to the north and northeast, many of them having probably roosted in wooded areas of the coastal plain and lower foothills. The main movement at Akrotiri occurs early to mid-morning, with usually fewer until *c.* 1330 hours, and generally little passage after that. Many soar in flocks over the seaward side of the lake, sometimes up to 1000–1800m, at which heights they are difficult to see, before gliding southwards. Some individuals and small flocks do not gain height, but flap out to sea only a few 10s of metres above the cliff tops. The bearings taken by departing birds vary between southeast and south-southwest. In Sep 1971 many *apivorus* which left Cape Gata at low level flew southeast (P. R. Flint). The main passage occurs Sep to early Oct, daily totals usually in 10s or 100s, occasionally over 1000, maximum 1645 (405 *apivorus* and 1240 buzzard spp), 26 Sep 1969. The highest autumn total, also in 1969, is 2757 (860 *apivorus* and 1897 buzzard spp), but this figure is undoubtedly too low as in no autumn have there been continuous daily observations of the buzzard passage throughout the migration period. Occasional observations in autumn at Cape Andreas, Cape Greco and Cape Kiti have shown individuals and small flocks departing from those locations also, mainly southeast, maximum 39 Cape Kiti, 25 Sep 1971. A southeastward departure from these eastern capes would involve a considerably shorter sea crossing than one from Akrotiri, and it may be that there is a considerable passage through the east of the island also.

73.   BUTEO RUFINUS   WV PM?

     Long-legged Buzzard

Scarce and irregular winter visitor (*B.r. rufinus*) mid Nov to mid Mar, some 11 recent winter records, mainly of singles, twice 2 together. Some individuals apparently remain for weeks or months, often near wetlands. In winter in the past, singles shot near Larnaca, 28 Dec 1912 and near Famagusta, 19 and 29 Jan 1913 (C.N.H.S.Ann.IV).

     Possibly also a scarce passage migrant: passage of more than 10 daily reported Cape Andreas, 26 Apr and 1–3 May 1972 (Stagg 1973), and singles there 10, 18 and 21 Apr 1973 (Stagg 1974); descriptions do not preclude *B.b. vulpinus*, but identity of one (1972) bird confirmed by S. J. Christensen from a colour slide. [During

1957–1968, 19 records of 30–31 birds on autumn passage mid Sep to early Nov were all rejected by Stewart & Christensen because descriptions were not separable from *B.b. vulpinus*. One similar Sep record since. "Clearly somewhat under-recorded on migration through Middle East generally" (Cramp & Simmons), so perhaps it may eventually prove to be a scarce passage migrant.]

74.   BUTEO LAGOPUS   AV
Rough-legged Buzzard

Occasional winter visitor, 4 records: one at Morphou, 24 Nov 1957 to 9 Feb 1958, a second there 25 Jan 1958 (R2, B6); 2 immature ♀♀ shot Zakaki marshes, Limassol, 27 and 28 Dec 1946 (skins in NRS), both of them *B.l. pallidus* (=*menzbieri*) (C. Edelstan *per* S. J. Christensen), being paler than a large series from Scandinavia. Vaurie mentions *B.l. lagopus* from Cyprus. [From 1957 to 1970, 15–18 records involving 25–28 birds early Aug to Oct, were all rejected by Stewart & Christensen who considered its occurrence improbable in Cyprus in autumn, the descriptions not separating it from pale specimens of *B.b. vulpinus*, with which they believed it had been confused. 7 similar Sep-Oct records since. Also once Jan and 3 times Apr without adequate details.]

75.   AQUILA POMARINA   PM
Lesser Spotted Eagle

Scarce passage migrant (*A.p. pomarina*), 12 records Mar to early May, and 12 records late Sep to early Nov, usually singly, sometimes 2–3 together. Records in spring from Famagusta 1965 (Christensen 1967) and Cape Andreas 1972–73 (Stagg 1973, 1974) and 1974 (P. R. Flint) indicate passage through the east of the island; highest total, 8 Cape Andreas, 30 Apr to 3 May 1972. In autumn mainly in the Limassol–Akrotiri area. One shot Alodha (Mogashia) marsh, 26 Dec 1912 (C.N.H.S.Ann.IV). [27 records of unidentified *Aquila* eagles late Aug to Oct, mainly late Sep to early Oct, most probably this species.]

76.   AQUILA CLANGA   AV
Spotted Eagle

Accidental visitor, only 3 records: one shot Akrotiri Salt Lake, 26 Sep 1967 (R14); one Lachi, 28 Sep 1986 and one Akrotiri Salt Lake, 5 Oct 1986 (R33).

77.   AQUILA HELIACA   RB PM?
Imperial Eagle

Very scarce resident (*A.h. heliaca*), formerly common. Perhaps 12 pairs in 1958 (R2), though in 1964 Bourne *et al.* described it as common over middle slope hills. Sightings now reduced to 0–3 a year.

Breeding distribution. Probably no longer breeds within the Kyrenia range, and doubtful if more than 1–2 pairs within the Troodos range. Waterer (prior to 1950) saw nests in both ranges; all of those found by him and D. F. Davidson were on Aleppo Pine *Pinus halepensis* (the Bannermans 1958).

Breeding data. The only detailed records are from the Kyrenia range: nest with 2 recently hatched young on *Pinus halepensis*, 15 Apr 1960 (R5); another on a tall pine with 2 slightly incubated eggs, 29 Apr 1909 (Bucknill 1909–10).

7 immatures heading north over Nicosia, 2 Feb 1965 (Christensen 1967) now considered probably indicating local dispersion and not migration (S. J. Christensen). An immature drifting north with other eagles, Cape Andreas, 3 May 1972 (Stagg 1973). [A skin in Dept. of Agriculture, Nicosia, collected by Horsbrugh and labelled as killed by a peasant with a stone while feeding on a dead sheep, is actually Bonelli's Eagle *Hieraaetus fasciatus* (S. J. Christensen, P. F. Stewart).]

78.   AQUILA CHRYSAETOS   AV

Golden Eagle

Accidental visitor, one record: an immature near Kormakiti, 14 Oct 1973 (NR4). [Descriptions of 2 at Curium, 21 Sep 1962 and one at Troodos, 31 Mar 1963, agree better with Imperial Eagle *A. heliaca* (Stewart & Christensen), as also another at Athalassa, 9 Nov 1974.]

79.   HIERAAETUS PENNATUS   PM

Booted Eagle

Scarce passage migrant. 14 records mid Mar to early May mainly from the east of the island; probably regular mid Sep to Oct, mainly late Sep, usually singly and mostly at Akrotiri; twice Nov, once early Dec (Christensen 1967). [One, without description, shot Platania, Feb 1972.]

80.   HIERAAETUS FASCIATUS   RB PM

Bonelli's Eagle

Scarce resident (*H.f. fasciatus*), formerly common. Bucknill (1909–10) recorded it many times in both mountain ranges, and in winter often saw 2–3 swooping over packs of coot and duck on the reservoirs. At least 50 pairs estimated in 1958 (R2).

Breeding distribution. Stewart & Christensen estimated 5–6 pairs in the Kyrenia range in 1970, with a larger population in the Troodos range. A few pairs remain within the Troodos range, where birds still regularly seen, maximum 5 there, 20 Oct 1985 (R32). Pairs bred there 1986 (R33) and 1988 (NR19). Last reported Kyrenia range 1974, now almost certainly extinct there because of the great increase in shooting. Guillemard (1888) obtained a young bird from a cliff near Limni. In late Mar 1909 a pair bred near the ruins of Buffavento Castle (Bucknill 1909–10), not within the ruins (*pace* the Bannermans 1958, 1971).

Breeding data. C/2 Troodos range, 12 Feb 1911 (Bucknill 1911). A nest between a tree stump and a cliff face near Halevga held C/1, 3 Feb 1958, and 2 juveniles by 7 Apr (R2). A pair raised 2 young at a nest in a pine tree in the Troodos range 1988; the 2 young, *c.* 10–15 days old, were found on 23 Mar and fledged 5 and 9 May. Extensive details of this nest, including lists of prey items, are given by Kourtellarides. The young were ringed and on 9 Jul 1988 one was found shot with a rifle bullet and dying.

Apparently also a very scarce passage migrant: one flew north from Kyrenia towards Turkey once mid Mar (Stewart & Christensen); 3 Cape Andreas, 30 Apr

1961, and one flew northeast there 4 May 1961; also a few records at Akrotiri, Sep–Oct.

PANDIONIDAE

81.   PANDION HALIAETUS   PM
Osprey

Passage migrant (*P.h. haliaetus*). Scarce late Mar to May, mostly Apr; occasional Aug to early Sep, fairly common mid Sep to mid Oct, especially at Akrotiri, usually singly, maximum 15 individuals autumn 1969 and 1972; occasional late Oct to Nov, once early-mid Dec. Most overfly, though some individuals stop to fish at the reservoirs, where they sometimes remain for a few days, exceptionally up to 3 weeks.

FALCONIDAE

82.   FALCO NAUMANNI   PM WV FB
Lesser Kestrel

Passage migrant in variable numbers Mar–May and Sep to early Nov (once mid Aug), most frequent late Mar to Apr and late Sep to mid Oct; in some years only a few, in others common in flocks of 10s, sometimes up to 100, usually most numerous in spring. Apparently very scarce and irregular in winter: 1–8 mid-late Dec, singles 3 times mid Jan and, in the past, 3 times Feb (Payn, MCZ).

Former breeding. Formerly a breeding summer visitor, but no breeding records since 1929 and no recent summer sightings despite search. Lilford considered it much more numerous than Kestrel *F. tinnunculus* in 1875, describing it as "exceedingly abundant, breeding principally in the holes and crannies of old walls, notably in those of the aquaduct that spans the road to Limassol at a short distance from Larnaca". Bucknill (1909–10) described it as a very common summer visitor, and found fresh full clutches on 5 May. However, he stated "though Lord Lilford regarded it as more abundant than *tinnunculus,* such is not our experience, as the large majority of the many Kestrels we shot and of the nests we took belonged to *tinnunculus*". This statement, based on birds and nests examined in the hand, suggests that *naumanni* was not by then at least a common breeding bird. Jourdain (1929a) saw a pair mating at Nicosia, 17 Apr 1929, and on 22 Apr located a mixed colony of *naumanni/tinnunculus* in the walls of Famagusta, from which he took one C/1 and two C/5 of *naumanni,* one of which (C/5) in BMNH was confirmed by M. Walters as typical of *naumanni* in both size and colouration. M. Walters has also located others in BMNH: C/5 collected by Schrader, 16 May (probably 1877), C/4 collected by R. Tancré, 14 May 1885, and 4 eggs from Lilford, Larnaca, 1887, all of which are typical of *naumanni,* and would be most atypical of *tinnunculus*. Thus there can be no doubt that *naumanni* formerly bred. The reason for its extinction is unknown; possibly the choice of man-made breeding sites rendered it vulnerable to shooting.

83.   FALCO TINNUNCULUS   RB PM WV
Kestrel

F.t. tinnunculus. Common resident.
Breeding distribution. Widespread outside forest areas, most numerous in coastal areas and lower Troodos foothills. A few pairs breed Kyrenia range, nests

found up to *c*. 700 m, and in Troodos range up to *c*. 300 m (Ashton–Johnson), though in late May and early Jun 1979 birds frequent in south and west Troodos up to *c*. 800 m (Flint 1980). Apparently absent from the higher Troodos, except on migration (Mason).

Breeding data. Eggs, usually C/3 to C/5, once C/6, found late Mar to May, and young late Mar to mid Jun; eggs of 13 nests examined by Ashton–Johnson showed "considerable variation in size and markings"; nests mainly in rock or earth cliffs, less commonly in buildings, though since 1976 has nested on multi-storey buildings at Nicosia; nests also found in *Eucalyptus*, Hawthorn *Crataegus azarolus* and in "palm trees", and once in old tree nest of Hooded Crow *Corvus corone* (Ashton–Johnson). The most frequent prey items brought to nests are small lizards; also recorded are small rodents, larks, a small snake and (in Nicosia) House Sparrows *Passer domesticus*. 2 young ringed Akrotiri, 3 Jun 1965, shot near Famagusta 6 Sep 1965 and Akrotiri 26 Dec 1966.

Common on passage and in winter; passage late Feb to early May and Aug to mid Nov, most Apr and Sep–Oct. Highest passage total, 157 northeast at Cape Andreas, 4–25 Apr 1973 (Stagg 1974).

84. FALCO VESPERTINUS   PM

Red-footed Falcon

Common passage migrant (*F.v. vespertinus*). Once mid Mar, twice late Mar, common Apr to mid May, mainly late Apr to early May, occasional to late Jun, once early Jul; occasional mid-late Aug, common Sep to early Nov, mainly late Sep to mid Oct, occasional to late Nov and once early Dec. Often in flocks, especially in autumn, when commoner than in spring. Highest passage total: 737 late Sep to mid Oct 1968, including 230 on 1 Oct and 208 on 4 Oct (R15). Observations in 1968–69 showed it often migrates at high altitude, often out of sight of the naked eye, and a large and sometimes unobserved passage may therefore occur regularly in autumn (Stewart & Christensen).

[Breeding, attributed to Müller or W. Schlüter, has been disputed by Bucknill (1909–10), Jourdain (1929b) and the Bannermans (1958). However, the eggs mentioned by Müller under *vespertinus* do not appear to refer to this species (Bourne 1959a). One consignment of *vespertinus* skins (sent to W. Schlüter) included many eggs, mostly Kestrel *F. tinnunculus* with a few Lesser Kestrel *F. naumanni* (Müller); no eggs were attributed to *vespertinus* and thus there is no suggestion that it has ever bred.]

85. FALCO COLUMBARIUS   PM WV

Merlin

Scarce passage migrant and winter visitor Sep–Apr, apparently more numerous in the past. Singles recorded frequently 1956–61 on low ground, Sep–Nov to Apr. Since then only 10 reliable records Dec–Feb, and scarce Mar–Apr and Sep–Nov, with no records in several years. 12 records of skins and shot birds in the past, mid Oct to early Apr.

3 skins in the RSM are listed as *F.c. aesalon*, one dated mid Mar and another Nov; specimens examined by Hartert were referred by him to *F.c. insignis* (the Bannermans 1958); some records from the eastern Mediterranean probably

represent *insignis,* or intermediates between *insignis* and *aesalon,* but the 2 races cannot always be identified with certainty (Vaurie).

86.   FALCO SUBBUTEO   PM FB?

Hobby

Common passage migrant (*F.s. subbuteo*): occasional late Mar, common Apr–May, occasional Jun; once early and late Jul, occasional Aug, common Sep–Oct, a few Nov, sometimes into Dec, these late individuals often hunting over reed beds. Maximum passage totals: in spring, 77 Cape Andreas, 6–25 Apr 1973, but mostly late Apr (Stagg 1974); in autumn, 106 Akrotiri, 27 Sep to 24 Oct 1967, mostly late Sep (R14). [One shot near Psevdhas, 30 Jun 1913, "contained an egg ready for laying within a few days", and a C/4 taken by a villager from an old crows nest near Psevdhas, 25 Jul 1913, was attributed to this species (C.N.H.S.Ann.IV), but the description of the eggs does not preclude Kestrel *F. tinnunculus.* R. R. Waterer "once found a nest" and D. F. Davidson "has evidence of breeding" (the Bannermans 1958), but no details are given.]

87.   FALCO ELEONORAE   MB PM?

Eleonora's Falcon

Locally common migrant breeder.
   Breeding distribution. Colonies on sea cliffs along south coast, from Cape Gata towards Petra tou Romiou. First arrivals at colonies usually mid or late Apr, occasionally Mar. Present at colonies May–Oct, though, especially during May and Jun, may be seen far from them, hunting over treetops at dusk to take large flying insects. In 1957 W.R.P. Bourne (*in* Vaughan) estimated 150–300 pairs, but appears to have over-estimated the Cape Aspro colonies. Censuses were made in 1971 (Flint 1972f), in 1972 (W. F. Corris *in* R19 and *in litt.*) and in 1977 (Walter & Foers); Corris, who surveyed the colonies by boat, obtained the most complete results, achieving the only successful count of the largest colonies, at Cape Aspro, and locating a previously unknown colony between Paramali beach and Evdhimou Bay. These observations, and other occasional surveys since 1957–58 of the more accessible colonies, suggest that the population is probably stable (*pace* Flint 1972f). From these censuses the population appears to be: Cape Gata and Akrotiri cliffs, *c.* 25 pairs; Episkopi cliffs (Curium, Kensington Village, Gibraltar Point), *c.* 23 pairs; Paramali beach/Evdhimou Bay, *c.* 12 pairs; Cape Aspro and west towards Petra tou Romiou, *c.* 50–60 pairs – total 110–120 pairs. None breeds on Petra tou Romiou itself, the most westerly colony being *c.* 3 km east of there. [Date of inland breeding near Kantara early May 1954 (the Bannermans 1958) suggests some other *Falco* sp involved. Doubtfully bred Polemidhia 1975 (NR6).] At Akrotiri, autumn 1957, 8 of 32 adults were dark phase (R2) and in autumn 1982, 20 of 42 (Mumford).
   Breeding data. Nests on cliffs, which fall directly into the sea, on ledges (often deeply overhung) 3–80 m above sea level. Clutch size C/2 or C/3, once C/4. Nests sometimes contain only one young but it is not known if these result from single egg clutches. At Akrotiri cliffs, eggs are laid late Jul and early Aug, hatching late Aug and early Sep (once mid Aug); young fledging early to late Oct. At one nest, incubation took 24–27 days, at another 27–30 days. At the latter nest young were just fledged in 44 days and at another nest young were almost fledged in 40–41 days (Flint 1972b); these are longer than the fledging periods given by Cramp &

Simmons. On 6 Oct 1978 a census at Cape Gata/Akrotiri cliffs located 21 nests containing a total of 36 young, an average of 1·71 young per nest (Foers 1983). Very soon after last young fledge, adults and young depart, usually late Oct or early Nov, exceptionally a few mid Nov.

An infertile egg taken Akrotiri 24 Sep 1960 contained the smallest detectable traces of insecticide: 0·4 parts per million of DDE and under 0·01 parts per million of DDT and TDE (B15). 27 bird spp were identified from remains taken from nest ledges at Akrotiri during ringing operations (B14, B16, B20, Stewart 1968a); also found were a locust wing, and, in 2 nests, crab claws. The most numerous prey species was Hoopoe *Upupa epops*, the other bird prey ranging in size from Garden Warbler *Sylvia borin* to Quail *Coturnix coturnix*, Corncrake *Crex crex*, Water Rail *Rallus aquaticus* and Rock Dove *Columba livia*. Vaughan suggested that remains of large species such as Quail and Rock Dove might be due to Peregrine Falcon *Falco peregrinus*, but this cannot be the case at Akrotiri, where Peregrine Falcons no longer breed.

9 flew south and west at Cape Andreas, 26–30 Apr 1972; 26 there 20–25 Apr 1973 (Stagg 1974), and 20 "migrating" near Halevga, 15 May 1960. These records could refer to passage or to arriving local breeders.

There are 7 local recoveries of birds ringed Akrotiri, at least 5 of them shot, one after 6 years. 2 chicks, ringed Akrotiri, recovered in Egypt and Madagascar. One ringed in Crete, recovered in Cyprus (Appendix 2).

88.   FALCO CONCOLOR   AV

Sooty Falcon

Accidental visitor, one record: one Cape Gata, 22 Sep 1962 (R9).

89.   FALCO CHERRUG   PM

Saker

F.c. cherrug. Passage migrant: scarce late Mar to early May, mainly Apr, no more than 3 records in any spring; usually fairly common Sep–Oct, mainly at Akrotiri, sometimes 1–3 almost daily, maximum 8 there 17 Sep 1961, occasionally a few into Nov. Very scarce and irregular winter visitor, mainly near wildfowl habitats or over the Mesaoria; only 2 recent records Dec, none Jan, and 3 in Feb. Formerly one shot early Dec (Baxendale 1915), and one obtained "in winter" (Bucknill 1913a). [During winter 1957–58, 12 records of *F. cherrug/biarmicus*, most probably the former; since then only 4 winter records of similar birds, Dec, Jan (2) and Feb.]

90.   FALCO PEREGRINUS   RB PM WV

Peregrine

Resident (*F.p. brookei*).

Breeding distribution. In recent times bred on cliffs at Akrotiri (1957), Cape Greco (1959) (Ashton–Johnson), Episkopi (1969,–70,–78,–79,–86,–87,–89 and probably in other recent years) and Baths of Aphrodite (1987). Pairs also at coastal sites at Cape Aspro, near Paphos, Akamas, Orga, along the Karpas, Cape Andreas and Cape Pyla; and inland at Kantara, St. Hilarion, Troodos, and within the Paphos

Forest. Formerly bred Buffavento (Bucknill 1909–10), and Klidhes Islands 1911–12 (Bucknill 1911, 1913a).

Breeding data. C/4 in an old nest of Raven *Corvus corax* found mid Mar (Ashton–Johnson) and young Mar to mid May.

Passage migrant Apr to early May and Sep–Oct, mainly autumn and usually in ones or twos; 31 moving southwest Cape Andreas, 9–24 Apr 1973 (Stagg 1974).

Specimens attributed to *F.p. peregrinus* were obtained near Famagusta, 1 Feb 1912 (C.N.H.S.Ann.IV) and 10 May 1914 (Baxendale 1915), though possibly confused with *F.p. calidus;* a winter killed specimen was identified as *calidus* by Jourdain (1930), and "large pale birds", recorded on passage Oct and around wildfowl concentrations in winter (R2), were presumably *calidus*.

PHASIANIDAE

91. ALECTORIS CHUKAR   RB

Chukar

Common and widespread resident (*A.c. cypriotes*), formerly abundant.

Breeding distribution. Occupies a variety of habitats, including garigue, vineyards, barren rocky areas, and pine forest, from sea level to summit of Troodos where birds remain until driven lower by snow (Mason). Marginal land, in the form of scrub or forest edge, has a significantly higher density of birds than forest and cultivation (Bell & Summers).

Breeding data. Eggs, C/8 to C/17 (mostly C/11 to C/15), late Feb to May, and young late Apr to Aug.

As 'partridge', mentioned by several authors in earlier centuries: the earliest, d'Anglure, who in 1396 received a gift of "one hundred partridges"; subsequently found plentiful or abundant by Cotovicus, in 1598–9, by Heyman in the early 18th century and by Kinneir in 1814 (all *in* Cobham). Mariti, during 1760–67, found it "among the commonest birds". Bucknill (1909–10) observed that "the introduction of modern weapons in large numbers has, within the last 20 years, caused a very marked decrease in the abundance of the species". Post breeding coveys are still heavily shot in late autumn and winter.

Although first described from Cyprus, *cypriotes* is not an endemic race, and it also occurs in southern Turkey, Crete and the southern Aegean islands. Cyprus birds however tend to average larger, and to be slightly paler and less slender billed than those from Crete and the Aegean (Cramp & Simmons).

92. FRANCOLINUS FRANCOLINUS   RB

Black Francolin

Locally common resident (*F.f. francolinus*), formerly very common and widespread. Now increasing in numbers and recolonising some of its former breeding range, both in the southwest and on the Karpas.

Breeding distribution. Local in the southwest from Phasouri through Kouklia (Paphos), Akhelia, Paphos, Akamas and Argaka to Pomos; mainly in low-lying coastal areas but some also in wide shallow valleys up to 200–400 m and up to 19 km inland, as in Stavros tis Psokas and Dhiarizos valleys. In 1989 the population in the southwest was estimated to be *c*. 150 birds (Boye). Also reported inland at Cedar Valley, Oct 1986 and near Yerakies, south of Lefka, Jun 1989. Habitat in the southwest usually agricultural: cereals, bananas or vineyards, with some scrub

(Flint 1980). Returned to breed Limni 1981 after an absence of some years and has since spread to Argaka and Pomos; has also returned to Paramali (Episkopi). A report of a bird by the Kormakiti Road, Oct 1986, suggests a possible return to an area where the species has been absent for many years. Also occurs on the Karpas where in spring 1987 found to be quite common and well distributed along the whole length of the peninsula from Cape Andreas to Galatia with others calling as far west as Boghaz. This is a considerable extension of distribution since 1974 when the species' range on the Karpas had declined to the easternmost 4–5 miles of the peninsula. At Cape Andreas itself the birds occur in dense high *Juniperus phoenicia* maquis. In 1989 the population on the Karpas was estimated to be *c.* 200 birds (Boye). It is very vulnerable to shooting, but responds well to effective protection (Bucknill 1909–10, Wilson 1925).

   Very common in the past: in 1738, Pococke (*in* Cobham), found it to be "among the chief birds" and, during 1760–67, Mariti listed it the first of "the commonest birds". In 1875 many were calling north of Salamis to Cape Andreas and eggs were taken at Trikomo (Lilford). In 1912 a few were still left at Cape Kormakiti (Bucknill 1913a). Wilson (1925a) lists Kouklia, Vatili, Tymbou, Aphania, Syrianokhori and Limassol marshes as places once "famous for their francolin", and states that "It is said that 40 years ago there were in Cyprus as many francolin as partridges". In 1958–59 still common in river beds on Karpas as far from the tip as Yialousa; common Akrotiri till 1958 and Episkopi till 1971. Calls mainly late Feb or Mar to mid Jul (call and behaviour described by Cole (1972a) and Hourston).

   Breeding data. Nest once under a small bush in the middle of standing corn (Bate 1903a). Eggs, C/8 to C/12 (mainly Müller), late Apr to early Jun; young late Apr, early Jul and late Aug.

93. COTURNIX COTURNIX   RB? MB? PM WV?

     Quail

(*C.c. coturnix*). Status obscure. Present all year in low cultivated areas; calling birds are very common and widespread Mar to early May, and in recent times bred Dhali, Episkopi, Famagusta/Dhekelia, Lakatamia, near Morphou and Strovolos. Whether breeders are resident or migratory or both is not known. Possibly breeds Troodos range: 2 calling on *cistus* covered hillsides at *c.* 1000 m, near Tripylos, 3 Jun 1979.

   Breeding data. Nest found once in an olive grove and Bucknill (1911) found it bred "fairly freely in the barley". Eggs, C/10 to C/15, found early Apr to mid May; young mid Apr to Jul.

   Usually common on passage Mar to early May, with fewer late Aug to Oct; in some autumns no obvious passage. In Sep 1926, autumn migrants were "caught in a storm and literally millions were drowned and washed ashore" (Wilson 1928). Sometimes many in winter, suggesting an influx.

RALLIDAE

94. RALLUS AQUATICUS   WV PM OB
     Water Rail

Usually common passage migrant and winter visitor (*R.a. aquaticus*) to marshes Sep–Apr, sometimes from Aug and into May.

Breeding. A deserted nest found in a large patch of *Juncus* at base of a *Tamarix* in Akrotiri reed beds, 19 Apr 1958, contained a broken egg typical for the species, and Water Rails were nearby (Ashton–Johnson). Individuals also seen there mid Jul 1963 and late Jun 1971. 4 there, May–Jul 1981 and a juvenile on 19 Jul. Adult and 3 small young there 27 Jun 1982. At Phasouri reed beds, at least 2 pairs with young and remains of 4 eggs found, Jul to early Aug 1982, a juvenile there, 2 Aug 1984 and an adult and 3 juveniles, mid-late Aug 1985; 3 juveniles Akrotiri/Phasouri reed beds Aug 1983.

95.   PORZANA PORZANA   PM

Spotted Crake

Scarce passage migrant Mar to mid May, mainly Apr, and Sep–Nov. Once each mid Jul and mid Aug. More numerous in the past: found very common on migration by Bucknill (1911), and "in abundance" by Lilford, Apr to early May 1875. Suspected to have bred Fresh Water Lake, May 1910, but all birds had gone by 3 Jun (Bucknill 1911). Singles collected 6 Dec 1911 and 27 Feb 1888 (skins in RSM). Bucknill (1911) stated that "a few stay for the winter", but no published records mid Dec to mid Feb.

96.   PORZANA PARVA   PM WV

Little Crake

Common passage migrant late Mar to Apr, peak numbers usually Apr, though 50 Akrotiri late Mar 1957; occasional mid Mar and May; only 11 records mid Aug to early Nov and 6 records Dec–Feb.

97.   PORZANA PUSILLA   PM OB

Baillon's Crake

Scarce (and irregular?) passage migrant (*P.p. intermedia*) late Mar to early May; only 8 records, Sep to early Nov; probably overlooked.
   Breeding. At least 6 individuals, including 2 unfledged juveniles and 3 older juveniles, at Phasouri reed beds, Jul 1982 (R29); an adult and a juvenile there, 2 Sep 1985 (R32).

98.   CREX CREX   PM

Corncrake

Passage migrant in variable numbers, usually scarce, probably much overlooked. Occasional Mar, scarce Apr to early May (mainly late Apr), usually singly though twice 6 in shooters bags in Apr at Philia and Kormakiti, and 10 shot Neokhorio (Akamas), 1 May 1983; once seen mid May. Very scarce and irregular Aug to mid Nov, though remains of 4 by nests of Eleonora's Falcon *Falco eleonorae,* Sep 1969 (R16). "Quite a number" shot, second and third weeks of Sep 1924, the species being usually "rather rare" then (Wilson 1925b).

99. GALLINULA CHLOROPUS   PM WV OB
Moorhen

Passage migrant and winter visitor (*G.c. chloropus*) in variable numbers late Sep to May, to wetlands, reservoirs and riverbeds with reed or cover; most numerous late Mar to May, usually 1–20 together, once 200 Akrotiri reed beds mid-late Apr; common in some winters, in others scarce or almost absent.

Breeding. One or two pairs remain and breed if wetlands suitable. Has bred in many recent years since 1957, mainly at Akrotiri and Phasouri reed beds, but also at Xeros and Asomatos, and on the dams or reservoirs at Akrounda, Athalassa, Kalopanayiotis and Phasouri. Eggs, C/3 once late May and small young seen late Apr to early Jul. In the past, bred at Akrotiri Salt Lake 1910 (Bucknill 1911). Scarce and irregular Jun–Aug in non-breeding years.

100. PORPHYRULA ALLENI   AV
Allen's Gallinule

Accidental visitor, 2 records: one, Happy Valley, Episkopi, 23 Dec 1968 and one (possibly the same bird) shot Nicosia, 25 Dec (both R15).

101. PORPHYRIO PORPHYRIO   AV
Purple Gallinule

Accidental visitor, 2 records: one near Kithasi, 4 Jan 1968 (R15); and one Larnaca Salt Lake, 31 Dec 1975 (R22). Race(s) not known.

102. FULICA ATRA   WV PM OB
Coot

F.a. atra. Passage migrant and winter visitor in variable numbers Sep–May, most numerous Nov–Mar, often in 100s, maximum 3000 Akrotiri Salt Lake, Jan 1970 and 3000 Yermasoyia, Feb 1976; in some winters very few.

Breeding. Some remain and breed if wetlands suitable. The first recent record was at Kouklia reservoir in 1967, since then has bred in several years, mainly at Akrotiri and Phasouri reed beds, but also on the reservoirs or dams at Akhna, Athalassa, Kouklia, Mavrokolymbos and Phasouri. Maximum numbers at Akrotiri where *c*. 25 pairs bred 1969; the species also bred "extensively" there 1975. Eggs, C/4 to C/9, found Apr–May and small young Apr to early Jul. In the past, "very large numbers" bred Kouklia reservoir 1910 (Bucknill 1911). Scarce and irregular Jun–Aug in non-breeding years.

GRUIDAE

103. GRUS GRUS   PM
Common Crane

G.g. grus. In spring, common passage migrant, mainly Mar to early Apr, but few flocks definitely identified (see Crane spp). Maximum flocks usually 200–500, though 1189 NNW Paramali, 17 Mar 1983 and *c*. 1000 north Nicosia, 12 Mar 1981. Occasionally a few to early May, once mid May. In autumn, very common passage migrant, in flocks of 10s, 100s and 1000s. Once 8 early Sep (NR3), and 2 in mid Sep, occasional late Sep, increasing early Oct, main passage mid Oct to early Nov, peak numbers usually late Oct. Large flocks occasional mid Nov, twice late Nov, once early and twice mid Dec. Flocks usually arrive on north coast from midday onwards, sometimes after dark. Some cross Kyrenia range, others coast west into Morphou Bay, then fly over Troodos or pass east or west of the range. Many flocks leave the island via Akrotiri peninsula, arriving from north or coasting in (usually from northeast) and departing south, occasionally southeast or southwest. Flocks arriving in the afternoon fly straight out to sea without landing, while those arriving in the evening and at night roost on the salt flats and fly on in the morning. The 2 very large flocks of 4000 and 6000, mentioned below, both overflew the south coast in the afternoon, 1515–1610 hours.

Prior to 1972 largest autumn flocks only in 100s, maximum 450, but since 1972 much larger flocks (or groups of flocks) have been recorded, and flocks of 1000 or more now occur in most autumns. One flock (4000+) over Akrotiri, 29 Oct 1972, was tracked by radar for 40 km and flew at a height of c. 1500 m on a steady bearing of 190° – a bearing which would have produced a landfall at Port Said. Also exceptional were a flock of 2000+ over Akrotiri, 29 Oct 1975, another of 2000 over Paramali, 2 Nov 1981, and flocks totalling at least 7300 birds which passed through Akrotiri, 20–31 Oct 1982. The largest single record is of c. 6000 which passed south over Episkopi, 25 Oct 1987; the birds were on a broad front c. 1 km wide and passed continually for 45 minutes. This huge passage was composed of many small individual flocks varying between 50 and 400 birds, with an average flock size of 170 (see **Migration & Movements**). [Also 5 similar records of large flocks of cranes late Oct to early Nov, all probably *G. grus*: 3 large flocks (c. 1000 in one flock) over Morphou, 21 Oct 1973; a total of c. 2000 moving south over Skouriotissa and Konia, 28 Oct 1975; 3750 south over Akrotiri, 30 Oct 1976; c. 2000 Akrotiri, 27 Oct 1977 and c. 2000 over Latsia, 10 Nov 1979.] Main passage formerly believed to occur Aug (the Bannermans 1958, 1971, Bourne *et al.*, Stewart & Christensen), but Flint (1971a, 1972a) and subsequent observers showed the Aug crane passage to be of Demoiselle Crane *A. virgo* only, the main passage of *G. grus* occurring c. 8 weeks later.

Occasionally a few briefly at wetlands in winter. [Several flocks of up to 150 cranes (presumably *G. grus*) on passage late Nov to early Dec, and 4 flocks Jan, including 150 south Akrotiri, 21 Jan 1959 were probably from Turkey, where considerable numbers of *G. grus* winter (Beaman).] In the past, flocks of 12–20 "throughout the winter months crossing the Mesaoria from the Famagusta to the Morphou marshes" (Bucknill 1909–10).

104. ANTHROPOIDES VIRGO   PM

Demoiselle Crane

Probably fairly common passage migrant late Mar to early or mid Apr, but very few flocks definitely identified (see Crane spp). The only large flocks recorded were 250, 4 Apr 1967 and c. 500, 28 Mar 1977, both at Akrotiri. Unusually the latter flock included 12 Common Crane *G. grus*. Occasional early-mid Mar and late Apr, twice early May. Very common during the brief and concentrated autumn passage mid Aug to early Sep, occasionally to mid Sep, mainly late Aug, with daily flocks of 10s and 100s. Occasional flocks early Aug and sometimes 1–3 birds till Oct. [50 cranes over Kyrenia, 31 Jul 1979, were presumably early *A. virgo*.] Flocks usually arrive on north coast in afternoon or evening, sometimes after dark. Some cross Kyrenia range, but many, perhaps most, coast west into Morphou Bay or on past Limni. Many flocks arrive in Xeros/Morphou/Myrtou area from north, late flocks often roosting there and flying on over Troodos or passing east or west of the range. Many leave island via Akrotiri peninsula, arriving from north or coasting in, mainly from northeast. Most flocks arrive at night, roost on the salt flats, and fly on early in the morning, heading SSW (Flint 1972a) or S–SSW (P.O. Swanberg *in* R27).

Maximum autumn count at Akrotiri Salt Lake was 10 flocks totalling 1468 birds, 19 Aug to 3 Sep 1971 (Flint 1972a), excluding crane spp or passage through other parts of the island; clearly too low a figure. [*c.* 3000 cranes passed through Cyprus in mid-late Aug 1972 (R19, NR3), all probably this species.] Largest autumn flock 580, not 770 (*pace* Cramp & Simmons), the latter figure being a total of 6 flocks (R17). Of 457 examined Akrotiri, 24 Aug to 5 Sep 1980, 40 were juveniles (P.O. Swanberg *in* R27). Autumn flocks arrive from north and must have overflown Turkey, where apparently overlooked, only very small numbers of migrants being recorded there (Cramp & Simmons). Mason mentions radar observations of small flocks assumed to be this species.

The only 2 systematic autumn counts at Akrotiri have been those mentioned above – in 1971 and 1980. The 1980 total was considerably lower than that for 1971, and casual observations since 1980 also suggest that the number of Demoiselles passing in autumn has declined. Further systematic counts are needed to establish whether this apparent decline is real. A decline at Akrotiri could be the result of a change in migration route, but it could also be caused by a reduction in the population, which would be cause for concern.

GRUS/ANTHROPOIDES
Crane spp *G. grus/A. virgo*

Flocks on spring passage occur late Feb to mid May, mainly Mar; most overfly unidentified without landing, often at night, but passages of both species clearly overlap to some extent, though no large flocks of Demoiselle Crane *A. virgo* are seen before late Mar. In most years *c.* 10–20 flocks recorded, maximum 22 flocks in spring 1973. Spring flocks usually in 10s or 100s. The spring passage in 1981 was exceptionally large, with a total of *c.* 8800 unidentified cranes passing, 9–26 Mar. This included daily totals of *c.* 4000 over Maroni, 12 Mar, and *c.* 2500 over Nicosia, 26 Mar. The spring passage is usually smaller than the autumn passages, and many passing through in autumn must return by a different route in spring. (Late Apr records attributed to R. Frost (*in* NR4) should be late Aug.)

There are 2 distinct autumn passages, the earlier of *A. virgo,* Aug to early Sep, the later of Common Crane *G. grus,* Oct to mid Nov, with few records between. Many autumn flocks land and are identified, but many overfly or migrate at night. 4 records of flocks of less than 20 mid Sep could refer to either species, though 250, 11 Sep 1976 and *c.* 250, 12 Sep 1980, were most probably *A. virgo.*

Until 1971 the Aug to early Sep passage was much larger than the Oct to mid Nov passage, but since 1972 the reverse has been the case. This has been caused by an apparent decline in the number of Demoiselles passing, and by the previously unrecorded passage of very large flocks of 1000s of Common Cranes.

OTIDIDAE

105. TETRAX (=OTIS) TETRAX   WV
      Little Bustard

Formerly a scarce to fairly common winter visitor to low ground Nov–Feb; once Aug. Only one recent record: one on cultivated coastal strip north of Coral Bay, 30

Dec 1979 (R26). [Sep 1967 record withdrawn by observer.] In the past, 2 collected Feb to mid Mar 1820 (Stresemann); one obtained Nov 1876 or –77 by Schrader; occasional Nicosia market (Guillemard 1888); "met with (*c.* 1888–89) on 3 or 4 occasions on uncultivated ground between Limassol salt lake and the hills" and one obtained (*in* 'The Field' 1889:653); shot "in winter" on "several occasions" and 3 near Paphos, 18 Dec 1908 (Bucknill 1909–10); "quite a number", Dec 1909–Jan 1910 (Bucknill 1911); 7 or 8 in east, Dec 1910 (C.N.H.S.Ann.II); one Akhyritou, 10 Dec 1911 (skin in RSM); 2 Larnaca market, Jan 1913 and one near Nicosia, 27 Aug 1913 (C.N.H.S.Ann.IV). Seen (prior to 1946), usually in pairs, "most winters" (Wilson 1954), and (prior to 1950) "a good many times", particularly in Morphou area (Waterer).

106. CHLAMYDOTIS UNDULATA   AV

Houbara Bustard

Accidental visitor (*C.u. macqueenii*), one recent record: one on stubble between Mandria and Kouklia (Paphos), 3 Nov 1979 (R26). In the past, one shot Engomi, Famagusta, 9 Nov 1912 and another obtained "later" (Baxendale 1915); a secondhand record mentioned by Bucknill 1909–10; Wilson (1954) saw birds "several times in autumn" (prior to 1946).

107. OTIS TARDA   WV

Great Bustard

Scarce and irregular winter visitor (*O.t. tarda*) Jan–Feb, only one recent record: 50–60 Rizokarpaso area, early Feb 1974 (NR5). In the past, mentioned by Guillemard (1888); seen "very rarely" near Famagusta, and one near Nicosia, 29 Jan 1905 (Bucknill 1909–10); one near Larnaca, 21 Jan 1910 (head in RSM); 3 near Stroullos, Feb 1911, 3 near Styllos, *c.* 21 Feb and 5 "said to be" near Beila (Pyla?) (all Bucknill 1911); one near Akhyritou, Jan 1925, and 2 in Famagusta District and one near Limassol "heard of" as shot (Wilson 1925b). Has occurred on east Mesaoria and Karpas (D. F. Davidson *in* the Bannermans 1958). Waterer considered that "a few regularly visit Cyprus".

HAEMATOPODIDAE

108. HAEMATOPUS OSTRALEGUS   PM

Oystercatcher

Scarce passage migrant (*H.o. ostralegus*), mainly in spring when probably regular on south and east coasts. 32 recent records: Feb, Mar (6), Apr (11), May (2), Aug (4), Sep (6), Oct and Nov; usually 1–4 together, maximum 20 Cape Pyla, 12 Nov 1970 and 10 on "NW Islands", 24 Aug 1985 (J. A. van der Ven). In the past, one Armidia (Ormidhia?) beach, 17 Apr 1787 (Sibthorp); 2 Famagusta harbour, 24 Apr 1938 (Payn); and "seen Famagusta harbour flats, in small numbers, every year since 1931" (Wilson 1954), presumably till 1946.

RECURVIROSTRIDAE

109. HIMANTOPUS HIMANTOPUS   PM OB

Black-winged Stilt

Common passage migrant (*H.h. himantopus*) in spring: once mid Feb, common early or mid Mar to May, peak numbers late Mar to mid Apr, usually in 10s, once 76 late Mar. Very scarce on autumn passage Aug–Oct. Occasional Nov–Dec, once Jan to early Feb. 22 coasting west, Pendayia, 14 Aug 1983 and other recent records from the northwest suggest a small regular autumn passage there.

Breeding. Some remain and breed probably in all years when water-levels suitable, usually in colonies of 6–14 pairs: breeds mainly Akrotiri Salt Lake, where it has bred in most years since 1969, also bred Kouklia reservoir 1969, Spiro's Beach 1985 and Akhna Dam 1988–89. In the past, bred Akhyritou reservoir 1905 (Bucknill 1909–10), Larnaca Salt Lake 1911, Fresh Water Lake 1912 (Bucknill 1913a) and Kouklia reservoir 1913–14 (Baxendale 1913, 1915); also bred Larnaca 1950 (the Bannermans 1958).

Breeding data. Nests at Akrotiri usually on small islands in the lake. Eggs normally laid mid-late May, sometimes from early May; small young seen mid-late Jun, once early Jun (Fisher); a presumed replacement clutch laid late Jun hatched mid Jul (Cole 1972b). Normally C/4, once C/7 (Fisher). Post-breeding departure, Aug to early Oct, depending on water-levels.

110. RECURVIROSTRA AVOSETTA   PM WV

Avocet

Scarce to fairly common passage migrant. Spring passage Mar–May, mainly Mar to early Apr, with flocks coasting east on the south coast and north on the west coast, with others at wetlands; usually less than 10 together, sometimes several 10s, exceptionally 100 or more, maxima 300 east off Kermia Beach, 25 Mar and 118 Larnaca Salt Lake, 6 Apr, both in 1983; sometimes up to 20 remain at wetlands into Jun; 1–3 occasionally Jul. Return passage Aug–Nov, mainly mid Aug to early Oct, with flocks of 10s coasting west, Kyrenia to Akamas, and at the salt lakes, maximum 200 Akrotiri Salt Lake, 29 Aug 1980. Sometimes 10s into Dec, maximum 114 Akrotiri early Dec 1981, perhaps late migrants. Scarce Jan–Feb, usually in ones or twos; up to 8 overwintered Akrotiri Salt Lake, Dec 1969 to early Mar 1970, and 27 there 10 Jan 1982.

BURHINIDAE

111. BURHINUS OEDICNEMUS   RB PM WV?

Stone Curlew

Scarce resident breeder (*B.o. saharae*).

Breeding distribution. On the Mesaoria, and probably elsewhere on open low ground. Only 4 recent records: one nearly fledged Pergamos, early May 1963; C/2 near Athalassa, 6 Jun 1974; a juvenile caught Astromeritis, 24 May 1982 and C/2 by Dhiarizos River mouth, 15 Apr 1988. Pairs present all year Nicosia Airport, 1957 and during the breeding season at the following places: Athalassa, 1976, 78, 80–82 and 87; Anglanzia and Latsia, 1976; Yeri, 1978; Argates, 1982; Asprokremmos Dam, 1983; Ayios Nikolaos and Larnaca Airport, 1988, and Kouklia (Paphos) 1981 and 89. Probably much overlooked. In the past, young obtained Aug (Bucknill 1909–10); fresh egg Famagusta, 7 May 1910 (Bucknill 1911); bred Akhyritou 1910 (C.N.H.S.Ann.II); C/2 Athalassa, 30 Apr 1929 (Jourdain 1929a). Stated to have bred Paphos District (Jourdain 1929b) and on the Karpas (Davidson 1954).

Flocks or roosts occur Aug–Feb, sometimes till Apr, mainly near Nicosia, Athalassa, Dhekelia, Xeros Potamos and Kouklia (Paphos), with others at Salamis, Larnaca Salt Lake, and on the Karpas, usually in 10s, maximum 139 Kouklia (Paphos), 27 Dec 1980. Flocks perhaps include migrants or winter visitors or both, as well as residents.

Fairly common on passage late Mar to early May, possibly to mid May, in ones and twos, occasionally up to 30 together. Common on passage Sep–Oct, mainly Sep; largest recorded passage Sep 1959 – over 100 on night passage Larnaca, 18 Sep; "many 100s" on night passage Cape Kiti, 19 Sep; a flock of 50 before dusk and "large numbers" out to sea on night passage Cape Zevgari, 21 Sep (R4). Race of migrants unknown.

GLAREOLIDAE

112. CURSORIUS CURSOR   PM

Cream-coloured Courser

Scarce and irregular passage migrant (*C.c. cursor*) usually around wetlands; 13 records since 1957 of ones and twos, mid Mar to early May, mainly at Akrotiri and Larnaca salt lakes and at Ayia Napa/Cape Greco; also 1–5 birds late Aug 1973 at Akrotiri Salt Lake.

113. GLAREOLA PRATINCOLA   PM FB

Pratincole

Fairly common passage migrant (*G.p. pratincola*) often around wetlands. Occasional late Mar, fairly common Apr–May, occasional to mid Jun, once late Jun; usually in 10s, maxima 200 Kouklia (Paphos), 8 Apr 1974 and 100 Zakaki, 13 Apr 1970. Scarcer on autumn passage late Jul to mid Oct, mainly late Aug to early Oct; also once mid Jul and twice early Nov; usually in ones, occasionally 10–20, maximum 70 Kouklia reservoir, late Aug to early Sep 1969.

Breeding. One record: 5 nests with eggs at the Fresh Water Lake, 14 Jun 1913 (C.N.H.S.Ann.IV).

114. GLAREOLA NORDMANNI   PM

Black-winged Pratincole

Scarce passage migrant: once mid Mar, scarce Apr to mid Jun, usually singly or less than 20 together though 60 Akrotiri Salt Lake area, 24 Apr 1982 (NR13); once each late Jun, late Jul and early Aug. Scarcer on return passage late Aug to mid Oct, exceptionally *c.* 400 Kyrenia, 13 Sep 1961 (R8).

CHARADRIIDAE

115. CHARADRIUS DUBIUS   PM OB

Little Ringed Plover

Common passage migrant (*C.d. curonicus*) around wetlands, usually in 10s, sometimes up to 100. Common Mar–May, mainly mid Mar to Apr; absent or scarce Jun. Common on return passage Jul to Sep–Oct; occasional Nov–Feb, mainly before mid-winter.

Breeding. One recent record: a "freshly fledged" juvenile Akrotiri gravel pits, 3 Jun 1963 (R10). Probably bred Akrotiri 1962 and 1969 (Stewart & Christensen). In the past, eggs obtained Fresh Water Lake, early May 1911 (Bucknill 1911).

One ringed in Cyprus, recovered in Italy (Appendix 2).

116. CHARADRIUS HIATICULA   PM WV

Ringed Plover

Fairly common passage migrant around wetlands late Mar to May or early Jun, in 10s or less; occasional mid Jun to Jul, perhaps oversummering; sometimes common on passage mid Aug to Oct, occasionally into Nov, sometimes up to 100 or more mid Sep to mid Oct, in other autumns only ones and twos. Usually scarce in winter, Nov or Dec to mid Mar, singly or less than 10 together, exceptionally 350 Larnaca Salt Lake, 17 Dec 1967 (R14).

Both *C.h. hiaticula* and *C.h. tundrae* could occur (Vaurie). 54 ringed Akrotiri, Sep–Oct 1967, had wing lengths (see Appendix 3) corresponding with measurements given by Prater *et al.* for *C.h. tundrae* from North Scandinavia and U.S.S.R.

One ringed Akrotiri, 6 Nov 1959, recovered Akhyritou reservoir, 25 Dec 1960.

117. CHARADRIUS ALEXANDRINUS   MB (or RB) PM WV

Kentish Plover

Fairly common migrant breeder (or resident) (*C.a. alexandrinus*).

Breeding distribution. Up to 25 pairs breed Akrotiri Salt Lake with fewer Larnaca Salt Lake, and has bred Paralimni, Famagusta–Salamis, Kalopsidha and Spiro's Beach. In the past, "considerable numbers" bred Fresh Water Lake 1910–11 (Bucknill 1911).

Breeding data. Nest usually on open salt or mud flats around wetlands, sometimes on small islands at Akrotiri Salt Lake. Nest sometimes placed in shadow of vegetation. Eggs, usually C/3 (occasionally C/4), found late Feb to mid Jun; small young late Mar to early Aug, probably double brooded.

Occurrence of passage and wintering birds obscures status of breeders, but in 1959 and 1970–71 numbers at Akrotiri fell sharply in Aug after breeding, suggesting breeders are not resident. Often all wetlands dry out in late summer or autumn and then presumably birds must leave the island. Passage migrant and winter visitor Sep–Apr, usually 10s to 100, occasionally up to 500 together. Sometimes no obvious passage and very few in winter.

One ringed Akrotiri, 24 Oct 1959, recovered there, 20 Feb 1960.

118. CHARADRIUS LESCHENAULTII   PM WV

Greater Sand Plover

Scarce to fairly common passage migrant around wetlands Mar–Apr, mainly early-mid Mar, usually singly or less than 10 together, maximum 43 Akrotiri, 17 Mar 1958; occasional May to early Jun. Scarce on return passage mid Jun to Aug or Sep. Very scarce and irregular winter visitor Oct–Feb. Usually 1–4 together, maximum 10 Akrotiri, 26 Dec 1961.

119. CHARADRIUS ASIATICUS   AV

Caspian Plover

Accidental visitor, 5 records: one in a newly ploughed field next to the sea at Paphos, 25–30 Apr 1984 (Oreel 1986); one Akrotiri Salt Lake, 3 Jun 1984 (R31); one on the cliff top west of Paphos lighthouse, 15–16 Apr 1987, and another in water meadows by Asprokremmos Dam, 20 Apr 1987 (both R34); one Baths of Aphrodite, 31 Mar 1990 (NL90/3).

120. CHARADRIUS (=EUDROMIAS) MORINELLUS   PM

Dotterel

Scarce and irregular passage migrant, probably overlooked. 12 recent records: late Mar to early Apr (7), early Nov (2), and Dec (3). Usually singly or a few together, maxima 7 Cape Andreas, 27 Mar 1970, and 14 Paralimni Lake, 3 Nov 1977 (Kephalas 1979). Usually recorded from dry flats around wetlands, as at Ladies Mile/Zakaki, or from open coastal headlands, e.g. Paphos, Akrotiri. In the past, one bought Nicosia market, 15 Dec 1909 (Bucknill 1909–10) and 4 bought Famagusta market, 9–11 Nov 1912 (Baxendale 1915).

121. PLUVIALIS APRICARIA   WV PM?

Golden Plover

Fairly common winter visitor (race unknown) Nov to Mar or early Apr, peak numbers late Dec to Feb, usually 10s to 100–200, maximum 500 Paralimni, 22 Dec 1957, most frequent on the Mesaoria and in the southeast, often near water. 32 south at Akrotiri, 11 Nov 1973, suggesting passage. Occasional mid Apr to mid May and mid Jul to Oct.

122. PLUVIALIS SQUATAROLA   WV PM

Grey Plover

Scarce passage migrant and winter visitor to wetlands and coasts, late Aug to May, usually singly or less than 10 together, occasionally up to 30; sometimes little or no obvious passage and very few, or absent, in winter. Occasional Jun to mid Aug, not oversummering.

123. HOPLOPTERUS (=VANELLUS) SPINOSUS   PM OB

Spur-winged Plover

Fairly common passage migrant mid-late Mar to early-mid May, mainly Apr; occasional Feb to early Mar and late May to mid Jul; 2 oversummered Famagusta late Apr to mid Jul 1962. Scarcer on return passage late Jul to Oct, mainly Sep. On both passages usually singly or less than 10 together, maximum up to 24 Akhna Dam, Sep 1990. Occasional Nov–Dec, twice early Jan.

Breeding. One recent record, Phasouri reed beds, 1988: a pair seen mating and scraping a nest hollow 6 May, C/4 found 8 May and chicks heard calling within the eggs 1 Jun (NL88/5). In the past, "nested at the reservoirs . . . in some seasons, when height of water favourable" (E. H. D. Nicolls *in* Bucknill 1909–10), but only one dated record: C/5 Kouklia reservoir, 1 Jun 1913 (C.N.H.S.Ann.IV, Jourdain 1913).

124. CHETTUSIA GREGARIA (=VANELLUS GREGARIUS)   AV

Sociable Plover

Accidental visitor, one record: an adult ♂ at Derelict Farm, Phasouri reed beds, 24 Mar 1986; this coincided with an influx into West Germany (R33).

125. CHETTUSIA LEUCURA (=VANELLUS LEUCURUS)   PM

White-tailed Plover

Very scarce and irregular passage migrant. 16 records from wetlands: mid-late Mar, mid Apr to early May (12), mid May, late Jun and late Oct, usually singly though 2 once mid Apr and 2 once early May. All recorded since 1970 and probably a result of the westward expansion suggested by Dean *et al.*

126. VANELLUS VANELLUS   WV PM

Lapwing

Very common winter visitor to low ground, especially fields on the Mesaoria, Oct–Nov to Feb or early Mar, peak numbers (100s or 1000s) Dec to early Feb. A few mid-late Mar, occasional Apr–Jun, once Jul (Kephalas 1989), occasional Aug–Sep. 6 records of passage at Akrotiri late Oct to early Dec, maximum 250 moving south 20 Nov 1960.

SCOLOPACIDAE

Calidridinae

127. CALIDRIS CANUTUS   PM

Knot

Very scarce and irregular passage migrant (*C.c. canutus*). 9 records from wetlands or coasts, mainly Akrotiri: Jan (2), mid Apr, early Aug, mid Sep to mid Oct (4) and mid Nov. In detail: one Morphou, 13 Oct 1961 (R8); 3 Bishops Pool, 26 Sep to 7 Oct 1967 (R14); one Akrotiri Salt Lake, 26 Sep 1969 (R16); one Akrotiri Salt Lake, 12 Jan 1970, and one Akrotiri Salt Lake, 11 and 13 Sep 1970 (both R17); one Famagusta harbour, 8 Jan 1973 (*per* P. F. Stewart); 3 Akrotiri Salt Lake, 18 Apr 1974 (NR5); 10 Akrotiri Salt Lake, 2 Aug 1976 (R23); one Larnaca Salt Lake, 15 Nov 1985 (R32).

128. CALIDRIS ALBA   PM WV
Sanderling

Scarce to fairly common passage migrant to wetlands and coasts late Mar to early Jun and Aug–Nov, most frequent May and Sep, usually 1–10 together, exceptionally 53 Larnaca Salt Lake, 24 Mar 1987 (P. Boye). Once mid Jun. Very scarce and irregular Dec to mid Mar, mainly 1–4 together. [Several doubtful winter and early spring records of flocks of 20–500.]
One ringed in Cyprus, recovered in Tunisia (Appendix 2).

129. CALIDRIS MINUTA   PM WV
Little Stint

Very common passage migrant around wetlands early or mid Apr to early Jun, in 100s, up to 1000 at the salt lakes; scarce or absent mid Jun to early Jul; returning mid Jul to Sep or Oct, in 10s or 100s. Winter visitor Oct–Mar in variable numbers, usually 10s, sometimes up to 200 Larnaca Salt Lake, fewer after mid-winter and scarce or absent by Mar.
One ringed Akrotiri Salt Lake, late Oct 1959 still present Dec; another ringed there 6 Nov 1959, recovered nearby 2 Feb 1960.

130. CALIDRIS TEMMINCKII   PM
Temminck's Stint

Scarce to fairly common passage migrant around wetlands Mar–May and mid Jul to Sep, mainly Apr to mid May and mid Aug to mid Sep, in ones or 10s, sometimes up to 50 at the salt lakes; often 1–5 remain Oct–Nov, exceptionally to mid Dec. Once Feb and twice early Jun.

131. CALIDRIS FERRUGINEA   PM
Curlew Sandpiper

Passage migrant: once late Feb, occasional Mar, fairly common around wetlands early or mid Apr to May, peak numbers usually mid May, in ones or 10s, exceptionally 225 Larnaca Salt Lake, 12 May 1982; usually scarce or absent Jun–Jul, though once 22 in mid Jun; usually scarce on return passage Aug to mid or late Oct, singly or less than 10 together, exceptionally 200 Akrotiri Salt Lake, 6 Sep 1970; occasional singles Nov or Dec. ["Quite common in the winter" and several shot (Bucknill 1911); Dunlin *C. alpina* which he does not mention, seems more likely.]
One ringed Akrotiri, 28 Sep 1967, and recovered there, 18 Oct 1969.

132. CALIDRIS ALPINA   PM WV
Dunlin

Passage migrant and winter visitor around wetlands (a few on coasts) Aug–May; in variable numbers, sometimes very few but usually 10s or 100–200, peak numbers often Nov to Jan or Feb at the salt lakes, maximum 330 Larnaca early Jan 1971. Scarce or absent Jun–Jul. Probably both *C.a. alpina* and *C.a. schinzii* occur, though neither definitely identified.

133. LIMICOLA FALCINELLUS   PM
Broad-billed Sandpiper

Scarce passage migrant (*L.f. falcinellus*) around wetlands, mainly at the salt lakes. Occurs mid Apr to early Jun, mid Jul to mid Sep, and once mid-late Oct. Some two thirds of the records are in spring, when most frequent May to early Jun. Usually 1–4 together, occasionally more, maximum 11 Akrotiri Salt Lake, 23 May 1982. Probably overlooked, may well be regular. Birds seen at Akrotiri Salt Lake 1970–71 usually occurred amongst large flocks of Little Stint *Calidris minuta,* and several were discovered by speculative searching of the flocks of stints, the Broad-billed Sandpipers being detected by their darker backs and longer heavier bills (NR2).

134. PHILOMACHUS PUGNAX   PM WV
Ruff

Very common passage migrant late Feb to early Jun, peak numbers Mar to mid May, in 100s, sometimes 1000–2000 at the salt lakes, widespread, occurring wherever there is water, and also in dry fields; scarce or absent mid Jun to Jul; usually scarce Aug–Oct, singly or less than 10 together, twice 100 Sep. Usually absent or very scarce Nov to mid Dec, once 60 mid Nov. Sometimes 10s late Dec to mid Feb, mainly at Larnaca Salt Lake, maxima 88 there Jan to early Feb 1972 and 150 mid Feb 1978, probably early migrants.

One recovery of a bird ringed in Norway (Appendix 2). 3 birds seen Kato Paphos, 18 Mar 1984, had been colour-dyed in Senegal, West Africa, between 5 Feb and 5 Mar that year (R31, C. J. L. Bennett).

Gallinagininae

135. LYMNOCRYPTES MINIMUS   PM
Jack Snipe

Scarce passage migrant to marshes Apr and Oct to early Dec, usually singly; occasional early May, Aug–Sep, and mid Dec to Mar, twice 1–2 overwintering till Jan or early Feb. In the past, 20 shot, 16 Nov 1907 (Bucknill 1909–10).

One ringed Akrotiri Salt Lake, 6 Nov 1959, was still present 5 Dec.

136. GALLINAGO GALLINAGO   PM WV
Snipe

Fairly common passage migrant and winter visitor (*G.g. gallinago*) Aug to early or mid May, mostly Nov–Apr, usually 1–10 together, exceptionally 100 or more Dec. Occasionally only a few in winter, but usually widespread at many small wetlands. Often a marked spring passage Mar–Apr. Occasional late May, twice early Jun, occasional Jul. [Reported at the reservoirs "in the summer" of 1908 (Bucknill 1909–10).]

94   Scolopacidae

137. GALLINAGO MEDIA   PM
Great Snipe

Scarce to fairly common passage migrant to marshes mid Mar to May, mostly late
Mar to mid May, usually singly, maximum 6 Kouklia, 5 Apr 1970. Twice early Sep,
once each late Sep, early Oct (skin in RSM) and late Oct, twice Dec. Described as a
winter visitor by Bucknill (1909–10), but no acceptable records Jan to early Mar. "In
40 years snipe shooting [up to 1946] I never saw one in autumn, or winter, it arrives
c. 15 Mar and stays till May" (Wilson 1954).

Scolopacinae

138. SCOLOPAX RUSTICOLA   WV
Woodcock

Usually common winter visitor to wooded areas Nov–Feb, mostly Dec to early
Feb, most frequent in the hills and mountains, often near streams; in variable
numbers, sometimes very common, up to 30 Drousha, 20 Dec 1978. A few singles
early-mid Mar, occasional to late Apr, twice early and once mid May. Occasional
Oct. On Troodos birds move to lower altitudes when feeding areas frozen
(Mason).

Tringinae

139. LIMOSA LIMOSA   PM WV
Black-tailed Godwit

Fairly common passage migrant around wetlands (*L.l. limosa*) Feb–May, mainly
late Feb to mid Apr, usually singly or less than 20 together, exceptionally 120 leaving
east from Akrotiri, 20 Feb 1982. 1–6 occasionally in all other months, with fewest
records Jul and Nov; 25 coasting west Kyrenia, 14 Sep 1960.

140. LIMOSA LAPPONICA   PM
Bar-tailed Godwit

Very scarce and irregular passage migrant (*L.l. lapponica*), 9 records from wetlands
or coasts: mid-late Mar, mid-late Apr (3), mid May, early Jun and late Sep to early
Nov (3). In detail: one Famagusta, 29 and 30 Sep 1961 (R8, B13); up to 7 Larnaca
Salt Lake, 18–30 Mar 1963 (R10); singles Akrotiri Salt Lake, 11 May, 29 Sep and 14
Oct 1969 (R16); one "Clapsides Beach", 31 Oct to 10 Nov 1973 (R20); one Akrotiri
Salt Lake, 1 Jun 1977 (R24); 2 Phasouri reed beds, 15 Apr 1984 and one Spiro's
Beach, 27 Apr 1984 (both NR15); one Spiro's Beach, 27 Apr 1985 (R32).

141. NUMENIUS PHAEOPUS   PM
Whimbrel

Scarce (and irregular?) passage migrant (*N.p. phaeopus*) Apr–May and Aug–Sep,
mostly Apr and Sep, singly or up to 6 together. Usually at wetlands or coasting; a
total of 11 at Cape Andreas, 7–20 Apr 1973 suggests it may be somewhat
overlooked. Once early Jul and once early Oct. In the past, one shot late Feb 1888
(Guillemard 1889).

142. NUMENIUS TENUIROSTRIS   AV

Slender-billed Curlew

Accidental visitor, 3 records: one Famagusta harbour, 23 Apr 1958 (R2, B6); 2 at a
small lake near Eylenja (Nicosia), 22 Dec 1964 (Christensen 1967); one Cape
Andreas, 28 Apr 1972 (NR3).

143. NUMENIUS ARQUATA   PM WV

Curlew

Passage migrant and winter visitor (*N.a. arquata*) in variable numbers Aug to mid
May, most frequent after mid-winter and only regular mid Mar to mid Apr; usually
rather scarce, usually singly or up to 10 together, exceptionally flocks of up to 80
Larnaca Salt Lake, late Mar 1957. Once early-mid Jun, twice late Jun, once mid and
once late Jul.

144. TRINGA ERYTHROPUS   PM

Spotted Redshank

Fairly common passage migrant to wetlands mid Mar to mid May, maximum 45
Akrotiri Salt Lake, 20 Mar 1969; occasional late May to Aug. Scarce on autumn
passage, mainly Sep to mid Oct, usually in ones or twos, occasionally up to 6
together, exceptionally 34 Akrotiri Salt Lake, 28 Aug 1982. Occasional late Oct to
early Mar.

145. TRINGA TOTANUS   WV PM

Redshank

T.t. totanus. Fairly common winter visitor and scarce to common passage migrant.
Usually 10s or less, from late Jun or Jul to Nov; exceptionally 120 on 26 Jul and 300
on 21 Aug 1970 at Akrotiri Salt Lake; usually an increase Dec–Mar, with 10s or
100s at wetlands; sometimes common on passage Mar, maximum 300 Larnaca Salt
Lake, 30 Mar 1987; fewer Apr to mid May and scarce or absent late May to mid
Jun.

146. TRINGA STAGNATILIS   PM

Marsh Sandpiper

Common passage migrant in spring, once mid Feb, occasional from late Feb,
normally 10s at wetlands late Mar to Apr, maximum 70 Larnaca, 18 Apr 1962, and
110 Akrotiri Salt Lake, 6 Apr 1980; last seen mid-late May. Once mid Jun. Usually
scarce on autumn passage late Jun to Sep, singly or less than 10 together, though 40
Akrotiri Salt Lake, 27 Sep 1981; occasional Oct, once early Nov and once early Dec.
[A Jan record attributed to Guillemard (the Bannermans 1958) was actually of a
specimen sent by Guillemard to Lilford in England, and "received, without any
particulars" in Jan 1889 (Lilford).]

147. TRINGA NEBULARIA   PM WV

Greenshank

Common passage migrant to wetlands in spring, sometimes a few from early Mar, 10s late Mar to early May, occasionally 100–200 at the salt lakes Apr, with a few to late May, occasional Jun. Scarce on autumn passage Jul–Sep, usually singly or less than 10 together, occasionally up to 20; scarce and irregular Oct–Feb, though occasionally a small influx to coasts and wetlands Dec–Jan, usually less than 10 together.

One recovery of a bird ringed in South Africa (Appendix 2).

148. TRINGA OCHROPUS   PM WV

Green Sandpiper

Common and widespread passage migrant early or mid Mar to Apr in 10s, maximum 100 Kouklia, 26 Apr 1967; occasional 10s early-mid May, scarce late May to early Jun; fairly common on passage mid or late Jun to Sep or Oct, mostly Jul to early Sep, usually 10 or less together, maximum 50 Lachi, 30 Aug 1978; occasional passage into Nov. Scarce winter visitor Nov–Feb, mainly at reservoirs, singly, exceptionally in 10s.

One recovery of a bird ringed in Finland (Appendix 2).

149. TRINGA GLAREOLA   PM

Wood Sandpiper

Very common and widespread passage migrant in spring, occasional Feb to mid Mar, 10s or 100s late Mar to May, peak numbers at wetlands mid Apr to mid May; sometimes 10–15 early Jun, scarce or absent mid Jun. Fairly common on passage late Jun to Oct, mostly Jul to early Sep, in 10s or less, maximum 30 together Akrotiri Salt Lake, 24 Aug 1970; occasional Nov, once early Dec. [Doubtfully reported in winter: one recent mid Dec record, and in the past, "common" Oct–May (Bucknill 1911) and once Jan (Schrader).]

150. XENUS CINEREUS   PM

Terek Sandpiper

Scarce and irregular passage migrant mainly to the salt lakes, probably overlooked, 6 records: late Mar to early May (5) and one late Aug to early Sep. In detail: one Akrotiri reed beds, 27 Aug to 2 Sep 1970 (R17); one Akrotiri Salt Lake, 4 May 1971, and one Larnaca Salt Lake, 8 May 1971 (both NR2); one Akrotiri Salt Lake, 10 Apr 1980 (R27); one Ladies Mile, 7–13 Apr 1983 (R30); 2 Zakaki pools, 23 and 24 Mar 1990 (M. Hayes *et al.*).

151. ACTITIS (=TRINGA) HYPOLEUCOS   PM WV

Common Sandpiper

Common passage migrant to coasts and wetlands, occasional early-mid Mar, in 10s or less late Mar to early or mid May, maximum 30 together Kiti Dam, 29 Apr 1975; a few till late May; absent or very scarce Jun. Return passage Jul–Sep, occasionally into Oct, peak numbers mid Jul to Aug, 20 or less together, exceptionally 57 Polis, 2 Aug 1957. Scarce winter visitor Nov–Feb.

Arenariinae

152. ARENARIA INTERPRES   PM
Turnstone

Scarce passage migrant (*A.i. interpres*), singly or up to 10 together at wetlands. In spring occasional mid Mar to Apr, most frequent May, occasional to mid Jun. Usually less scarce on passage Aug–Oct, mostly late Aug to Sep, once late Nov and once early Dec. One wintered Famagusta harbour, 11 Jan to 3 Mar 1972.

Phalaropodinae

153. PHALAROPUS LOBATUS   PM
Red-necked Phalarope

Scarce passage migrant to reservoirs and salt lakes, late Mar to mid May (mainly mid Apr to mid May) and late Jul to Sep (mainly mid Aug to mid Sep), usually 1–2 together, maximum 13 Larnaca Salt Lake, 11 May 1947 (Morris 1954). Once early Jun, once late Jun (Baxendale 1915) and twice Oct.

STERCORARIIDAE

154. STERCORARIUS PARASITICUS   PM
Arctic Skua

Scarce passage migrant. 22 records since 1957: early Feb, Apr (17), May (2) and late Sep (2). During 1957–84 there were only 8 records of single birds: 6 in spring along the south coast (including one dead Episkopi and one at Akrotiri Salt Lake) and 2 in Sep off Kyrenia. However in spring 1990 a total of 13 were recorded at Akrotiri 8–13 Apr, including a flock of 6 on 8 Apr, and flocks of 3 on 11 and 13 Apr, all moving east off Cape Gata or Cape Zevgari (RAFOS *per* C. J. Sparks, G. W. Rayner). If these 1990 records reflect a normal spring passage, then clearly the species is a regular passage migrant in some numbers and has been greatly overlooked in the past. Further seawatching off Akrotiri is needed to confirm the size and regularity of this spring movement. [7 records of *Stercorarius* spp: Apr (6) and late Nov.]

LARIDAE

155. LARUS ICHTHYAETUS   AV
Great Black-headed Gull

Accidental visitor, apparently becoming more frequent, 4 records: a winter plumage adult at Paralimni Lake, 23 Jan 1958 (R2, B6); 2 immatures Episkopi Bay/ Akrotiri Salt Lake, 12–23 Apr 1984 (NR15, R31); 1–2 birds Akrotiri Salt Lake/ Phasouri reed beds, 13–17 Mar 1987 (R34); 2 adults at Cape Greco, 22 Feb 1991 (R. Frost).

156. LARUS MELANOCEPHALUS   PM WV
Mediterranean Gull

In recent times a scarce passage migrant and winter visitor to coasts, harbours and salt lakes; recorded every month, mostly Dec–May, usually in ones or twos, exceptionally 60 Akrotiri, 17 May 1978 and also 15 Larnaca Salt Lake, 8 Apr 1987; in spring mainly on passage in the south and east. Apparently a very common spring migrant in the past. 3 records of large numbers on passage Apr in the southeast: "often" on passage Larnaca, 16–21 Apr 1875 and "some thousands" in Famagusta harbour, 22 Apr, which had moved 8 miles northeast along the coast next day (Lilford); an "enormous flock" feeding inland at the head of Larnaca Bay, 19 Apr 1887 (Guillemard 1888); and "very abundant" Larnaca, 11 Apr 1927 and the week following (Riddell).
        2 recoveries of birds ringed in the U.S.S.R. (Appendix 2).

157. LARUS MINUTUS   WV PM
Little Gull

Scarce to fairly common winter visitor to coasts, harbours and salt lakes, occasionally to inland waters. Occurs Dec to Mar or Apr, occasionally into May, usually in 10s or less, sometimes 100–200, maximum *c.* 300 Larnaca Salt Lake, 14 Mar 1981. Occasional increases on the south coast in spring, probably passage migrants from the south, and some birds also coast east then, maximum 200 east off Cape Greco, 28 Mar 1983. Occasional Jun, exceptionally 14 Limassol Bay, 29 Jun 1969, and once late Jul. Occasional ones and twos at wetlands Aug–Nov, though westward coasting flocks of 10s have been observed on the north coast then, and this passage is probably regular.

158. LARUS RIDIBUNDUS   WV PM
Black-headed Gull

Common winter visitor, sometimes from early Nov, usually mid or late Nov to Mar–Apr, peak numbers Dec to early Mar, often 1000–2000 at coasts, harbours and Larnaca Salt Lake, fewer at inland waters and at Akrotiri Salt Lake, where sometimes scarce or absent. Occasional May–Sep, when some records are probably due to confusion with Slender-billed Gull *L. genei.* A westward passage of flocks of 10s has been observed on the north coast late Oct, and early and late Nov; maximum many flocks of 20–100 moving westwards at Pendayia, 26 Nov 1975.
        2 recoveries of birds ringed in the U.S.S.R. (Appendix 2).

159. LARUS GENEI   PM WV
Slender-billed Gull

Common passage migrant. Spring passage Mar–Apr with a few into May, peak numbers mid Mar to Apr with flocks of 10s or 100s coasting east on the south coast or roosting at the salt lakes, especially Akrotiri, maximum up to 600 Akrotiri, late Mar to early April 1981. Occasional Jun. Autumn passage Jul–Oct, mainly mid Jul to Sep; if Akrotiri Salt Lake holds water, flocks roost there, often well out on the lake and concealed by heat haze, usually in 10s, occasionally 100s, maximum 1200 there

Aug 1982, increasing to 2500 by mid Sep; some autumn flocks also on the north coast. Occasional Nov. [Reports of large influxes late Oct to Nov should probably refer to Black-headed Gull *L. ridibundus* (Flint 1972c).] Usually a scarce winter visitor to sheltered and shallow water areas along shore, notably the southern end of Famagusta harbour, where 1–6 birds regular Jan–Mar, sometimes mid Dec to mid Apr. Exceptionally 10s overwinter at the salt lakes (200 mid Dec 1981), with birds in summer plumage from late Dec or Jan, and sometimes an increase at Akrotiri Jan or Feb, perhaps early migrants.

15 recoveries of birds ringed in the U.S.S.R. (Appendix 2).

160. LARUS AUDOUINII   RB or MB
Audouin's Gull

Resident or migrant breeder.

Breeding distribution. First proved at the Klidhes Islands 1960, a colony of 12 nests on the main island 14 May (B8); 6 nests there 4 May 1961 (B10), none 5 Jun 1966 (B19) and one mid Jun 1968 (R15). In 1966 2–4 birds present and probably breeding on the small island closest to the mainland, where 7 nests 6 May 1971 (Took 1971a), 8 nests 13 May 1972 (R19), 9 nests 12 May 1973 (R20), at least 10 nests 17 May 1974, with a maximum of 43 birds present 1 May (NR5). No access was possible for some years after 1974, and on 24 May 1987 no birds were seen on the small island, but on the main island a colony of 36 adults and 15 occupied nests was found (Murray 1987d). Eggs and young suffer very heavy predation from fishermen (B8, B10, B19, R15), which is probably responsible for the 2 recent changes of breeding site. Ideally a warden should be appointed May–Jul to protect this rare breeding species.

Breeding data. First arrivals at the colony usually early Apr, main arrival mid or late Apr, and birds present till Jul, probably into Aug. In 1961 nests were only the pretence of a scrape, with no nesting material of any kind, the eggs laid directly on the bare rock (B8); in 1971 nests lightly made of grasses and bits of dry vegetation (Took 1971a); in 1987 nests were "built on bare ground with a light covering of soil", varying from either little or no lining of vegetation to well formed nests (Murray 1987d). Eggs, C/1 to C/3, found May, normal hatching dates apparently late May and early Jun, and young late May to Jul. [In view of possible confusion with Herring Gull *L. argentatus*, a colony of 6 nests with eggs ascribed to *L. audouinii* near Rizokarpaso, 10 May 1974, requires confirmation (NR5).]

Adults apparently disperse around the coasts, especially those of the Karpas, outside the breeding season; with perhaps most young birds leaving the island.

161. LARUS CANUS   WV
Common Gull

Scarce winter visitor to coasts, harbours, coastal wetlands and inland waters late Nov to Apr, mainly Dec–Mar, usually in ones and twos, occasionally more. Maxima: 8 Zyyi, 11 Mar 1954 (the Bannermans 1958); 14 Famagusta harbour, 23 Jan 1964 (Stewart & Christensen); 9 Famagusta Floods, 29 Jan 1972; and up to 8 Akhna Dam, 15–31 Dec 1989. Previously, one collected 22 Dec 1946 (skin in NRS) is small and definitely *L.c. canus* (C. Edelstan *per* S. J. Christensen); others are mentioned by Müller, Bucknill (1911) and Madarász (1904b), who was sent 6 taken in Jan.

162. LARUS FUSCUS   PM WV
Lesser Black-backed Gull

Common passage migrant (*L.f. fuscus*), usually in 10s, sometimes 100s daily. In spring an eastward passage of flocks on the south coast and north from Cape Andreas, Mar–May, mostly late Mar to early May, with a smaller passage north on the west coast. Maxima, a total of 808 north at Cape Andreas, 5–25 Apr 1973, including 300 on 12 Apr and 200 on 20 Apr (Stagg 1974); and (exceptionally) up to 300 an hour north at Salamis, 13 Apr 1971 (I. Beames). Occasional Jun–Jul. In autumn mainly westward passage on the north coast Aug–Oct, mostly late Aug to mid Oct, with a smaller southward passage on the east coast; autumn maxima 160 off Xeros, 18 Sep 1972 and 200 there, 13 Oct 1973. In both spring and autumn, birds also occur anywhere around the coasts, in the harbours and at coastal wetlands. A few remain over winter, occasionally in 10s, exceptionally 150 Famagusta, 20 Dec 1958.
2 recoveries of birds ringed in Denmark and Finland (Appendix 2).

163. LARUS ARGENTATUS   RB WV PM
Herring Gull

Resident breeder (*L.a. michahellis*).
Breeding distribution. Coastal cliffs and offshore islands. Colonies: Klidhes Islands, 400 adults there 1987 and 55 nests found (R34); Akrotiri, 10–25 pairs; Yeronisos Island, "many apparently sitting on eggs or chicks" Apr 1987 (R34); and Ayios Yeoryios Island, *c.* 25 pairs. Colonies probably also at Cape Aspro, Episkopi (bred 1982), Mazaki Island and possibly elsewhere. Bred Kyrenia in the past (Bucknill 1909–10).
Breeding data. Eggs, C/2 and C/3, found Apr–May and (replacement clutches?) early Jul, young late Apr to Jul; normal hatching dates apparently late Apr and early May; fledging observed late May and late Jul. Eggs and young at the Klidhes Islands suffer heavy predation from fishermen (B8, B10, R34). Adults are present at or near the colonies throughout the year. Some resident birds apparently prey on exhausted passerine migrants. On 17 Mar 1970, a bird circling over the sea south of Cape Gata attempted to capture an arriving Wheatear *Oenanthe* sp (Flint 1971b). Also remains of many small passerines found among Herring Gull pellets on the Klidhes Islands, 24 May 1987, spp included Serin *S. serinus,* Goldfinch *C. carduelis,* Spanish Sparrow *P. hispaniolensis* and Pipit *Anthus* sp (Murray 1987d).
A post breeding roost develops Akrotiri Salt Lake from Jun onwards, maximum 150—250 there Jul–Aug, sometimes 100–200 till Mar. This roost includes passage and wintering birds as well as residents. Winter visitor in variable numbers to coasts, harbours and inland waters Nov to early Apr, usually in 10s, sometimes 100–200 together, maximum 400+ Asprokremmos Dam, 17 Feb 1985. 5 flocks of up to 20 flying north on the west coast mid Apr 1980 (T. R. Mitchell), otherwise little obvious passage.
The races of passage migrants and winter visitors are not known. Most are probably *L.a. michahellis* with some *L.a. cachinnans.* An adult showing characters of *L.a. armenicus* was at Akrotiri Gravel Pits, 27 Feb 1988 (Rayner 1988); another was on the north coast near Phlamoudhi, 24 Oct 1990 (P. R. Flint); and up to 4 were at Ormidhia fishing shelter, 22–26 Feb 1991 (R. Frost). On distribution (Grant) *armenicus* might be expected to occur regularly in winter. Dark-mantled birds amongst the Akrotiri Salt Lake roost in autumn 1970 and 1971 (P. R. Flint) may

have been the '*barabensis*' form of *L.a. cachinnans,* dark individuals of *L.a. armenicus,* or *L.a. heuglini.* Birds of the *argentatus* group with flesh coloured legs could also occur. A study of the Herring Gull complex in Cyprus would be interesting and scientifically rewarding (Thiede), particularly in the case of *armenicus* and the dark-mantled birds. (Note – some authors now consider *cachinnans, argentatus* and *armenicus* to be distinct species, and *heuglini* to be a race of *L. fuscus.*)

164. LARUS MARINUS   AV

Great Black-backed Gull

Accidental visitor, 5 records: one adult Morphou Bay, 11 Feb 1958 (the Bannermans 1958); one adult Akrotiri, 30 Mar 1958 (B6); one immature Akrotiri Salt Lake, 30 Mar and 21 May 1970 (R17); one Akrotiri Salt Lake, 9 Apr 1987 (R34); one Dhiarizos River, 15 Apr 1989 (M. S. Cooper *per* C. J. L. Bennett). [14 other recent records give inadequate detail. Mentioned in the past by Baxendale (1915), Lilford and Sibthorp. The black-backed *L. fuscus fuscus* is often reported as this species, particularly in Apr.]

165. RISSA TRIDACTYLA   AV

Kittiwake

Accidental visitor, 2 records: 1–3 immatures Famagusta harbour, 2–13 Feb 1961 (R7, B13); one immature Kyrenia, 1 Oct 1961 (R8).

STERNIDAE

166. GELOCHELIDON NILOTICA   PM

Gull-billed Tern

G.n. nilotica. Scarce to fairly common passage migrant in spring, usually in the south and east, at coastal wetlands or offshore, occasionally at inland waters. Occasional Mar (though 44 Akrotiri, 19 Mar 1972), main passage Apr in 10s or less, maximum flocks of 28 and 60 east at Zakaki, 14 Apr 1971; few till late May, sometimes Jun. Occasional early-mid Jul and Aug to mid Sep. One off Dhekelia, 28 Jan 1980, was probably an early migrant.

167. STERNA CASPIA (=HYDROPROGNE TSCHEGRAVA)   PM

Caspian Tern

Very scarce passage migrant late Mar to mid May, mainly Apr, offshore or at coastal wetlands, occasionally at inland waters. Usually in ones and twos, maximum 4 north off Paphos lighthouse, 16 Apr 1990 (D. Raw). Twice late Aug and occasional Sep.

168. STERNA SANDVICENSIS   WV PM

Sandwich Tern

S.s. sandvicensis. Scarce winter visitor and passage migrant to inshore waters mainly Nov–Apr, highest numbers usually after mid-winter; occasional Sep–Oct, and seen once each May, mid Jun and mid Jul. Most frequently recorded in Larnaca Bay (notably on jetties and buoys at Dhekelia, and at Larnaca beach), where up to 14 birds in some recent winters. Also occurs in harbours at Famagusta, Limassol and Paphos, and elsewhere around the coasts. Occasional at inland waters. The Jan–Feb easterly shift of birds in the Mediterranean (Cramp & Simmons) is perhaps responsible for the increase in numbers after mid-winter.

First recorded 1953 (B6), but then not for 18 years. The next records were in 1971 (R18), 1972 (NR3), 1973 (NR4) and 1981 (R28). Since 1981, it has been recorded annually, and in some years there have been over 20 records. Although some birds will undoubtedly have been overlooked offshore previously, the many records in the 1980s indicate a considerable increase in wintering numbers. 2 recoveries of birds ringed in the U.S.S.R. (Appendix 2).

169. STERNA HIRUNDO   PM WV FB

   Common Tern

S.h. hirundo. Passage migrant in variable numbers in spring, occasionally scarce but usually fairly common or common Apr–May, mainly in the south and east, at wetlands or coasting, peak numbers mid Apr to early May, in 10s, sometimes 100 or more at Akrotiri Salt Lake, maximum 200 there, late Apr to early May 1969; once seen mid Mar and occasionally Jun–Jul, though 21 Atkrotiri Salt Lake, 9 Jul 1978. Scarce and irregular on passage Aug to mid Oct in ones and twos, mostly Sep. Occasional early Nov and once late Nov. Occasionally 1–7 in winter (mainly Jan), offshore or at coastal wetlands. [At least 12 records of 1–17 *sterna* sp Dec to mid Mar, mainly offshore, most probably *S. hirundo* or Sandwich Tern *S. sandvicensis*.] In winter in the past, one mid Feb 1888 (Guillemard 1889) and "fair numbers" Akhyritou reservoir, 25 Jan 1908 (Bucknill 1909–10).

   Breeding. One record: eggs taken Akhyritou reservoir, May 1905 (Bucknill 1909–10). [Breeding near Famagusta 1912 (Jourdain 1929b), not mentioned by Bucknill or the C.N.H.S., is probably an error.]

170. STERNA PARADISAEA   AV

   Arctic Tern

Accidental visitor, 3 records: one Akrotiri, 11 May 1963 (R10); 10–60 Akrotiri Salt Lake, 29 Apr to 17 May 1969 (R16); one Larnaca, 30 Apr 1984 (R31). [Others, without descriptions, May and Sep.]

171. STERNA ALBIFRONS   PM FB

   Little Tern

S.a. albifrons. Very scarce to scarce passage migrant in spring mainly at coastal wetlands or offshore, occasionally at inland waters. Occasional Mar to mid Apr, most frequent late Apr to mid May, usually 1–4 together, exceptionally 32 and 20 flying southwest off Larnaca, mid May 1957; occasional late May, once early and once mid Jun. 7 records of 1–2 birds mid Jul to Sep.

   Breeding. 3 records in the past: "a few pairs" with eggs Akhyritou reservoir, May 1905 (Bucknill 1909–10); nested 1910 "in some numbers" Fresh Water Lake and on islands round Famagusta harbour, fresh eggs taken Jun (Bucknill 1911); one nest C/2, Larnaca Salt Lake, 16 Jun 1946 (Morris 1946a). [No evidence for 1912 breeding attributed by Jourdain (1929b) to Baxendale (1915), who does not mention the species. No evidence for 1911 breeding (*pace* Stewart & Christensen, the Bannermans 1971).]

172. CHLIDONIAS HYBRIDUS (=HYBRIDA)   PM

Whiskered Tern

Scarce passage migrant (*C.h. hybridus*) to wetlands and coasts Apr–May, mainly mid Apr to mid May, usually less than 10 together, maximum 16 Akrotiri Salt Lake, 7 May 1982; once seen late Mar and occasionally Jun to early Jul. Scarcer on return passage mid Jul to mid Oct, mostly late Jul to Aug, usually 1–4 together, occasionally more, maximum 15 Zakaki, 2 Aug 1981. Occasional late Oct, once early Nov.

173. CHLIDONIAS NIGER   PM

Black Tern

Fairly common passage migrant (*C.n. niger*) to wetlands, less frequently to coasts: occasional Mar to early Apr, 10s or less mid Apr to May, maximum 28 Akrotiri Salt Lake, 2 May 1972; occasional Jun, once early Jul. Return passage mid Jul to early-mid Oct, usually less numerous but more widespread than in spring, maximum 25 Akhna Dam mid-late Aug and 11 Oct 1989. Once late Oct and once early Nov. [A *Chlidonias* sp off Akrotiri, 30 Dec 1971, thought to be *C. niger*. 40 *Chlidonias* sp Akrotiri Salt Lake, early and late Jul and present in numbers throughout Aug, maximum 30 mid Aug, all 1970.]

174. CHLIDONIAS LEUCOPTERUS   PM

White-winged Black Tern

Common passage migrant to wetlands, less frequently to coasts, most numerous in spring: once mid Feb and twice early Mar, occasional mid Mar to mid Apr, common late Apr to May, peak numbers late Apr to mid May, often 100 or more, maxima 250 Akrotiri Salt Lake, 23 Apr 1968, and 300+ Akhna Dam, 23 Apr 1990; often a few seen Jun and occasionally early-mid Jul. Return passage late Jul to Sep, 10s or less, maxima 50 Akrotiri Salt Lake, 23–27 Aug 1968, and 50 Akrotiri reed beds, 15 Aug 1982; occasional Oct, once early-mid Nov.

PTEROCLIDIDAE

175. PTEROCLES ORIENTALIS   RB PM?

Black-bellied Sandgrouse

P.o. orientalis. Scarce resident, now usually only c. 2–4 records a year, usually of birds flying over or drinking at rivers or pools; usually less than 10 together. Until the early 1970s flocks of up to 40 occurred, the largest since was of 15 in 1984.

Breeding distribution. Apparently now confined to the rocky southwestern edge of the Mesaoria, mostly within the area Larnaca, Pergamos, Tymbou, Athalassa, Nicosia Airport and Xeri. Formerly a "not uncommon" resident on the

Mesaoria (Waterer), eggs taken there and breeding mentioned near Vatili (Bucknill 1909–10); also 7 pairs Athalassa, 25 Apr 1929 (Jourdain 1929a). No well documented breeding records. Its numbers and distribution require investigation. It appears to be still decreasing and unless it is given effective protection this most attractive breeding species may be lost.

G. F. Wilson (*in* Bucknill 1909–10) considered the numbers of residents "to be augmented considerably by migrants in autumn and probably in spring", and some of the 100s which came to drink at the river near Pyroi, mid Sep to mid Nov 1910, were believed to be immigrants (Bucknill 1911). In recent years: *c.* 200 feeding in a rocky area near Analiondas, 4 Jan 1976 (NR7), were probably immigrants. Individuals at Akrotiri, once early Nov, once early Dec and once late Mar, and 2 Kouklia reed beds (Paphos district), late Dec, were either migrants or wandering residents.

176. PTEROCLES ALCHATA   FB? former PM?
Pin–tailed Sandgrouse

P.a. caudacutus. 2 old records: one shot near Larnaca, 3 May 1787 (Sibthorp), and ♂ and ♀ collected *c.* 15 Mar to *c.* 22 Apr 1820 (Stresemann). Stresemann disputed Sibthorp's record, apparently because of the Greek name mentioned, suggesting it referred to Black-bellied Sandgrouse *P. orientalis*; in fact the name could refer equally to either species, and the description and plate (*in* Russell) mentioned by Sibthorp confirm the identification of *P. alchata*. [Shot once by G. F. Wilson, presumably before 1910 (Bucknill 1909–10).] That specimens were obtained by the first 2 collectors to visit the island suggests that it was previously not scarce, perhaps as a migrant or breeding bird.

COLUMBIDAE

177. COLUMBA LIVIA   RB
Rock Dove

Common resident (*C.l. gaddi*).
Breeding distribution. Nests colonially on rock faces in the hills and mountains, on sea cliffs and on offshore islands, some also on lowland cliffs inland. Very numerous within the Kyrenia range, scarce or absent in many parts of the Troodos range because of a lack of suitable rock faces. Flocks make daily movements to feed and drink, notably down from the Kyrenia range on to the Mesaoria and northern foothills, and from offshore islands to the mainland; largest flocks in late summer and autumn, often in 100s, maximum 1000 Kolossi, late summer 1957. The largest number seen flying in from the Klidhes Islands was 664 in the early morning of 11 Apr 1973 (NR4).
Breeding data. Nest in cave (R28) and Bucknill (1909–10) mentions nests "in ancient ruined vaults, and even in old deep-cut wells". On the Klidhes Islands, "nests were on the ground beneath dense patches of Atriplex and grass scrub with access via a tunnel of matted vegetation" (Murray 1987d). Eggs, usually C/2, found mid Mar to Jul; young heard in nest Feb.

178. COLUMBA OENAS   WV PM?
Stock Dove

Winter visitor (*C.o. oenas*) mainly to low ground, occasionally common, but more usually scarce; perhaps overlooked. Has occurred mid Aug to early May, most records Oct–Feb, very few later; usually in 10s or less, occasionally in 100s, maximum 800 Palekhori, 26 Nov 1972. 13 flying due south Akrotiri, 21 Nov 1981, suggests passage.

179. COLUMBA PALUMBUS   RB WV?

Woodpigeon

C.p. palumbus. Common resident.

Breeding distribution. Forest areas; most common on the lower and middle slopes of the Troodos range, particularly within the Paphos Forest; less common in the Kyrenia range; also breeds on the Karpas and the Akamas.

Breeding data. Nests found in *Pinus,* Olive *Olea europaea* and Alder *Alnus orientalus* (McNeile, Ashton–Johnson). Eggs, C/2, late Apr and mid May; young late Apr and "nests" Jun to early Jul.

Some flocks flight to low ground to feed, especially Jul–Apr. Often in 100s from Jul, particularly in the Troodos range, once 600 there Dec. The crops of 12 birds shot Troodos range, Aug–Sep, contained mainly seeds of coniferous trees (Bucknill 1909–10). A marked increase Nov–Dec 1978 and *c.* 2000 Kannaviou, 13 Nov 1983, suggest winter influx.

180. STREPTOPELIA DECAOCTO   RB PM?

Collared Dove

Locally fairly common resident (*S.d. decaocto*), having increased considerably in numbers and distribution in the last 10–20 years.

Breeding distribution. Nicosia, Athalassa, Limassol (Coca-Cola factory, Hospital and New Port areas). Individuals and pairs also reported from many other towns and villages including Platres (1100 m).

Breeding data. Nests found in *Pinus, Eucalyptus,* Cypress *Cupressus sempervirens,* Almond *Prunus communis,* Pepper Tree *Schinus molle,* conifers and once on a vine trellis. Height of 3 nests above ground *c.* 7–*c.* 14 m. Breeding season protracted. Eggs, C/2 once mid Jun; "nesting" reported Mar–Jul and Sep; single young seen Mar, Jun, Jul and Sep, and single fledged young Apr and Jul. In the past, mentioned in Sibthorp's list of 1787; seen Larnaca 1875 (Lilford); and Nicosia 1910, "always a few ... frequenting old secluded Turkish gardens ... in an almost semiferal state" (Bucknill 1909–10), and 1933 (Ferrier), Waterer considered it a fairly common resident in Nicosia; also occurred in other towns (G. F. Wilson *in* Bucknill 1909–10).

Recent increases in numbers first noticed in 1972 when 30 Kermia (Nicosia), late Oct (R19), and 60 there autumn 1973 (R20). Present Athalassa from at least 1986 (R34) and a colony found Limassol in 1988 (NL88/1). In Apr 1988 seen "everywhere" in Nicosia (NL88/4) and in May 1989 "commonly seen" Nicosia and Athalassa (NL89/5). An autumn flock at Athalassa has increased from 50–60 in Oct 1987 (R34) to 110 in Oct 1989 (NL89/10). These autumn flocks are presumably composed of local post–breeding birds. Flocks also in winter: up to 40 Limassol, Jan 1988, and 50+ Stroumbi, mid Dec 1989.

The species was favoured by Muslims in the Ottoman Empire (Cramp 1985) and the earlier records from Nicosia are presumably a result of this, but the recent expansion in the island may be the result of immigration of new genetic stock. There are 2 records from Cape Andreas, mid and late Apr, and 4 from Cape Greco, spring and autumn, suggesting immigration/emigration.

181. STREPTOPELIA TURTUR   PM MB
Turtle Dove

S.t. turtur. Very common passage migrant: twice seen early Mar, occasional mid-late Mar, first arrivals usually early Apr, in 100s or 1000s mid Apr to early or mid May, maxima *c.* 3250 Angulos (Dhiorios), 9 May 1971, *c.* 4000 Lefkoniko, 30 Apr 1972, and in late Apr 1976 several 1000s found dead Paphos/Akamas coast by the sea shore following 2 days of severe storms (NR7); last seen late May. Less numerous on return passage Aug–Oct, mainly late Aug to Sep in 10s or 100s; occasional early Nov.

Common migrant breeder.

Breeding distribution. Pine forest and lightly wooded areas at all altitudes. No recent records from the Mesaoria, bred "fairly commonly" in suitable localities on the plains in the past (Bucknill 1911).

Breeding data. Nests found in *Eucalyptus, Juniperus phoenicia,* Almond *Prunus communis* and Pepper Tree *Schinus molle.* Eggs, C/2, found late Apr to early Jun; fledged young late May and late Jul. A pair raised 2 broods at Kyrenia 1978, young flying by 21 Jul and 14 Sep.

3 ringed in Cyprus, recovered in the U.S.S.R. (2) and Greece (Appendix 2).

S.t. arenicola: 2 collected Ayia Irini, 18 May 1969 by J. M. Harrison and one (undated) seen by the Bannermans (1958).

182. STREPTOPELIA SENEGALENSIS   AV
Palm Dove

Accidental visitor (*S.s. senegalensis*), one record: one Larnaca, 30 Sep 1968 (R15). ["Small numbers – in parties of 3 or 4" on Government Farm, Athalassa, early May 1909 (Bucknill 1909–10), possibly introduced. Seen "in small numbers" by D. F. Davidson (the Bannermans 1958).]

CUCULIDAE

183. CLAMATOR GLANDARIUS   PM MB
Great Spotted Cuckoo

Fairly common passage migrant in spring: has occurred Feb to early May, but mainly mid Mar to Apr, usually in ones and twos, sometimes up to 6 together. No observed autumn passage.

Scarce to fairly common migrant breeder, parasitic, laying in nests of Magpie *Pica pica.* [Probably also occasionally lays in nests of Hooded Crow *Corvus corone*: mentioned by Bucknill (1909–10), G. F. Wilson (*in* Ferrier), and "juvenile reared by a Hooded Crow" (R27), but no documented records yet.]

Breeding distribution. All breeding records are from below *c.* 400 m, though possibly breeds higher.

Breeding data. Eggs found Apr to mid May; fledged young May to early Jul. An original C/8 of *P. pica* was reduced, by 9 Apr, to C/6 plus 2 eggs of *C. glandarius* from different hens (Ashton–Johnson). At Lara, 7–16 Jul 1989, 5 juveniles were associating together, sometimes in the same tree, and usually accompanied by a Magpie (N. Petrou). Very few records Jul–Aug, once early Sep, probably locally bred birds.

184. CHRYSOCOCCYX CAPRIUS   AV

Didric Cuckoo

Accidental visitor, one record: one Akrotiri, 27 Jun 1982. The first record for the Palaearctic (Lobb 1983, R29).

185. CUCULUS CANORUS   PM OB?

Cuckoo

C.c. canorus. Common passage migrant in spring; occasional early Mar, common mid or late Mar to Apr or early May, sometimes a few till late May. Spring migrants usually in ones and twos, occasionally up to 10 or more together; in 1980 25 shot Ayios Epiphanios, 20 Apr, and 15 were at Maroni, 27 Apr (of these 40 birds 6 were rufous phase – NR11). 25 also at Ayios Yeoryios, 15 Apr 1981. Of 150 limed and sexed Paralimni, 20 Mar to 12 May 1968, 94 were ♂♂, and of the ♀♀, 13 were rufous phase (Horner & Hubbard). Scarce and irregular on passage late Jul to mid Oct, most records Sep; once mid Nov.

Possibly breeds: a juvenile at Kakopetria, 10 Jul 1973 (NR4); several heard calling Paphos Forest early Jun 1979 (Flint 1980); an adult Troodos, 14 Jun 1981 (R28); 2 adults Ayios Epiphanios, 17 Jun 1983 (NR14); one adult Orga, 15 Jun 1984 (R31); and one calling Xeros Potamos, 13 and 20 Jun 1990 (NL90/6).

TYTONIDAE

186. TYTO ALBA   RB

Barn Owl

Fairly common resident (*T.a. erlangeri*).

Breeding distribution. All breeding records are from low ground (up to 250 m), though occasionally seen higher, once Troodos late Aug. In recent times nests found Aronas (Athalassa), Dhali, Episkopi, Famagusta, Kokkini Trimithia, Lakatamia, Limassol, Lymbia, Nicosia, Nicosia Airport, Polis, Tseri and Varisha (Morphou); in the past at Larnaca and near Nicosia (Bucknill 1911). Apparently most numerous around towns and villages.

Breeding data. Nests in cliffs, quarries and buildings; eggs, C/3 mid Mar and C/2 early May; young, broods of 2–4, late Mar to Jun.

Although a protected bird, many are killed in road accidents, and by limesticks and shotguns. Pellets (total mass 0·5 kg) collected from a deserted building near Kophinou, 11 Oct 1977, contained mainly bones of rats and mice *Muridae* (NR8).

There appears to be a considerable variation in degree of paleness, some individuals are considered to be of "the white form" (NR10 & 11), and a dark-breasted bird was limed once Feb (NL87/7). The latter was possibly *T.a. guttata,* though Cyprus is far removed from its breeding range, and it seems more likely to have been an unusually dark individual of *erlangeri.*

STRIGIDAE

187. OTUS SCOPS   RB MB? PM

Scops Owl

Common resident (*O.s. cyprius,* an endemic race).

Breeding distribution. Lightly wooded areas at all altitudes, often in or near towns and villages.

Breeding data. Calls mainly Feb–Mar to Jul, less frequently Aug–Oct, occasionally Nov–Jan. Breeding density may be high, up to 10 calling around Tsadha, early Apr 1981 (NR12). Nests in trees and buildings, in holes in walls, once in a nest box (*per* P. F. Stewart), and once in a well (Bucknill 1911); 3 clutches were in old nests of Magpie *Pica pica* in Olive *Olea europaea* and *Juniperus phoenicia* (Ashton–Johnson). Eggs, C/2 to C/5 (mainly C/4), Apr–May, young May–Jul.

O.s. cyprius has a longer wing than those populations of nominate *scops* breeding to the north of Cyprus (Dement'ev & Gladkov). Wing lengths of *cyprius:* ♂♂ (8) 153–165 mm, mean 157·5 mm, ♀♀ (14) 154–168 mm, mean 161 mm (measurements from Madarász (1901), BMNH skins and Cramp 1985). It is possible that *cyprius* is partly migratory, as are other Mediterranean island races (Vaurie), though probably only a very small number of birds leave the island in winter. 4 heavy long–winged birds trapped Akrotiri Sep (see Appendix 3) may have been departing *cyprius.* Also 14 *cyprius* limed Paralimni, 12 Mar to 3 Apr 1968, suggesting arrival (Horner & Hubbard). If these were returning to the island, they might be expected to occur earlier than the more northerly breeding *O.s. scops,* which was the case (see below).

Compared with nominate *scops, cyprius* is darker and greyer, with more prominent white spotting on the back, often extending to the crown and scapulars, and with much wider black streaks and narrow cross bars below, often isolating distinct white spots (Vaurie, Cramp 1985). The 2 races should be separable in the field.

Common passage migrant early–mid Mar to early May (mainly Apr), and Sep–Oct; 136 (apparently nearly all nominate *scops*) limed Paralimni, 16 Mar to 8 May 1968 (Horner & Hubbard). Probably nearly all passage migrants are *O.s. scops,* of which 6 were collected Mar, Sep and Oct (Madarász 1904b); the mean wing length of birds trapped Paralimni (see Appendix 3) is also similar to that of *O.s. scops* (Dement'ev & Gladkov). *O.s. cycladum,* which breeds in southern Turkey (Cramp 1985), can also be expected to occur, and 3 birds limed Paralimni, spring 1968, may have been of this race (G. Watson *in* Horner & Hubbard). *O.s. pulchellus,* from eastern Russia/Siberia, could also possibly occur in small numbers.

188. ATHENE NOCTUA   RB

Little Owl

Common resident.

Breeding distribution. Open, lightly wooded and rocky country, mainly on low ground and the lower mountain slopes, occasionally up to Troodos, but no breeding records above *c.* 700 m; also in and around towns and villages.

Breeding data. Nests in holes in trees and walls, in buildings and low cliffs; eggs, C/3 to C/6, mainly C/5 (Müller), mid Apr to early Jun; fledged young mid May to early Jul.

Cyprus birds vary in darkness of colouration (Madarász 1904b, Bucknill 1909–10, R. Meinertzhagen *in* the Bannermans 1958); Vaurie lists them as *A.n. indigena,* but states that they "show a certain tendency towards the paler *lilith*", and Cramp (1985) lists them as *lilith.*

189. ASIO OTUS   RB? WV? PM?

Long-eared Owl

Probably resident (*A.o. otus*).
    Breeding distribution. Probably often overlooked. 1–2 pairs bred Salamis 1968–71 (Stagg 1968, R16, R18, P. F. Stewart), probably also bred there 1963 and birds present 1973; has also occurred in breeding season at Astromeritis, Dhekelia, Kapedhes, Larnaca, Pyrga, Skarinou, Tala and Xyliatos and has possibly bred Athalassa (NR2).
    Breeding data. Bred Salamis in fir plantation in old nests of Hooded Crow *Corvus corone,* remains of 2 young and an egg found early Mar, half grown young seen early Jun (R16), fledged young early Apr and mid May. Present at the breeding site late Dec to mid Jul. Occasional winter records, mainly from low ground, both recently and in the past (Lilford, Madarász 1904b, C.N.H.S.Ann.IV), some at least probably being local breeding birds, some possibly immigrants.
    One passage record, a bird arrived from over the sea and fell exhausted on to the beach at Larnaca, early Apr 1988.

190. ASIO FLAMMEUS   PM WV

Short-eared Owl

Scarce passage migrant and winter visitor (*A.f. flammeus*) mid Sep to Apr, most frequent mid Mar to mid Apr on passage in the south and east; in winter mainly at marshes and in open country. Possibly more numerous in the past: Lilford met with it frequently near Salamis and Akrotiri, Apr 1875.

CAPRIMULGIDAE

191. CAPRIMULGUS EUROPAEUS   PM MB

Nightjar

Common passage migrant and migrant breeder. Occasional Mar, common on passage Apr–May, mostly late Apr to early May.
    Breeding distribution. Common in summer in wooded areas at all altitudes, though not on Mesaoria. Has bred Akrotiri, Polemidhia, Troodos, Skarinou and Cape Andreas; breeding probably overlooked elsewhere.
    Breeding data. At Akrotiri, C/2 amongst twig litter on stoney ground surrounded by juniper and pine scrub (A. S. Norris). Hatching once mid Jun, fledged young once early Aug. Passage and departure Aug to early Nov, exceptionally to late Nov, twice Dec.
    Breeding birds are *C.e. meridionalis*; the wing length range of trapped migrants (see Appendix 3) suggests both *meridionalis* and *europaeus* occur on passage.
    One ringed in Cyprus, recovered in Tanzania (Appendix 2).

APODIDAE

192. APUS APUS   PM MB

Swift

A.a. apus. Abundant passage migrant in spring; occasional from late Jan, a few mid or late Feb, main passage Mar–Apr, maxima "a continual stream ... of some thousands" north at Larnaca, 4 Apr 1965 (R12), up to 1000 per hour north along coast at Salamis, mid-late Apr 1971 (I. Beames), and a constant eastward movement of 1000s at Episkopi, 14 Mar 1982 (R29); last spring migrants late May. Much scarcer on return passage mid Jun to Sep, 10s to 100, though 2000 Zakaki, 21 Aug 1970 and 500–600 flying eastwards at Episkopi, 14 Aug 1985; occasional Oct, once late Nov and once early Dec.

Very common migrant breeder, main arrival early Mar.

Breeding distribution. Nests in towns, villages, and isolated buildings; probably also nests on cliffs, though the only recorded natural sites are on the Klidhes Islands, where many nest in crevices in the rocks (Smith, Murray 1987d).

Breeding data. Few detailed records: eggs, usually C/3, on low ground late Apr (Bucknill 1909–10, Jourdain 1929a), small young on Troodos mid May (Ashton–Johnson), fledging there early Jul. Numbers decrease on low ground in Jun and all have departed by early or mid Jul; last seen on Troodos late Aug (Mason).

Breeding birds are duller and less blackish than typical nominate *apus* from western Europe, but are much more similar to *apus* than to *pekinensis* (see Vaurie).

193. APUS PALLIDUS   MB PM

Pallid Swift

Locally fairly common migrant breeder (race unknown), present Mar–Apr to Sep; overlooked owing to confusion with Swift *A. apus.*

Breeding distribution. Small colonies, "often associated with larger colonies of *A. apus*" (R1), at Troodos, Nicosia, Famagusta, Pyrgos, Morphou, Cape Greco, Paphos, Bellapais, Cape Andreas, Makheras Monastery, villages on the Karpas and probably elsewhere.

Breeding data. Nests mainly in buildings, also on cliffs (Stewart & Christensen). Poorly documented, only records being from Troodos, where it breeds apparently 1–3 weeks later than *A. apus*: 2 nests under eaves held 2 newly hatched young and 2 small young late May (Ashton–Johnson); some young in nest there till late Aug and early Sep, and a pair still feeding young there, 11 Oct 1987 (R34). Numbers gradually lessen on Troodos from mid Aug (Mason), but some are present throughout Sep; the last seen there early-mid Oct. On Troodos, birds feed generally at a lower level than *A. apus,* sometimes even among dense trees (Mason).

Occasionally a few on passage Apr–May and Aug–Sep, once 40 mid Sep.

194. APUS MELBA   MB PM

Alpine Swift

Common migrant breeder (*A.m. tuneti*). Once mid Jan and early Feb, main arrival mid Feb to early Mar; most apparently depart late Aug to early Sep, though sometimes 100s around breeding sites till late Oct and a few till late Nov, once 20 Episkopi late Dec.

Breeding distribution. Colonies (*c.* 10–20 up to *c.* 150 pairs, possibly more) on rock faces and in caves in the Kyrenia range, notably at Karonia Forest Station (Kantara), Halevga, Pentadaktylos, Buffavento and Kornos Peak; on cliffs at Ayios Theodoros, Troodos range; also on sea cliffs on the south coast at Episkopi and Cape Aspro.

Breeding data. Nest sites more or less inaccessible, so breeding details unkown.

A.m. melba is a common passage migrant in spring, scarce in autumn. Spring passage mid Feb to early May, most mid-late Apr, sometimes 100s daily, maxima *c.* 7000 coming in over the north coast, 21 Apr 1965, and *c.* 1000 moving northwest along the road Skarinou–Episkopi, 18 Mar 1978. In autumn 28 moving south very high at Akrotiri, 28 Sep 1975, and 200 southeast at Anglanzia, 29 Sep 1976, otherwise several records of flocks from Sep to early Dec which could refer to passage or to local birds.

ALCEDINIDAE

195. HALCYON SMYRNENSIS   WV

White-breasted Kingfisher (Smyrna Kingfisher)

Very scarce visitor (*H.s. smyrnensis*), mainly in winter; apparently becoming more regular, individuals overwintering in 3 recent winters since 1985. Some 7–9 records: one near houses at Ayios Nikolaos (Famagusta), 16 Aug 1977 and for *c.* 3 weeks previously (R24); singles at Phasouri reservoir, 15–16 Aug and 10 Nov 1985 (R32), 21 Jan to 20 Mar 1986 (R33), 25 Jan to 1 May 1987 (R34), 16 Feb and 11 and 18 Mar 1988, 2 there on 22 Mar (NL88/2 & 3) (some of these records probably refer to the same wintering individual), and one 26 Aug 1990 (J. C. Le Gassick); one Kyrenia, 22 Dec 1987 (R34); one found dead on the main road near Pissouri, 16 Jun 1989 (J. C. Le Gassick). [One, probably this species, early Apr 1957 and second-hand records mentioned by Lilford and Guillemard (1888).]

The nearest breeding population is in southern Turkey (Cramp 1985), and recent birds are presumably from there. Its recent increase in Israel coincides with the growth in agriculture there (Cramp 1985), and with the recent similar growth in Cyprus much suitable habitat now exists for it. It, therefore, can be considered a potential breeding species.

196. ALCEDO ATTHIS   PM WV

Kingfisher

Passage migrant and winter visitor (*A.a. atthis*) to coasts and wetlands. Common on passage from late Jul or Aug to Oct; much less numerous Nov–Feb, sometimes an increase after mid-winter; fairly common on passage Mar–Apr, mainly Apr, absent or very scarce May to mid Jul. Usually occurs in ones and twos on both spring and autumn passage, sometimes up to 10 or more at favoured locations, maximum 20 Akrotiri, mainly at the reed beds, 16 Aug 1969 (R16); 26 were trapped at Akrotiri that autumn, all first year birds (P. R. Flint). [There are no breeding records. "Several pairs . . . nesting . . . in Othello's Tower", Famagusta, after early Apr 1925 (Wilson 1925c) were presumably spring migrants mistaken for breeding birds. There is no basis for a breeding record at Akrotiri 1973 (attributed to W. F. Corris *in* NR4), which was presumably transposed from another species.]

One ringed Akrotiri, 17 Aug 1969, recovered Tymbou, near Nicosia, 23 Apr 1972; one ringed Akrotiri, 16 Sep 1969, retrapped there 11 Jan 1970; one ringed

Akrotiri, 9 Nov 1980, retrapped there 10 Oct and 1 Nov 1981 (M. G. Lobb). The mean wing length of trapped birds (see Appendix 3) is similar to that of birds from the south European U.S.S.R. (Cramp 1985).

197. CERYLE RUDIS   WV

Pied Kingfisher

Very scarce and irregular winter visitor (*C.r. rudis*) to coasts and wetlands. Only 10 recent records, Oct–Mar (9) and May. In detail: one Famagusta harbour, 3 Oct 1957, and two there 24 Nov 1957 to Jan 1958 (R2); one Potamos Creek, 16 Nov 1970 (R17); one Zakaki, 21 Nov 1971 (NR2); one Kalopanayiotis Dam, 26 Nov to 7 Dec 1978 (R25); one Larnaca marina, 16 Mar 1982 (R29); one Potamos, 3 May 1988 (Kephalas 1989); 2 Akhna Dam, 5 Jan and one there 6 Jan and 22 Mar 1989 (Kephalas 1989, NL89/1 & 3); one Kanli (Kanlıköy) reservoir, 23 Mar 1989 (P. Hellyer). Apparently more numerous in the past: mentioned by Guillemard (1888), Madarász (1904b) and Bucknill (1909–10); also seen by Morris (1954), at Nicosia, Nov 1944; Waterer, "a number of times at both Famagusta and Syrianokhori", and Wilson (1954), "every year, in small numbers, hovering over Famagusta harbour flats", though his only detailed published record is of 3 there, mid Nov 1924 to early Apr 1925 (Wilson 1925b,c).

MEROPIDAE

198. MEROPS SUPERCILIOSUS   PM

Blue-cheeked Bee-eater

Scarce passage migrant (*M.s. persicus*), probably regular in spring, late Mar to May, mostly Apr, usually less than 10 together, though 40 Akrotiri Salt Lake, 11 Apr 1966. May remain at marshes or reed beds for 2–3 weeks. Occasionlly 1–2 in Sep–Oct, and 12 Phasouri, 13 Sep 1988.

199. MEROPS APIASTER   PM MB

Bee-eater

Passage migrant, very common in spring, abundant in autumn. Twice mid and twice late Mar, occasional early Apr, main passage mid or late Apr to May, occasionally in 1000s late Apr and early May (many 1000s Rizokarpaso, 1 May 1960), a few early Jun. Return passage from mid Jul, mainly Sep to early Oct, flocks of 10s or 100s passing high overhead on a broad front almost continuously mid-late Sep by day, some also by night, usually few mid-late Oct, occasional Nov. Early autumn migrants in Jul–Aug are often wrongly claimed as breeding birds. Autumn migrants are a favourite prey of hunters, and many 1000s are shot.

Scarce migrant breeder, singly or in colonies up to 20 pairs (R34).

Breeding distribution. Mainly in river and stream banks in coastal areas and hills of the Troodos range, some also in the Kyrenia range, and on the Karpas.

Breeding data. Few details: C/5 Khandria at *c.* 1100 m, 25 May 1959 (Ashton–Johnson), the highest altitude reported; young Jun.

7 recoveries of birds ringed in the U.S.S.R. (4), Bulgaria (2) and Israel (Appendix 2).

CORACIIDAE

200. CORACIAS GARRULUS   PM MB
Roller

C.g. garrulus. Common passage migrant, most numerous in spring; occasional Mar to early Apr, common mid or late Apr to mid or late May, maximum 100s on the Karpas mid May 1972. Return passage from late Aug, common Sep, sometimes to mid Oct, last seen usually late Oct or early Nov; occasional singles overwintering.

Scarce to fairly common migrant breeder.

Breeding distribution. Below *c.* 800 m in open, usually cultivated, lightly wooded country, nesting in holes in isolated, often ruined buildings, and in cliffs and banks. Apparently more numerous in the past: Lilford described it as breeding abundantly, and Wilson (1925c) saw "many" breeding in holes in walls of Famagusta.

Breeding data. Eggs, C/4 and C/5, found late May and early Jun (Müller); young late May to Jul, and fledged young late Jun.

One recovery of a bird ringed in the U.S.S.R. (Appendix 2).

UPUPIDAE

201. UPUPA EPOPS   PM MB
Hoopoe

U.e. epops. Common passage migrant, most numerous in spring. Occasional Feb, a few early Mar, main passage mid or late Mar to Apr or early May, sometimes a few till late May. Return passage Aug–Oct, mainly Sep; once early and once late Nov.

Fairly common migrant breeder.

Breeding distribution. Forest and wooded areas in both mountain ranges, mainly at higher altitudes, scarce and local on low ground.

Breeding data. Nests usually in holes in trees, once in a crack in a rock (Bucknill 1913a). Eggs, C/5, once late May; young late May to early Aug.

PICIDAE

202. JYNX TORQUILLA   PM WV
Wryneck

J.t. torquilla. Common passage migrant Mar to early May, mainly late Mar to Apr; less common Aug–Oct, mainly Sep, sometimes only 1–2 in autumn. A scarce winter visitor to open wooded areas, often near water or reed beds, mainly on low ground, a few records up to *c.*800 m. Heard calling Phasouri, Jan–Feb 1972.

One ringed Bishops Pool, 14 Oct 1968, retrapped there 16 Feb 1969; another ringed Bishops Pool, 7 Jan 1969, retrapped there twice, 14 Oct 1969 and 15 Oct 1972.

PASSERINES

ALAUDIDAE

203. AMMOMANES DESERTI   AV
Desert Lark

Accidental visitor, one record: one Cape Andreas, 23 Apr 1973 (NR4, Stagg 1974).

204. MELANOCORYPHA CALANDRA   RB PM WV?
Calandra Lark

M.c. calandra. Common resident.

Breeding distribution. Flat arable land on the eastern Mesaoria, mainly in the area bounded by Nicosia, Kythrea, Lefkoniko, base of the Karpas, Famagusta, and south to Larnaca and Kiti; less common and local on the western Mesaoria, some all year Yerolakkos and Ayios Vasilios, but apparently none Morphou area in summer. Probably also breeds on the coastal plain to the southeast of Paphos (Akhelia/Mandria/Kouklia). Also at least 10 singing ♂♂ in fields between old and new Paphos, spring 1990 (R. & D. Frost).

Breeding data. Song mainly Dec–May. Nests on the ground, usually in cover, occasionally on open bare ground (R20). Eggs, C/3 to C/6, found Apr to mid May; young from early Apr (Took 1971a). Possibly a polyandrous or loose colonial nester (Took 1971a).

Flocks of up to *c.* 1000 form on the Mesaoria after breeding, mainly late Jun to Oct–Nov, usually smaller flocks later. In autumn and winter small flocks also on low ground away from breeding areas, occasionally in hills up to *c.* 900 m. Probably some winter visitors occur. A few records of passage late Feb to Apr, notably many at Cape Greco, 5 Mar 1972 and 22 northeast at Cape Andreas, 24 Apr 1973. No proof of autumn passage, though several flocks of up to 50 moving southwest, Larnaca area, late Sep to early Oct 1957.

205. MELANOCORYPHA BIMACULATA   PM
Bimaculated Lark

Scarce passage migrant in spring: once mid Mar, main passage late Mar to Apr, peak numbers early-mid Apr; once early May (R. & D. Frost); usually singly or up to 10 together, maximum 16 Spiro's Beach, 16 Apr 1987. Almost all spring records are from near-coastal habitats: salt flats with low open *salicornia/suaeda* scrub, other sparsely vegetated open ground near coasts, and newly ploughed coastal fields. Regular locations have been Spiro's Beach, Moni Beach, Zakaki and the narrow coastal strip from Paphos to Coral Bay. Only 3 autumn records: one or more birds in the Akrotiri area, 12 Nov 1982; a tired migrant landed on a ship in transit from Mersin (Turkey) to Famagusta, 28 Jul 1984 (NR15); one on the north coast at Peristeria, 27 Oct 1990. [5 at Akrotiri Salt Lake, 28 Nov to 1 Dec 1981, were also this species from their calls (F. J. Walker).]

The species has an interesting history in the island, it remained undiscovered for many years and was almost certainly overlooked as Calandra Lark *M. calandra.* The first record was of 2 limed and collected at Paralimni, 31 Mar 1968 (Horner & Hubbard), having been apparently identified at the time as *M. calandra* (Hubbard 1968). Unfortunately observers in Cyprus were not aware of this record and were thus not alerted to the probability of the species' occurrence. The record was finally published in Cyprus at the end of 1982, by which time the species had been rediscovered in the island by F. J. Walker, in Mar 1982, and since then it has proved to be a regular spring migrant. Migrants are presumably of the race *M.b. rufescens* which breeds in central Turkey (Cramp 1988).

206. CALANDRELLA BRACHYDACTYLA (=CINEREA)   MB PM
Short-toed Lark

Common migrant breeder (*C.b. brachydactyla*) present Mar–Oct, occasionally Nov.

Breeding distribution. Flat arable land on the eastern Mesaoria, mainly in the area bounded by Nicosia, Boghaz and Famagusta, less common in the west, from Nicosia to Morphou. Probably breeds Kormakiti and perhaps elsewhere.

Breeding data. Nests on the ground, in the open or in cover. Eggs, C/3 to C/4, found mid Apr to May; young also mid Apr to May. Breeds in the same areas as Calandra Lark *M. calandra,* but in shorter grass (Bourne *et al.*). Mixed colonies with *M. calandra* near Kalopsidha (Ashton–Johnson); at Prastio/Kouklia song territories of the 2 spp overlap and birds feed side by side (Took 1971a). Flocks of up to 400 form after breeding, early Jun onwards.

Common passage migrant Mar to mid May, mainly late Mar to Apr, in 100s, maximum *c.* 2000 Cape Andreas, 7 Apr 1974. Less common on passage Aug–Nov, mainly late Aug to early Oct, usually in 10s, though 300 over Akrotiri, 5 Oct 1969. Occasionally a few on the Mesaoria or the south coast Dec–Feb.

Migrants probably belong to races *brachydactyla* and *artemisiana.* Note that Vaurie and others treat *C. brachydactyla* as conspecific with and under the name *C. cinerea.* [One collected Famagusta, 16 Apr 1938, identified as *C.b. longipennis* (Payn), but the skin (in BMNH) is of identical colouring to *C.b. brachydactyla* (P. F. Stewart). 3 records of flocks of 50–150 *C. brachydactyla/C. rufescens* around Akrotiri Salt Lake in winter, twice Dec and once early Feb.]

207. CALANDRELLA RUFESCENS   PM WV?

Lesser Short-toed Lark

Very scarce and irregular passage migrant mid Nov to Apr, most frequent Feb–Apr, usually singly or in 10s. Probably often overlooked. Occasional on mud flats or waste ground around the salt lakes in winter, though only once Dec and twice Jan.

Birds showing heavy bills typical of *C.r. ahoronii* have occurred (Stewart & Christensen); on distribution *C.r. heinei* is also likely to occur. [Reported, without descriptions, Sep, Oct and May and several times in winter; notably 50–300 at Bishops Pool, 3–31 Dec 1972.] (See also Short-toed Lark *C. brachydactyla.*)

208. GALERIDA CRISTATA   RB PM WV?

Crested Lark

Very common and widespread resident (*G.c. cypriaca*).

Breeding distribution. Open, natural and cultivated, low ground (including salt flats) and lower hills; highest nest found at *c.* 450 m, though some birds present in suitable habitat up to *c.* 1000 m.

Breeding data. Song in spring from early Feb and also until late Aug to Sep. Nests on the ground, in cover or in the open. Eggs, C/3 to C/6, found mid Mar to May; young late Mar to Jun. At Prastio/Kouklia breeds in the same territories as Calandra Lark *M. calandra* and Short-toed Lark *C. brachydactyla,* but does not appear to feed alongside them (Took 1971a).

Several records of birds becoming scarce or absent in some areas on low ground Jun–Aug, returning Sep (suggesting some movement within the island), this best observed at Pendayia 1972 (R19), though 6 recoveries/retraps of birds ringed Nicosia (3), Akrotiri (2) and Polemidhia, 4 of them where ringed and 2 within 7 km, show sedentary nature of residents. Occasional records on Troodos and Mt. Olympus in summer and autumn, once "numerous" Prodhromos, late Jun. Winter numbers apparently sometimes vary, both increases and decreases noted. Flocks of

10s, occasionally 100s, have been noted Oct–Apr, these probably include both residents and immigrants.

Formerly considered to be an endemic race, *G.c. cypriaca* (Bianchi) was discarded by Vaurie, who included it with *G.c. caucasica*. However *G.c. cypriaca* is recognised by Cramp (1988), who includes birds from Karpathos and Rhodes, though mentioning that birds from Cyprus have relatively short and thin bills. There is possibly some plumage variation within the island, birds on reddish-brown soils in the Cape Greco area appear browner and less grey on the upperparts than those around Limassol. Bergmann noticed that Cyprus birds commonly give a very conspicuous harsh call, in alarm or arousal situations, not heard by him in several years observations in Germany, France and Spain.

Only one record of passage: at Cape Andreas, 5–14 Apr 1973, small numbers, maximum 6, flying in off the sea from ESE, mostly early mornings (F. J. Walker); those seen closely were very pale compared with residents, and were possibly *G.c. subtaurica,* which breeds in Turkey (Anatolia and Taurus) (Vaurie). Neither Vaurie nor Hüe & Etchécopar mention migration for any races in the Near East, though flocks of possible migrants occur in Lebanon (Benson), and apparently there is some movement towards southern areas of Turkey in mid-winter (Vittery & Squire).

209. LULLULA ARBOREA   RB WV PM?

Woodlark

Common resident (*L.a. pallida*).

Breeding distribution. Lightly wooded open ground of the higher Troodos range, down to *c.* 1000 m on the southern side and to *c.* 650 m on the northern side. Common from Stavros towards Kykko at *c.* 1000 m on ridge tops with good Rockrose *Cistus villosus* cover and scattered Aleppo Pine *Pinus halepensis,* birds singing in all suitable habitat (Flint 1980).

Breeding data. Song late Feb to Jun, possibly later. Few breeding records: C/4 near Platania Forest Station, 14 May 1954 (McNeile); fledged young Troodos, early Jun 1957 (B2); 2 unfledged young near Tripylos, 3 Jun 1979 (R26). Present Platres all year, higher altitude birds usually moving below *c.* 1200 m or the snowline in winter, though once "fairly common" Troodos, Jan.

Common winter visitor to open low ground and lower hills, mid-late Oct to early-mid Mar, mainly Nov–Feb, occasional mid Aug to Sep and Apr, once early May. Usually 10 or less together, sometimes flocks of up to 50. Some winter in Egypt (Goodman & Meininger), and one flying south over the sea 10 miles north of Port Said, 21 Nov 1906 (Lynes & Witherby), suggests passage over Cyprus. 2 skins in BMNH collected Famagusta, 20 Sep 1917, were identified as *L.a. arborea* by R. Meinertzhagen (*per* I. C. J. Galbraith). *L.a. pallida* may also occur as a winter visitor or passage migrant.

One recovery of a bird ringed in Hungary, presumably *L.a. arborea* (Appendix 2).

210. ALAUDA ARVENSIS   WV PM

Skylark

A.a. cantarella. Very common winter visitor to open low ground, some up to *c.* 800 m. Occasional Sep to early Oct, increasing mid-late Oct, common Nov–Feb, in flocks of 10s and 100s, especially on the Mesaoria; some depart mid Feb, most late Feb, 10s remain Mar and occasional singles Apr. Song heard mid Feb and late Mar; also mid Apr at Cape Kiti, Pissouri and near Paphos (J. D. Summers-Smith, P. Tate), but no evidence of breeding.

Passage migrant in variable numbers in autumn: "large numbers" out to sea Cape Gata, 12 Oct to 21 Nov 1962 (R9), some passage southeast there the following autumn, and constant passage south at Akrotiri, Oct 1981, but apparently overlooked in other years. Small numbers, maximum 39, flying northeast and east from Cape Andreas on 4 dates, late Oct to Nov 1971 (Flint 1972e). No observed spring passage.

[One collected spring 1938 and attributed to nominate *arvensis* (Payn) is referable to *A.a. cantarella* (skin in BMNH).]

HIRUNDINIDAE

211. RIPARIA RIPARIA   PM
Sand Martin

R.r. riparia. Very common passage migrant in spring, abundant in autumn. Occasional Feb to mid Mar, 100s from late Mar or Apr to mid-late May, once "many 100s" northwest Larnaca early May, 1000 Akrotiri late May, and once 200 there early Jun. Occasional Jun to early Jul. A juvenile was trapped at a roost at Akrotiri reed beds, 29 Jun 1982. Autumn passage sometimes from mid Jul, and "huge flocks" Akrotiri, 22 Jul 1967; otherwise passage usually mid Aug to Oct, peak numbers (1000s daily) mid or late Sep, sometimes to early Oct. The most numerous hirundine on passage at Akrotiri in autumn. At Cape Gata, *c.* 2000 moved east of south in 30 minutes, 16 Sep 1971, *c.* 5000 south in 40 minutes 20 Sep, only 10s, 21 Sep and very few later (NR2). Occasional singles Nov and twice Jan. One overwintered Bishops Pool, late Dec 1972 to early Mar 1973.

One recovery of a bird ringed in Nigeria; 2 ringed in Cyprus recovered in the U.S.S.R. (Appendix 2).

212. PTYONOPROGNE (=HIRUNDO) RUPESTRIS   RB PM
Crag Martin

Locally fairly common resident.

Breeding distribution. Isolated pairs and small colonies in both mountain ranges, mainly above *c.* 400 m, a few down to *c.* 100 m. Within the Kyrenia range present in the breeding season at Buffavento, Pentadaktylos, Kantara, St. Hilarion, Halevga, Kyrenia Pass and Bellapais; nest sites not described. Within the Troodos range has bred at Troodos village, Mt. Olympus (Mason), Amiandos, Platres, Prodhromos, Macheras, Platania, Stavros and within the Paphos Forest. Has also bred Episkopi.

Breeding data. In the Troodos range nests mainly under eaves of huts and houses; some also nest under bridges in valleys of the Paphos Forest; possibly also breeds in a cave near Ayia and on cliffs at Troodhitissa. Few detailed breeding records: eggs, C/4, found mid-late May (Ashton-Johnson); young late May to early Aug, last fledged Troodos, mid Aug.

Some remain in the Kyrenia range in winter, descending to lower northern slopes on "cool cloudy days" (R18). A few occur occasionally in the higher Troodos range and on Mt. Olympus in winter, but (mainly from Nov to Feb) most descend to sheltered cliffs and valleys in the lower hills or on the south, west and northwest coasts, as at Episkopi, Yermasoyia, Lara, Lachi, the Akamas, Skouriotissa, Stavros and Vroisha, areas which probably provide the favourable micro-climates which they seek in winter (Voous 1960). Winter flocks usually 10–50, once 100. No evidence that any breeders migrate, and "considerable numbers" were on the south coast even in the bitter winter of 1911 (Bucknill 1911).

Scarce to fairly common passage migrant Feb–Apr, mainly Apr; maximum, 8 flocks of 6–12 departed from Kormakiti, 12 Apr 1959 (R3). 250 west at St Hilarion, 27 Oct 1957, possibly autumn migrants.

213. HIRUNDO RUSTICA   MB PM

Swallow

H.r. rustica. Common migrant breeder.

Breeding distribution. At all altitudes, mainly around towns, villages and isolated buildings.

Breeding data. A few arrive early-mid Feb, main arrival on low ground late Feb to Mar, 4 weeks later on Troodos. In Mar 1987, 100s of swallows died in Limassol during 3 weeks of exceptionally heavy rainfall (NL87/3). Nest building late Feb onwards. Nests in buildings. Eggs, C/4 to C/6, found once early Mar (Nicosia) to mid May, once a brood of 7 young (R26). First broods fly mid Apr to May, and second broods until early-mid Jul, occasionally late Jul, no records of third broods. Breeding sites on low ground usually deserted by mid or late Jul. Post-breeding roosts form in reed beds May–Oct, notably at Morphou, Akrotiri and Larnaca, maximum *c*. 20,000 Akrotiri, Jul to early Aug 1972, (these roosts probably contain an increasing proportion of passage birds as autumn progresses). 5 ringed, at Morphou Bay (2), Pendalia, Akrotiri and Nicosia, were recovered near where ringed in subsequent years, one after 5 years; a pullus ringed Lakatamia, 29 Apr 1972, was retrapped at the Akrotiri roost, 8 Aug 1972.

Very common passage migrant in spring, abundant in autumn. Spring passage mid Feb to May, mainly Apr, when a heavy passage leaves from northern capes. Autumn passage Aug–Oct, mainly mid Sep to early Oct, maximum *c*. 2000 moving south in 30 minutes Cape Gata, 20 Sep 1971. Occasionally seen Nov, and less frequently Dec and Jan; no evidence of overwintering.

Birds with reddish underparts occur from time to time, notably one at Bishops Pool for 2 weeks from 27 Aug 1968 (R15), but occurrence of races *transitiva* and *savignii* not proven.

2 ringed in Cyprus, recovered in the U.S.S.R. and Saudi Arabia (Appendix 2).

214. HIRUNDO DAURICA   MB PM

Red-rumped Swallow

H.d. rufula. Very common migrant breeder.

Breeding distribution. In both mountain ranges, on adjacent coastal lowlands, and on the Karpas – within the Troodos range the commonest breeding hirundine, with a nest under almost every culvert and bridge. Relatively few breed on the Mesaoria, though some breed Nicosia.

Breeding data. Occasional arrival from mid Feb, pairs return to old nests late Mar to early Apr, but many others are still nest building Jun. Nests mainly under culverts and bridges, also in buildings (mainly under eaves and roof overhangs, and in porches, verandahs, carports and garages), caves, cliff overhangs and old tombs, usually singly, sometimes 2 or 3 nests together. Old nests are regularly used in later years; one nest at Limni was used for 5 successive years (R22). The nest lining feathers are usually from Woodpigeons *Columba palumbus* (Ashton-Johnson). Eggs, C/4 to C/5, found mid Apr (Jourdain 1929a) to May; young mid May to mid Aug. Third brood in nest Skouriotissa, 10 Aug 1975 (R22). Post-breeding flocks mid Jun on, and roosts of *c*. 500 noted in reed beds at Margi (Myrtou) and Akrotiri, Jul– Aug. Most depart early-mid Sep, occasionally a few Oct and once early Nov.

Fairly common passage migrant. Spring passage Mar–May, mainly late Mar to Apr when 10s daily at northern capes. Autumn passage Aug–Sep, mainly late Aug to mid Sep, maxima, 250 Cape Gata, 6 Sep 1963, and 100s daily Khrysokhou Bay, 25 Aug to 4 Sep 1984, but usually little obvious passage at southern capes.

215. DELICHON URBICA   MB PM

House Martin

D.u. urbica. Locally common migrant breeder.

Breeding distribution. Breeds colonially on town and village buildings and other structures, mainly in the Troodos range and adjacent coastal lowlands, and now increasingly elsewhere on low ground. Some colonies also on rock faces in the Kyrenia range at Buffavento, Kantara, Halevga and Pentadaktylos, and on south coast cliffs from Curium to Paramali. In the past, a cliff colony at Amargeti, Paphos district (Bucknill 1910) and other colonies on cliffs near the Paphos–Polis road (the Bannermans 1958). There are probably many other unrecorded cliff colonies. Town and village colonies usually 10–100 pairs, though some cliff colonies are up to 300 pairs, and 864 occupied nests on radar domes Mt. Olympus, 7 Jun 1973. Large colonies also on television mast at Mt. Olympus and on framework of mine conveyor belt at Xeros. Numbers and distribution are increasing. Increases noted at several colonies in the 1970s and has bred Nicosia since 1977 and Limassol since at least 1979. Also bred Akrotiri 1975, Moni 1981, Dhekelia 1987–88, and probably also now breeds Paphos, Kormakiti and Orga. Now common and still increasing at Nicosia and its suburbs – Eylenja, Engomi, Strovolos, Athalassa, Laxia and Nicosia Airport.

Breeding data. 10s return to the Episkopi colony early–mid Feb, some nest rebuilding there late Feb, but main arrival generally late Feb to Mar. Eggs, C/5, found mid May (Ashton–Johnson); young Apr to early Aug. Post-breeding flocks form Jun onwards. Departure from Nicosia area late Jun onwards, elsewhere most birds depart mid Jul to Aug, though sometimes 100s remain Mt. Olympus into Sep. Occasional Oct–Nov, 4 records Dec and once early Jan. One ringed Pano Platres, 1 May 1957, recovered there 4 May 1960; one ringed Episkopi, 8 May 1969, shot Akrotiri area, 6 May 1972.

Common passage migrant in spring, mainly Apr to mid May, though some passage from mid Feb and to late May. Usually few among the main hirundine and swift passage, but, unless forced lower by bad weather, flies higher and in large flocks – maxima *c*. 500 north at St. Hilarion, 14 Apr 1959, and *c*. 900 north at Cape Kormakiti, 16 May 1971, and 100s more inland. Usually not very obvious on autumn passage, late Jul to mid Oct, though 3 records of flocks of 100s south Akrotiri, mid Aug, late Sep and early Oct.

MOTACILLIDAE

216. ANTHUS NOVAESEELANDIAE   PM
Richard's Pipit

Scarce passage migrant (*A.n. richardi*). Once late Mar, most frequent Apr and mid Oct to early Nov, occasional to early Dec, once mid Dec. Usually 1–4 and mainly on the south coast, though 13 on ploughed land at St. Hilarion, 14 Dec 1957 (the Bannermans 1958). Probably regular at Phasouri reed beds in autumn.

217. ANTHUS CAMPESTRIS   PM
Tawny Pipit

Fairly common passage migrant (*A.c. campestris*) in spring: occasional Feb to mid Mar, main passage late Mar to Apr, usually singly or less than 10 together, though 80 Cape Andreas, 18 Apr 1973; last seen mid–late May, once mid Jun. In autumn occasional Aug to early Sep, scarce on passage mid Sep to Oct, occasionally to Nov, usually in ones and twos. Occasional Dec and twice Jan, not overwintering.

218. ANTHUS SIMILIS   AV
Long-billed Pipit

Accidental visitor, one record: one Cape Andreas, 27 Apr 1972, showing characters of *A.s. captus* (NR3).

219. ANTHUS HODGSONI   AV
Olive-backed Pipit

Accidental visitor, one record: one in a pine wooded garden at Episkopi, 10 Feb 1989 (R. Murray *per* C. J. L. Bennett). The bird showed characters of the race *A.h. yunnanensis*, which breeds from northeastern Russia east to Kamchatka, Mongolia, Manchuria and northern Japan (Vaurie).

220. ANTHUS TRIVIALIS   PM
Tree Pipit

Common passage migrant (*A.t. trivialis*) in spring: once late Feb, occasional early-mid Mar, main passage late Mar to Apr, usually singly or less than 10 together, occasionally in 100s mainly at northern capes; last seen early-mid May. Usually scarce or almost unrecorded on return passage: occasional late Aug to early Sep, most frequent mid Sep to mid Oct, occasional late Oct to Nov. Found to be "common" at Akrotiri, early Oct 1957, many passing high over Akrotiri, 21 Sep 1978, and 100 Xeros Potamos, 20 Sep 1981. [No acceptable records Dec to mid Feb.]

221. ANTHUS PRATENSIS   WV PM
Meadow Pipit

A.p. pratensis. Very common and widespread winter visitor to open low ground, usually scarce above *c*. 500 m. Occasional late Aug to mid Oct, increasing late Oct to early Nov, peak numbers mid Nov to Feb, usually in 10s, though 100s at town rubbish tips and sewage farms; fewer Mar, last seen Apr to mid May. 2 ringed Nicosia and Akrotiri retrapped where ringed in subsequent winters.

Passage or departure at Cape Andreas once mid Feb, and presumed passage flocks of 50–100 at Akrotiri twice Mar. Passage out to sea Akrotiri twice late Oct to Nov.

222. ANTHUS CERVINUS   PM WV

Red-throated Pipit

Common passage migrant: spring passage Mar–May, mainly Apr when 100s around wetlands; once mid Aug, occasional mid–late Sep, autumn passage Oct to mid–late Nov, peak numbers late Oct when up to 400 at Akrotiri sports fields. Winter visitor in variable numbers to low ground, mainly near water, occasionally scarce, but in most winters fairly common and widespread in 10s or less, with exceptionally 100s around town rubbish tips Dec–Jan. Numbers may increase or decrease in mid-winter, suggesting that some movement takes place (Stewart & Christensen).

223. ANTHUS SPINOLETTA   PM WV

Water Pipit

Fairly common passage migrant late Mar to Apr, usually in small flocks of up to 20, maximum 100 Salamis, 7 Apr 1957 (Thomas); occasional early May. Less common on autumn passage mid Oct to Nov, mainly early Nov, usually in ones and twos, sometimes 10–20 together, notably on Mt. Olympus or at Akrotiri sports fields. Once early Oct. Winter visitor in variable numbers around wetlands mainly Nov–Feb, usually rather scarce, in some winters only 1–2 singles, in other years singles or up to 6 together, more widespread, exceptionally 30 Bishops Pool, 2 Jan 1973. Often fewer after mid-winter. One ringed Akrotiri, 17 Dec 1972, retrapped there 7 Feb 1973.

8 skins in BMNH collected spring 1938 and attributed to *A.s. spinoletta* (Payn) are all *A.s. coutellii*, as also is one in BMNH collected spring 1909 (P. F. Stewart). [*A.s. petrosus/littoralis* (Rock Pipit): 5 doubtful records with little or no detail.]

224. MOTACILLA FLAVA   PM MB

Yellow Wagtail

Common passage migrant. First arrival early–mid Mar, once 300 mid Mar, main passage usually from late Mar or early Apr to early May, once 100s mid May; occurs in flocks of 10s or 100s, up to 10,000 Akrotiri/Phasouri, 5 and 7 Apr 1981 were quite exceptional; occasional late May and early Jun, twice late Jun. In autumn occasional from early Aug, main passage mid Aug to mid Oct, in flocks of up to 1000, peak numbers mid Sep to early Oct; last seen early–mid Nov, occasionally late Nov. Occasional singles around wetlands or on low ground in winter, but not shown to overwinter.

At least 3 races occur regularly on passage: *M.f. flava*, common on both passages; *M.f. feldegg*, occasionally more common than *M.f. flava* in spring, but scarcer in autumn; *M.f. thunbergi*, least common, usually only a few on both passages. Usual arrival dates: *feldegg* mid Mar, *flava* late Mar or early Apr and *thunbergi* Apr, corresponding with departure times from wintering grounds in Africa, those races breeding furthest south departing first, the northernmost breeders last (Moreau 1972). *M.f. beema* is possibly a scarce regular migrant, a total of at least 9 records in Apr in 6 recent years (1957, 1977, 1979, 1980(2), 1981(3) and 1987), mainly in the Akrotiri area, usually singly, exceptionally 20♂♂, 2 Apr 1980, though some of these records are perhaps due to variation in *M.f. flava* (Dement'ev & Gladkov). Also 5 records of *M.f. lutea*: 11 May 1957, 15 Sep 1969, 12 May 1970, 2 Apr 1980 and 9 Apr 1987. Birds resembling *M.f. cinereocapilla* reported once mid Mar and occasionally Apr and mid Aug to Sep, perhaps due to confusion with young ♂ *M.f. feldegg*, with *M.f. flava/thunbergi* hybrids, or with *M.f. 'dombrowskii'*, (of which many reported spring 1957) (Williamson 1955). One or 2 birds approaching *M.f. leucocephala*, spring 1957, probably pale variants of *M.f. beema* (Cramp 1988). A record of *M.f. flavissima*, 25 Apr 1980, should perhaps refer to *M.f. lutea*.

Breeding distribution. Scarce migrant breeder (*M.f. feldegg*): *c.* 10 pairs Akrotiri/Phasouri, mainly in or near reed beds; has also bred on the Karpas (Stewart & Christensen), and seen in the breeding season at Zakaki, Syrianokhori, Kermia, Akhna Dam and near Cape Drepanum.

Breeding data. Present Akrotiri late Mar to mid Aug. At Akrotiri, a nest of 6 young fledged 3 Jun 1957; a nest with 5 half fledged young in tuft of grass on dried mud flats, 20 May 1970 (P. R. Flint); C/4 there, 15 May 1976, and another nest with 4 young, 16 Jun 1976; fledged young Akrotiri late May onwards, conspicuous there by early Jul.

One bird ringed in Cyprus recovered in Turkey (Appendix 2).

225. MOTACILLA CITREOLA   PM

Citrine Wagtail

Scarce passage migrant in spring, 16 records of ones and twos: late Mar (2), Apr (11), early, mid and late May. Most records are of ♂♂. All records are from the Zakaki/Akrotiri/Phasouri area, the coastal southwest, or Akhna, and usually from or near wetlands, either marshes, river valleys or reservoirs. First recorded in 1971 (NR2), subsequent records were in 1980 (R27), 1985 (R32), 1986 (2-W.E. Oddie), 1987 (R34), 1988 (2-NL88/4), 1989 (2-NL89/3&4) and 1990 (6 records involving 7 or 8 birds – J. Diley, R. & D. Frost, NL90/3,4&5), and it is now apparently a regular migrant. P. R. Colston compared a colour photograph of the 1980 bird with the long series of 3 races in BMNH and considered it most closely resembled *M.c. werae*. These records conform with the pattern of other recent records from Greece, Israel and Turkey, which suggest a small, regular passage through the Middle East (Inskipp). The breeding range of *werae* is expanding southwest within the U.S.S.R. (Wilson, Dement'ev & Gladkov), and recent records in the Near and Middle East perhaps result from this expansion.

226. MOTACILLA CINEREA   WV PM OB?

Grey Wagtail

M.c. cinerea. Fairly common winter visitor around wetlands and along streams, mainly on low ground, usually in ones and twos, maximum 30 Athalassa, 1 Jan 1977. Occasional Aug to mid Sep, records of flocks at this time perhaps due to confusion with Yellow Wagtail *M. flava*. First arrivals usually late Sep or early Oct, fairly common mid–late Oct to Feb, fewer Mar; last seen Apr, occasionally May. 2 ringed Akrotiri (one in early Oct) retrapped there in subsequent winters.

Passage migrant in variable numbers Oct–Nov, sometimes to early Dec, mainly mid Oct to mid Nov, when sometimes fairly common on high and low ground in small flocks of up to 10–20, maximum 40 Akrotiri, 20 Nov 1960.

Possibly an occasional breeder on Troodos, though breeding not yet proven: in 1968, "Singles seen around Troodos area throughout year" (R15); in 1969 present there "throughout the breeding season", and juveniles seen early Jun and 12 Jul (R16); in 1987 a pair by a stream just below Troodos village, 17 Jun (J. E. Francis).

227. MOTACILLA ALBA   WV PM OB

White Wagtail

M.a. alba. Very common and widespread winter visitor on open low ground, few above *c.* 400 m. Particularly common along roadsides and on newly cultivated fields. Sometimes 100s at town rubbish tips, maximum 1000 Mia Milea tip, 30 Jan 1972. Roosts of 100s form in reed beds and citrus plantations, also a large roost in central Nicosia since at least 1980. Twice seen early Aug, first arrivals, possibly passage birds, usually late Aug to Sep, main arrival mid–late Oct, very common till early–mid Mar, few after late Mar.

Common passage migrant. Spring passage mid Mar to early May, mainly Apr, in 10s or 100s, maximum *c.* 350 Akrotiri, 3 Apr 1981. Occasional mid–late May, late migrants or breeding birds (see below). More numerous an autumn passage late Sep to mid Nov, mainly mid–late Oct, when marked passage out to sea Akrotiri, maximum *c.* 600 there, 12 Oct 1970. Also 150 out to sea, Timi beach, 21 Oct 1987. Migrants present Troodos and Mt. Olympus late Sep to early Nov 1975 (Mason).

Breeding. Occasional: a young bird fed by parents and only just able to fly, west of Kyrenia, 15 Jul 1962, and on 22 Jul an adult carrying food at another location west of Kyrenia (R9); a fledged juvenile Liveras, 15 Jul 1973 (NR4); a pair nested in a building at Tunnel Beach, Episkopi, May 1988, one young fledging 30 May (NL88/5). Also 2 adults at Episkopi early Jun 1978, and one there mid Jun 1979. In the past, 3 wagtails seen "at the end of May 1909 . . . perhaps young of this species" (Bucknill 1909).

One showing well marked characters of *M.a. personata* Akrotiri, 22 Sep 1966 (R13). [Another, less well marked, 13 Apr 1973. Bucknill (1909–10) supposed Sibthorp's *Motacilla ficedula* to be the Pied Wagtail *M.a. yarrellii*, but this was disputed by Jourdain (1910a). The Greek-Cypriot name given by Sibthorp (literally 'fig-eater') is now applied to the Golden Oriole.]

7 recoveries of birds ringed in Sweden (5) and Finland (2); one ringed in Cyprus recovered in Czechoslovakia (Appendix 2).

BOMBYCILLIDAE

228. BOMBYCILLA GARRULUS   AV

Waxwing

Accidental visitor, one record: 5 caught Karpasha, near Myrtou, 2 Jan 1966, coinciding with a large invasion into Western Europe, winter 1965–66 (R13).

CINCLIDAE

229. CINCLUS CINCLUS   FB
Dipper

Former resident along the few perennial streams of the higher Troodos range; last recorded 1945. First mentioned by Guillemard (1888), one at *c.* 700 m on the stream below Kalopanayiotis, 24 May 1887, and one or more Mt. Olympus, mid Jun. Bucknill (1909–10) described it as a "far from abundant" resident, being "more common than elsewhere on the very highest slopes of the range", and in May–Jun 1909 "tolerably common in suitable localities". Bucknill also mentions young in full plumage late May, and a nest with young near Kykko Monastery, the nest "of similar character to that of the British *Cinclus*". Often seen Caledonian Falls, summer 1910, and 3 young there, unable to fly, early Jul (Bucknill 1911). 8 collected Troodos, 1901 and 1909 (skins in BMNH), include 3 juveniles obtained May (P. R. Colston). Bourne *et al.* mention a 1939 record, and Davidson (1954) records that in 1945 "a few still resident in the river Kryos Potamos (near Troodos) at 4000 feet". Also seen 1945 by an unknown visitor to Troodos, sometime between 26 Jul and 5 Aug (Haifa Nat. Club Bull.). No later records. Wilson (1946b) mentions a nest at Caledonian Falls, but is probably referring to that of 1910. In 1957–58 COS members failed to locate it, despite an extensive search. The Bannermans (1958) also failed and were informed it had disappeared and had not been found for many years. Regular observations since 1957 have produced no records.

The reasons for the Dipper's extinction are not known, though shooting seems most probable. Despite protection birds continued to be shot for food (Bucknill 1909–10), and the small population in its limited habitat must have been particularly vulnerable. In Turkey it is a fairly widespread and not uncommon resident, somewhat more widespread in winter when some dispersal occurs (Beaman), and occasional immigration into Cyprus is a possibility. Its re-establishment, either by immigration or re-introduction, seems unlikely unless shooting can be effectively controlled.

Although Madarász (1903), from a skin sent by Glaszner, considered it an endemic race, the Cyprus population had not evolved very distinct racial characters, Hartert (1903–23) including it with *C.c. caucasicus*, and Vaurie with *C.c. aquaticus*, Vaurie stating, however, that "The population of Cyprus ('*olympicus*') requires further study. Its bill is similar to that of *aquaticus*, not so slender as in *caucasicus*, but the colouration of old specimens from Cyprus resembles that of old specimens from the Caucasus".

TROGLODYTIDAE

230. TROGLODYTES TROGLODYTES   RB WV?
Wren

Common resident (*T.t. cypriotes*).

Breeding distribution. Restricted to the higher and middle slopes of the Troodos range, mainly in thick cover along streams in valley bottoms in pine forest; many also sing (though not yet proved to breed) in very steep shallow dry valleys with dense Golden Oak *Quercus alnifolia*. Particularly common within the Paphos Forest, where many breed to below 600 m, and song heard down to *c.* 400 m (Flint 1980). Also occurs in irrigated orchards (Ashton-Johnson).

Breeding data. Song at least mid Jan to Aug. Nests usually in the side of a running or dry stream bank, in the side of a road cutting, twice on or under a verandah, and once 16 feet up in the fork of a pine tree (Ashton-Johnson, Bucknill 1909–10). Eggs, mainly C/5 and C/6, once C/4 (Ashton-Johnson) and C/7 (Bucknill 1909–10), found early Apr (C. F. Belcher *in* the Bannermans 1958) to early Jul, and many broods fly late May to early Jun. Only 2 summer records from the Kyrenia range: one in song on the northern slopes of Buffavento, 26 Jun 1969, and 2 in song Kantara, 25 May 1987 (NL87/5).

A scarce winter visitor to low ground mainly Nov–Feb. One Zakaki, 2 Aug 1989 (D. J. Odell) and one Pomos, 28 Aug 1978 were unusually early, also occasionally reported mid Sep to Oct and Mar. Most frequently recorded from woodland near water in the well-watched Akrotiri/Phasouri area, where "plentiful" early 1960, and 4 there Dec 1982. In Nicosia song heard Dec to early Feb in acacia thicket near the river. Winter records on low ground may be result of immigration or local altitudinal movement or both. In the U.S.S.R. many move south in winter (Dement'ev & Gladkov), and it is more widespread in winter in Turkey, probably partly as a result of immigration (Beaman). One on board ship entering Cyprus waters, 22 Aug 1956 (Thomas), also suggests immigration.

Formerly considered an endemic race (Bate 1903b, the Bannermans 1958), *T.t. cypriotes* was united by Vaurie with birds from Crete, Rhodes and the near East. Compared with nominate *troglodytes, cypriotes* has a longer bill and is more extensively barred below, the barring reaching to the upper breast in some specimens (Vaurie).

PRUNELLIDAE

231. PRUNELLA MODULARIS   WV PM?
Dunnock

Winter visitor in variable numbers, probably often overlooked in the hills. Occasionally scarce, but more usually fairly common and widespread in scrub and wooded areas, most numerous in the hills and mountains, where sometimes up to 10 at some locations, for example Ligi (Kapoura), Troodos, Kalavasos and Lythrodhonda. Occasional Oct, most records Nov–Feb, fewer Mar, occasional early Apr, once mid Apr. Song heard Platres and Dhiarizos river, early Apr 1988 (D. & M. Hawkins). 3 limed Paralimni, 11 Nov 1967, and 6 moving WSW Akrotiri, 6 Nov 1975 (M. Komulainen) suggests passage.

One trapped Akrotiri, 21 Nov 1970, showed characters of *P.m. obscura* (R17) and judging from sight records, all birds probably belong to this race (Stewart & Christensen). We know of no records of nominate *modularis*, though on distribution it could occur. Compared with *modularis, obscura* is more brownish and less grey on the sides of the face and neck, and is mottled to a varying degree with off-white on the chin, throat and breast; the noticeably paler and duller brown ground colour of the upperparts is probably the best field character (Vaurie, Cramp 1988).

TURDIDAE

232. CERCOTRICHAS GALACTOTES   PM
Rufous Bush Chat

Scarce passage migrant (*C.g. syriacus*), only 1–3 records a year and most frequent in the east of the island. Has occurred mid Mar to early May (mainly mid-late Apr) and

Aug to early Oct (mainly mid Aug to mid Sep), usually singly, occasionally 2 together; maximum 5 limed Paralimni, 18 Apr to 8 May 1968 (Horner & Hubbard). 3 alighted on ship about midway between Cyprus and Latakia (Syria), 28 Aug 1957 (Horváth).

One winter record: 2 Evretou Dam, 20 Jan 1990 (C. J. L. Bennett).

233. ERITHACUS RUBECULA   WV PM
   Robin

E.r. rubecula. Very common and widespread winter visitor to scrub, wooded areas and gardens on low ground, and on high ground below the snowline. On Mt. Troodos winters usually very near to water (Mason). Occasional early–mid Oct, very common from late Oct or early Nov to Feb. Departure from late Feb, last seen early–mid Apr, once early May. Also seen once early Aug and once mid Aug (skin in the Department of Agriculture, Nicosia). Song mainly after arrival and after mid-winter. 19 ringed, Akrotiri (10), Episkopi (8) and Nicosia, retrapped where ringed in subsequent winters; 2 others ringed Akrotiri were recovered 48 km and 158 km northeast early in subsequent winters, presumably while returning to Akrotiri. Up to 500 a day limed Paralimni, early Nov 1967 (R14), must have been mainly passage migrants. Occasional increases Mar and once early Apr (Horner & Hubbard) on the south coast are probably passage migrants from the south.

E.r. caucasicus. Probably a regular winter visitor in small numbers, *c.* 5–6% of wintering birds showing well marked characters of this race, i.e. 4 (5·7%) of 70 trapped birds examined 1970–71 (NR1&2), and *c.* 5% of 111 examined Feb 1985 (Hjort *et al.*). Of the 70 examined 1970–71, 9 also showed characters intermediate between *caucasicus* and nominate *rubecula. E.r. caucasicus* has been recorded 'spring' 1938 (Payn), Feb 1970, mid Nov 1971 and Feb 1985. Also found in winter 1971–72 amongst limers' catches (P. R. Flint). It may be separated from nominate *rubecula* in the hand by its rufous upper tail coverts and tail base (Cramp 1988).

5 recoveries of birds ringed in Finland (3), Sweden and the U.S.S.R.; one ringed in Cyprus recovered in Lebanon (Appendix 2).

234. LUSCINIA LUSCINIA   PM
   Thrush Nightingale

Fairly common passage migrant. In spring perhaps most numerous in the east of the island. Occurs in spring late Mar to early May, mainly Apr with peak numbers probably mid Apr; once seen mid May. In autumn once mid Aug, main passage late Aug to Sep; occasional early–mid Oct, once late Oct. Mostly trapped birds, very few sight records. 113 were limed Paralimni, 7 Apr to 9 May 1968, ♂♂ arriving before ♀♀ and being more numerous, and most birds occurring 12–18 Apr (Horner & Hubbard). The correct totals, for this species and Nightingale *L. megarhynchos*, of birds limed at Paralimni in spring 1968 (Horner & Hubbard) are the reverse of those given by Hubbard (1968), and support the implication by Bourne *et al.* that this species is in fact the less numerous in spring.

235. LUSCINIA MEGARHYNCHOS   MB PM
   Nightingale

L.m. megarhynchos. Common migrant breeder.
   Breeding distribution. Valleys of the Troodos range near running streams with good cover of brambles, shrubs and trees, both within pine forest and in cultivated

Plate 25. Greater Flamingos at Akrotiri Salt Lake, with the reed beds beyond. (P. R. Flint)

Plate 26. Griffon Vulture at Quarry beach, Episkopi. (T. A. Box)

Plate 27. Baillon's Crake at Phasouri reed beds. (T. A. Box)

Plate 28. Black-winged Stilt, a common spring migrant and a regular breeder when water levels are suitable. (T. A. Box)

Plate 29. Spur-winged Plover, a fairly common migrant in spring. A pair bred at Phasouri reed beds in 1988. (T. A. Box)

Plate 30. The first White-tailed Plover recorded from Cyprus, Akrotiri Salt Lake, March 1970. A hunter later shot this beautiful bird. (P. R. Flint)

Plate 31. Audouin's Gulls at evening roost at Peristeria on the north coast, *c*. 48 km east of Kyrenia. (P. R. Flint)

Plate 32. Wryneck at a garden pond during the spring migration. (D. Frost)

Plate 33. Cyprus Pied Wheatear ♂, April. The most distinctive and interesting species of all the endemic birds. (D. Frost)

Plate 34. Cyprus Pied Wheatear ♀, April. (D. Frost)

Plate 35. Blue Rock Thrush, a breeding species along the upper ridge of the Kyrenia range. (M. E. J. Gore)

Plate 36. Great Reed Warbler at Phasouri reed beds, July 1982. (T. A. Box)

Plate 37. Cyprus Warbler ♂, a common and widespread endemic species. (M. E. J. Gore)

Plate 38. Cyprus Warbler breeding pair, ♂ left and ♀ right. (D. Frost)

Plate 39. Coal Tit of the distinctive endemic race. (G. van Duin)

Plate 40. Cretzschmar's Bunting bathing in a garden pond during the spring migration. (D. Frost)

areas, especially orchards. Most common 800–1200 m, though eggs taken at
c. 700 m in hills near Ora (Bucknill 1913a) and many sing down to 600 m in valley
bottoms of the Paphos Forest (Flint 1980).

Breeding data. Sings regularly Apr till at least early–mid Jul, last heard mid
Aug. Eggs, C/5, found mid May to mid Jun (Bucknill 1913a); fledged young Jun–Jul.
Song heard Jun at Skouriotissa and near Karavas (Wilson 1954) and Kazaphani on
the north coast, but breeding not proved.

Common passage migrant in spring: once early Mar, occasional mid Mar, main
passage late Mar to Apr; last seen late May. 249 were limed Paralimni, 15 Mar to 10
May 1968, ♂♂ arriving before ♀♀ and being more numerous (Horner & Hubbard).
Some birds, presumably migrants, remain and sing on low ground and in the lower
hills, sometimes into mid May. Scarce on autumn passage late Aug to early–mid Oct;
mainly trapped birds, very few sight records. In some autumns unrecorded.

One ringed in Cyprus controlled in Israel (Appendix 2).

236. LUSCINIA SVECICA   PM WV

Bluethroat

Fairly common passage migrant in autumn, usually occurring in reed beds. Twice
late Aug, occasional Sep, main passage mid-late Oct to early Nov, sometimes to
early Dec; often 2–6 at the same location, maximum 8 Phasouri, 7 Dec 1969. Scarce
winter visitor to reed beds till Mar or early Apr, usually singly, occasionally up to 4
at the same location. Singles at Cape Greco, once mid Apr (I. Beames), and at
Paralimni, once late Apr, are the only evidence of spring passage.

L.s. svecica is the most frequently reported race, occurring Oct–Mar; *L.s.
cyanecula* is much scarcer, with only 11 records: Oct (7), Feb (3) and late Mar
(C.N.H.S.Ann.IV). Geographically *L.s. volgae* is more likely to occur than
cyanecula (the Bannermans 1971), and perhaps the 2 races have been confused in
Cyprus. A bird with an entirely blue throat at Akrotiri reed beds, 16 Mar 1971, was
possibly *L.s. magna* (Cole 1972c).

237. TARSIGER CYANURUS   AV

Red-flanked Bluetail

Accidental visitor (*T.c. cyanurus*), 2 records: one Mt. Olympus, 8 Nov 1957 (R. S.
Dove *in* the Bannermans 1958), and one caught near Phrenaros, 18 Oct 1987
(Kephalas 1989).

238. IRANIA GUTTURALIS   AV

White-throated Robin

Accidental visitor, 2 records: one Dhekelia, 1 Apr 1962 (R9); one near Maroni, 16
Mar 1981 (R28).

239. PHOENICURUS OCHRUROS   WV PM

Black Redstart

P.o. gibraltariensis. Common and widespread winter visitor to open, often rocky,
ground, and to cliffs, scree slopes, dam faces and built up areas, usually below
c. 1200 m; also "often in olive trees" (Hjort *et al*.). Once early Sep (skin in NRS),

occasional from mid Sep, common from late Oct or early Nov to Feb, departure from mid–late Feb, fewer Mar; usually last seen late Mar to mid Apr, exceptionally to late May. Wintering birds usually in ones and twos, sometimes 10 or more at the same location, maximum 18 Peyia, 6 Feb 1983. Newly arrived birds in late Oct to Nov often briefly in larger concentrations, notably at the Akamas, where *c.* 40, 15 Nov 1986; also 40 Cape Andreas, 27 Oct 1987. 2 ringed Episkopi retrapped there in subsequent winters; one ringed Akrotiri, 15 Jan 1974, still there 16 Mar.

Occasional influxes of passage migrants Mar and mid Oct to early Nov. Song heard from migrants, Maroni, 4 Nov 1986. Perhaps more common on spring passage in the east, 71 limed Paralimni, 9 Mar to 5 Apr 1968, the majority being ♀♀ (Horner & Hubbard). A few migrants occur on Troodos Nov, but no birds there in winter (Mason).

P.o. ochruros. One obtained spring 1938 (Payn). One with a red belly and probably of this race was seen Nov 1956 (C. J. Bridgman *in* the Bannermans 1958), and another attributed to this race trapped Akrotiri, Nov 1968. One at Tunnel Beach, Episkopi, 6 Jan 1985 was attributed to *P.o. semirufus*, another near the Tekke Mosque, 8 Sep 1986, had a red-brown breast and belly and was possibly also *semirufus*. Vaurie mentions *semirufus* from Cyprus in winter, but not *ochruros*, and there is possibly some confusion between the 2 races.

7 recoveries of birds ringed in Czechoslovakia (4), Poland (2) and the U.S.S.R. (Appendix 2).

240. PHOENICURUS PHOENICURUS   PM

Redstart

P.p. phoenicurus. Common passage migrant. Spring passage early–mid Mar to early–mid May, mainly Apr; twice seen Feb and occasionally late May. Singing ♂ in an almond grove, Paphos, 6 May 1987 (M. H. Thurston). 1134 limed Paralimni, 8 Mar to 12 May 1968, ♂♂ arriving significantly before ♀♀ (Horner & Hubbard). Autumn passage mid Aug–early Sep to Oct (occasional Nov), peak numbers usually Oct. Reported in winter with doubtful reliability, only one satisfactory record: one ringed in East Germany found injured Episkopi, early Jan 1965 (R12). Also one recovery of a bird ringed in Israel and one ringed in Cyprus recovered in the U.S.S.R. (Appendix 2).

P.p. samamisicus. Fairly common passage migrant in spring, scarce in autumn. Once mid Feb, occasional early Mar, a few mid Mar, main passage late Mar to early Apr, earlier than that of the nominate race; fewer mid Apr, occasional to early May, once late May (Bucknill 1909–10). 212 ♂♂ limed Paralimni, 11 Mar to 12 Apr 1968, with 61 on 2 Apr. Only 2 ♀♀ could be positively identified as this race (Horner & Hubbard). 7 autumn records, Aug to Oct.

[Several vague and unsubstantiated summer and/or breeding records: *P.p. phoenicurus* "certainly nesting" Troodos, "summer" 1908 (Bucknill 1909–10); *P.p. samamisicus* "breeding" on south side of Halevga (D. F. Davidson *in* the Bannermans 1958). Also "a few Redstarts" on Troodos, "summer" (Bate 1903a).] A ♀, Phasouri, 3 Jun 1984, was probably a late migrant.

241. SAXICOLA RUBETRA   PM

Whinchat

Common passage migrant in spring, occasional from early Mar, main passage Apr to early May, peak numbers usually mid–late Apr, though in 1985 and 1987 they

were in early Apr; maximum 70 on the Akamas, 28 and 29 Apr 1981; last seen mid–
late May. Although a common spring migrant, only 3 were limed Paralimni, spring
1968 (Horner & Hubbard). Less common on return passage mid Aug–early Sep to
late Oct–early Nov, mainly mid–late Sep; once early Aug, twice mid and once late
Nov. No satisfactory winter records.

242. SAXICOLA TORQUATA   WV PM?
   Stonechat

Very common and widespread winter visitor (*S.t. rubicola*) on open low ground, less
common in the hills, mainly below *c*. 700 m. Once mid Sep, occasional from late Sep,
main arrival late Oct to early Nov, when sometimes briefly in concentrations of 10s,
maximum 50 Cape Greco, 24 Oct 1986. Birds then disperse to take up winter
territories, usually in pairs. Some depart mid Feb, most late Feb to early Mar; last
seen late Mar or Apr. 4 ringed Nicosia, Akrotiri and Episkopi (2) retrapped/
recovered where ringed in subsequent winters. No proof of passage, though some of
76 limed at Paralimni, 6 Mar to 6 Apr 1968 (Horner & Hubbard) were probably
spring migrants. In that survey ♀♀ were significantly more numerous than ♂♂.
   S.t. maura. 2 records: one trapped Akrotiri, 4 Dec 1971 (NR2), and one found
dead in a mistnet at Cape Pyla, 1 Jan 1991 (J. Bullock *per* C. J. L. Bennett). Pale birds
with large white rumps, presumably *S.t. maura, armenica* or *variegata*, are often seen
in winter, especially in bleaker parts of the Mesaoria. [One collected spring 1938 was
identified as *maura* (Payn), but the skin (in BMNH) does not show characters of that
race (P. Colston).]

243. SAXICOLA CAPRATA   AV
   Pied Stonechat

Accidental visitor, one record: ♂ Larnaca, 3–11 Nov 1986 (D. & L. Hutton *per* C. J. L.
Bennett, R33). On 6 occasions the bird visited a 7th floor balcony where it fed on
insects among the pot plants and imitation turf. This behaviour may seem unusual,
but the species does occur around houses and gardens, and is indifferent to man
(Dement'ev & Gladkov, Flint *et al.*, Cramp (1988), S. C. Madge). The species breeds
from Transcaspia and eastern Iran through the Oriental region to the Far East
(Vaurie). The western populations are migratory, generally moving south in winter;
however a few move west into western Iran and Iraq (Hüe & Etchécopar, Cramp
1988), and an extension of this movement was probably responsible for the above
record.

244. OENANTHE ISABELLINA   PM
   Isabelline Wheatear

Common passage migrant. Once mid Feb, spring passage usually late Feb to mid–
late Apr, with peak numbers mid Mar to early Apr; occasional early May, twice mid
May. 181 limed Paralimni, spring 1968, compared with 477 Northern Wheatear *O.
oenanthe* and 96 Black-eared Wheatear *O. hispanica* in the same period (Horner
& Hubbard). Less common in autumn mid Aug to Oct, mainly late Aug to Sep;
also once early Aug, occasional Nov and once early Dec. Very few records in some
earlier years, apparently because of difficulty of identification. Wing lengths of
trapped birds (see Appendix 3) correspond with those of birds from Turkey (Cramp
1988).

245. OENANTHE OENANTHE   PM

Northern Wheatear (Common Wheatear)

Very common passage migrant in spring, first seen Feb, main passage Mar–Apr, peak numbers from mid–late Mar to mid Apr, often in 10s, maximum 88 on newly ploughed land at Cape Greco, 25 Mar 1971 with 47 at Cape Andreas the next day; last seen May, once early Jun. Singing ♂ near Paphos, 18 Apr 1988 (P. R. Flint). ♂♂ preceed ♀♀ on spring migration (Horner & Hubbard). Usually less common on return passage, once mid Jul, usually first seen Aug, main passage Sep–Oct with peak numbers mid Sep to early or mid Oct; last seen Nov, once early Dec.

246. OENANTHE CYPRIACA (see below)   MB

Cyprus Pied Wheatear

Abundant and widespread migrant breeder, breeding restricted to Cyprus, wintering in the southern Sudan and Abyssinia (Vaurie).

Breeding distribution. Throughout the island. Most common in the hills and mountains, especially on rough open ground with scattered trees, but also occurs commonly in mountain pine forest; on broken rocky ground; on open, natural and cultivated lowlands; around houses and gardens, in industrial and suburban areas, and in woods and plantations. It is least common on the central plain (Stewart & Christensen).

Arrival and song. Once seen early Feb, occasionally late Feb, usually first seen early Mar, occasionally in numbers mid Mar, main arrival usually late Mar with others into Apr. Song Mar–Jul, possibly later, from a song post, usually a tree top, but also buildings, boulders and overhead wires. The top of a tall mast on top of a 3 storey building was a regular song post (P. R. Flint). One ♂ sang c. 70 m from its nest and that is probably the usual distance (Ashton-Johnson). The breeding density, especially in the hills and mountains, is extremely high, 4 or 5 singing ♂♂ often heard from one point (Christensen 1974).

Nest sites. Nests, usually in holes, in a wide variety of natural and man-made sites: in the earth banks of mountain roads (Ashton-Johnson), on the ground under a boulder or a stone (Took 1971a), in caves, and in crevices or holes in rocks or cliffs, including those by the sea. Also in holes or hollows in a variety of trees, once behind loose bark of a eucalyptus; in stream banks and stone or mud brick walls; in or under old tins (McNeile, S. Norris), in aircraft (Bridgman), under a low thick bush (McNeile), in a mine slag heap and down a shaft. Around buildings has used a variety of nest sites: a pile of building debris, electricity meter boxes, a flower pot, a fire escape ladder, a pair of secateurs in a garage, a concrete house beam, a wooden beam in a shed, between barrels and under eaves. Once in an airfield fire extinguisher within 6 m of daily aircraft engine running; 4 young fledged successfully (R23). Highest nest found, 3·7 m above the ground.

Nests, eggs and young. The nest is usually rather loose, bulky and untidy, but has a neat cup lined with hair, occasionally fine grasses and rootlets, once feathers (Ashton-Johnson). Some nests have a base or entrance ramp of twigs or pieces of wood up to 10 cm long, some as thick as a pencil, one urban nest had pieces of split building timber – 7 cm × 6 mm × 13 mm (Took 1971a). Of 12 clutches found by Ashton-Johnson, the average size was 4·8. The eggs are exceptionally beautiful, having a bright blue ground, with usually a zone of very fine warm red-brown spots near the large end, but there is considerable variation in the markings (Ashton-Johnson). Both ♂♂ and ♀♀ incubate (Ashton-Johnson). In general breeding starts in the latter half of Apr in the plains, in early May at around 600 m in the hills, and in mid May at 1500–1800 m in the Troodos forest (Ashton-Johnson). On low ground, eggs, C/4 to C/6, found 10 Apr (Müller) to early Jul; some fledged young early May, more mid May, and many late May to early Jun, with others till at least early Jul. Several records of young on low ground Jul, only detailed one being of a nest with one young one day old at Strovolos, 6 Jul 1971 (Took 1971a). On Mt. Troodos fledged young once mid Jun, with most young fledging there late Jun (Mason), but some still in the nest early Jul (Ashton-Johnson). A first brood fledged Skouriotissa, 22 or 23 May 1975, and a second brood fledged from the same nest, 29 or 30 Jun (R22). This is the only record of a second brood, though they may be overlooked in summer. When a ♀ has fledged young she has a call very reminiscent of the thin pipe of a Bullfinch *P. pyrrhula*, repeated frequently if an intruder is nearby (Took 1971a).

Post-breeding. After May birds become apparently less numerous or little recorded on low ground, with an increase in the Troodos range after early Jun, and it is believed by some (NR4, 7 & 11–15) that an altitudinal movement takes place at this time. However, there is relatively little observer coverage on low ground during the summer heat of Jun–Aug, and birds may go unrecorded then. The increase on high ground can be explained by the large number of young which fledge there in Jun. A small survey in 1972 showed birds numerous on low ground in summer on the Karpas, at Kormakiti and Yermasoyia, with an apparent reduction elsewhere (NR3). Birds have since been found numerous at Episkopi and Mavrokolymbos Dam in summer. There is other evidence that birds do remain on low ground after breeding: a family of adults and juveniles roosted in their breeding cave at Tjiklos, Kyrenia, until 30 Jun 1972 and remained in the area until 14 Sep (R19), and a family of 2 adults and 2 juveniles remained at Moni throughout Jul–Aug 1980 (R27). Further detailed observations of this nature are needed. That during Sep birds move from low to higher ground prior to departure (the Bannermans 1971, Stewart & Christensen) is not supported by surveys in 1971 and 1972, which revealed a marked *increase* on low ground along the south coast late Aug and Sep (NR2 & 3), presumably as birds from higher ground begin to move south. Mason noticed a reduction on Mt. Troodos in mid Sep. Seen in winter plumage from late Jul, departure Aug–Oct, mainly late Aug to Sep, when very common on the south coast. Occasional singles Nov, twice mid Dec. Once overwintering: ♂ Episkopi, 31 Dec 1978 to 1 Feb 1979. Pullus ringed Nicosia, 22 Apr 1959, recovered nearby, *c.* 13 Nov 1960; pullus ringed Episkopi, 27 Jun 1963, recovered there, 3 Apr 1964.

Vaurie listed this species as a race of Pied Wheatear *O. pleschanka*, Voous (1960) considered it intermediate between *O. pleschanka* and Black-eared Wheatear *O. hispanica*; but the Bannermans (1971), Sluys & van den Berg and the present authors (1983) listed it binomially as *O. cypriaca*, for which there seems adequate justification. In addition to the size and plumage differences between *pleschanka* and *cypriaca* mentioned by Meinertzhagen and Vaurie, recent studies (Christensen 1974, Bergmann) have shown *cypriaca* to differ morphologically and behaviourally more than was previously thought. Christensen studied *cypriaca* in Cyprus 1969–70 and 1973, and noticed that the plumage of ♀ *cypriaca* is very different from that of ♀ *pleschanka*, being, in mid-summer, almost identical to that of the ♂; he also noticed that *cypriaca* has a unique song, very different from that of *pleschanka*. In his paper (1974) the plumage of ♀ *cypriaca* is described and illustrated in detail. Took (1971b) describes the early summer plumage of ♀ *cypriaca* (but see Christensen 1974: 50–51). The song of *cypriaca* was recorded by Bergmann, and, with the aid of sonagrams, he gives a detailed comparison with the song of nominate *pleschanka*. In addition to the above differences *cypriaca* also occupies a much wider range of breeding habitats than *pleschanka*, which, in particular, does not occur in forest or heavily wooded country (Dement'ev & Gladkov, Vaurie, Cramp 1988).

A detailed comparison of the plumages and biometrics of *cypriaca* and *pleschanka* was made by Sluys & van den Berg. They confirmed the differences mentioned above and found that in non-breeding plumage *cypriaca* ♂♂ have a more orange-brown breast than *pleschanka* ♂♂. They also consider the wing length of *cypriaca* to be always diagnostically shorter than that of *pleschanka*, and while this is undoubtedly true for most birds, there is in fact a small range of overlap between ♂♂ of the 2 species, around 89–92 mm. Vaurie lists a wing length range of up to 90 mm for *cypriaca* ♂♂, and ♂♂ have been trapped in Cyprus with wings of 89, 90, 91 and 92·5 mm (W. Corris, M. G. Lobb, Horner & Hubbard). Adult ♂♂ have wings 2 mm longer on average than first year ♂♂ (Horner & Hubbard). Newly arrived birds in Mar have small gonads, suggesting that development must take place on Cyprus within one month (Horner & Hubbard).

247. OENANTHE HISPANICA   PM

Black-eared Wheatear

Fairly common passage migrant (*O.h. melanoleuca*) in spring; once late Feb, occasional early Mar, main passage mid–late Mar to mid–late Apr, peak numbers late Mar to mid Apr; last seen early–mid May, once obtained late May (skin in RSM). Black-throated ♂♂ are more numerous on spring passage than white-throated: in 1968 82·8% of an unspecified number (Horner & Hubbard), in 1970 84·6% of 39 (NR1), in 1971 65·5% of 55 (NR2), and in 1988 56·7% of 30 were black-throated (P. R. Flint). ♂♂ are more numerous and arrive earlier than ♀♀ (Horner & Hubbard). Usually very scarce on return passage late Aug to Oct, only 3 or 4 records per autumn, exceptionally 6 birds at Cape Greco, 10 Oct 1987 (U. Schroeter), and 16 Petounda Point, 15 Sep 1990. Also obtained mid Aug and late Nov (skins in BMNH), and once seen mid Nov. (See also Cyprus Pied Wheatear *O. cypriaca*.) [*O.h. hispanica*. 1980–81 records apparently due to confusion with the buff form of *O.h. melanoleuca*.]

248. OENANTHE DESERTI   PM

Desert Wheatear

Scarce passage migrant Mar to mid Apr, mainly mid Mar to early Apr, usually singly and most often on the south coast; also twice mid Feb. Only 6 autumn records: mid Aug, late Sep, late Oct (3) and late Nov. Once in winter, one Paphos lighthouse, 30–31 Dec 1987. Race unknown (*pace* Hüe & Etchécopar).

249. OENANTHE FINSCHII   WV PM?

Finsch's Wheatear

O.f. finschii. Winter visitor in variable numbers, occasionally scarce but in most winters locally common, to broken rocky bare ground below *c.* 600 m. Birds establish territories and apparently remain in the same area all winter. Almost all records are of ♂♂. Song heard once mid Feb (B2). Noted wintering areas are Ayia Napa/Cape Greco and Kythrea/Halevga, but occurs widely in suitable habitat. Maxima 15 along *c.* 6 km of road east of Ayia Napa, 14 Feb 1971, and 11 Cape Pyla,

14 Jan 1987. Occasional late Sep to Oct, common Nov–Feb, departure from late Feb, usually all have left by mid–late Mar.

Probably a scarce passage migrant in spring: occasional singles Apr, and once early May, usually on the south coast or at Cape Andreas, and 8 limed Paralimni, 12 Mar to 5 Apr 1968 (Horner & Hubbard). [As *Saxicola erythraea* Ehr. one was collected at Ktima, Jul 1877 (Schrader), the specimen listed by Müller as adult ♂. Bourne (1959a) believed this referred to Mourning Wheatear *O. lugens*, but Madarász (1904b) and Bucknill (1909–10, 1910) took it to be synonymous with *O. finschii*.]

250. OENANTHE MONACHA   AV
Hooded Wheatear

Accidental visitor, 2 recent records: ♀ Kensington Cliffs, Episkopi, 13 and 15 Apr 1987, and ♀ Larnaca Salt Lake, 17 Apr 1987 (both R34). In the past, 2 beside the road west of Larnaca, 5 May 1875 (Lilford), one, ♂, collected and now in RSM (where identification confirmed by I. H. J. Lyster).

251. OENANTHE LEUCOPYGA   AV
White-crowned Black Wheatear

Accidental visitor, 2 records: an adult showing characters of *O.l. leucopyga* remained in the same small area of scattered buildings and flat bare ground at Akrotiri, 11–24 Mar 1970 (R17), and another adult at the Temple of Apollo, Curium, 28 May 1985 (R32, P. J. Langston *per* C. J. L. Bennett).

252. MONTICOLA SAXATILIS   PM
Rock Thrush

Scarce passage migrant in spring: occasional Feb to mid Mar, main passage late Mar to Apr, sometimes to early May. ♂ singing from roof of large ruined stone building north of Coral Bay, 13 Apr 1988 (K. Flint). 11 limed Paralimni, 18 Mar to 20 Apr 1968 (Horner & Hubbard). 3 recent summer records: one Mavrokolymbos Dam, 16 Jun 1972; one St. Hilarion, 7 Jun 1987 and one Mt. Olympus, 2 Jun 1990 (J. C. Le Gassick). In the past, one Kantara, 24 Jul 1910 (Bucknill 1911). There are no breeding records (the Bannermans 1971), but in view of the summer records occasional breeding is a possibility. Only 8 recent autumn records, late Aug, Sep (5), early Oct and mid Nov. In the past, fairly common Troodos late Aug to Sep 1911 (Bucknill 1913a), and sometimes "dozens" daily Mt. Olympus, Sep (probably before 1914) (Wilson 1954).

253. MONTICOLA SOLITARIUS   RB WV PM
Blue Rock Thrush

M.s. solitarius. Locally common resident.
Breeding distribution. Along the peaks and upper ridge of the Kyrenia range. Breeding proved at Buffavento 1957 and 1969 (3 pairs in both years) and 1970 and 1971, St. Hilarion 1928 (C. F. Belcher) and 1959, Kantara 1913 (C.N.H.S.Ann.IV) and 1987, and "near Boghaz" (C. F. Belcher *in* the Bannermans 1958).

Breeding data. Song at breeding sites at least Jan–Jun. At Buffavento nests were placed in holes in the castle walls (W. R. P. Bourne). Eggs, C/5 to C/6, found early and late May; fledged young mid May to early Jun. Away from the Kyrenia range, unconfirmed reports of breeding from the Akamas (Stewart & Christensen) and Stavrovouni (NR8). Occasional on the south coast in summer, notably at Cape Greco and Episkopi, and several summer records from Troodos/Olympus/Amiandos since 1982, but no evidence of breeding from any of these areas.

Usually only ♂♂ recorded at breeding areas in winter. Fairly common winter visitor to rocky low ground, especially where coastal cliffs occur, mid Sep–Oct to Mar–early Apr. Song from wintering birds on low ground heard mid Oct and regularly mid Jan to Mar. Scarce to fairly common passage migrant late Feb to Apr (twice early May), maxima 10 limed Paralimni, 2 Apr 1968, and 8 on low cliffs at Ayia Napa, 12 Mar 1978. Little evidence of autumn passage, though some mid Sep to Oct records may refer to migrants (notably 11 Amathus, 11 Oct 1982).

254. TURDUS TORQUATUS   PM WV

Ring Ouzel

Usually a scarce and irregular passage migrant and winter visitor (*T.t. alpestris*) Oct to Mar, usually on high ground. Only frequent Nov, when occasional flocks on passage at Mt. Olympus, maxima 50 there, 6 Nov 1971, 40–60 on 19 Nov 1982, and 50–100 on 25 Dec 1982. In the past, "a regular swarm", mid Feb to early Mar 1911, even frequenting gardens in Nicosia (Bucknill 1911). [A pair Troodos, Jul 1907, "which from their behaviour, most probably had young" (Bucknill 1909–10). "A few years ago a nest and eggs of a Ring Ouzel were taken near the ruined castle of Kantara . . . and the old birds seen" (Bucknill 1909–10). It was not realised at that time that Blue Rock Thrush *M. solitarius* was the common breeding thrush of the Kyrenia range, so probably that species is implicated (Bourne 1959a).]

255. TURDUS MERULA   WV PM RB?

Blackbird

Usually common winter visitor to wooded areas on high and low ground, though in some winters rather scarce. First arrivals Oct, usually common from Nov or Dec to Feb, departure from late Feb, last seen late Mar–Apr; occasionally May (perhaps breeders). Song from Dec, more regular late Jan onwards. Occasional increases late Feb to Mar (once "abundant" Akrotiri late Mar) probably involve passage migrants. Only evidence of autumn passage, 2 moving northeast Cape Andreas, 20 Nov 1971.

Since 1979, several summer records, mainly from Mt. Troodos, suggesting that breeding range is extending to Cyprus, though this not proven yet. Troodos records: one 26 May 1979; up to 6 early Aug 1984; 2 early Aug 1985; song heard May and 2 seen mid Aug 1986; 2 early–mid Jul and 2–4 mid-late Aug 1987; song heard Apr, 1–4 seen mid–late May and 2 mid Aug 1988; one late May 1989; 3 in song, 21 Jun 1990 and territorial behaviour seen. Most of these records were from the wooded valley south of the Troodos Leave Camp near the sewage outfall. Also recently recorded in summer on lower ground at Smyies, one 4 Jun 1980; and at Avgas gorge (south of Lara), 2 on 14 Jul 1989 (N. Petrou).

2 ringed Athalassa and Episkopi recovered near where ringed in subsequent winters; one ringed Akrotiri, 25 Jan 1968, shot Kakopetria (45 km north) Feb 1970. 4 recoveries of birds ringed in the U.S.S.R. (3) and Egypt (Appendix 2). Vaurie

mentions only *T.m. aterrimus*, but the bird ringed near Ryazan was presumably nominate *merula*, and 2 ringed Sea of Azov were possibly migrants of either race. Wing lengths of trapped ♂♂ (see Appendix 3) are close to those of *aterrimus* given by Cramp (1988).

256. TURDUS NAUMANNI   AV

Dusky/Naumann's Thrush

Accidental visitor, one record: one Akrotiri, 10–11 Nov 1958, showing characters intermediate between *T.n. eunomus* and *T.n. naumanni* (Bourne 1959a). [Photographs and descriptions of one Cape Andreas, 14 Apr 1973 (Stagg 1974), do not confirm the identification beyond doubt.]

257. TURDUS PILARIS   WV

Fieldfare

Winter visitor in variable numbers to scrub and wooded areas on high and low ground; particularly fond of Strawberry Tree *Arbutus andrachne* berries in the hills (Bourne *et al.*). Occasionally scarce, more usually fairly common in 10s, sometimes 100s, maximum "many 1000s" Akrotiri, mid–late Dec 1970. Once seen mid Sep. First arrivals usually late Oct to Nov, peak numbers Dec–Jan, fewer Feb, occasional singles Mar to mid Apr.

3 recoveries of birds ringed in the U.S.S.R., West Germany and Czechoslovakia (Appendix 2).

258. TURDUS PHILOMELOS   WV PM

Song Thrush

T.p. philomelos. Very common and widespread winter visitor, mainly below *c.* 1200 m. Largest winter flocks often in olive groves, notably at Lythrodhonda, the Akamas, Flassou and Lefkara. In some winters very large influxes occur, notably winter 1967–68 when countless 1000s throughout the island (Stewart & Christensen). Singles seen 3 times Aug and once Sep, but first arrivals usually Oct, increasing Nov, peak numbers Dec to mid Feb, in 100s or 1000s, maximum 15,000 Lara, 30 Jan 1983; fewer Mar, last seen Apr, occasionally May. Wintering birds suffer very heavily from shooting: an estimated 3 million are now shot each winter (see **Bird Killing and Conservation**). Some evidence of spring passage: occasional increases on the south coast late Feb to early Mar, and 244 limed at Paralimni after 6 Mar 1968 (Horner & Hubbard).

10 ringed, Akrotiri (7) and Nicosia (3), recovered or retrapped in subsequent winters, 6 where ringed and 4 within 25 km. One ringed Cape Andreas, 26 Mar 1970, recovered there 18 Nov 1970, on return passage. 5 recoveries of birds ringed in the U.S.S.R. (4) and Rumania; one ringed in Cyprus recovered in Greece (Appendix 2).

259. TURDUS ILIACUS   WV PM

Redwing

T.i. iliacus. Winter visitor in variable numbers, usually scarce, occasionally fairly common. A few records late Oct to mid Nov, first arrivals usually late Nov, most frequent Dec–Jan, fewer Feb, last seen Mar, once early Apr. Maximum winter numbers are usually only in 10s, but an exceptional influx occurred in 1980: *c*. 1000 Lythrodhonda mid Jan to early Feb, and *c*. 2000 Lefkara Dam early Feb. Night passage heard late Nov, early Dec and late Jan.

    4 recoveries of birds ringed in England, Finland, Ireland and West Germany (Appendix 2).

260. TURDUS VISCIVORUS   WV PM

    Mistle Thrush

T.v. viscivorus. Winter visitor in variable numbers, mainly to low ground and foothills, usually scarce, occasionally fairly common in 10s. Occurs mid–late Oct to Mar (occasional early Apr), usually most frequent Nov–Feb. 4 records of passage flocks moving east and northeast at Cape Andreas, mid Oct to mid Nov, maximum *c*. 2000 thrushes, mostly this species, 24 Oct 1970. Sometimes flocks on passage Troodos/Mt. Olympus, Nov.

SYLVIIDAE

261. CETTIA CETTI   RB

    Cetti's Warbler

Locally common resident.
    Breeding distribution. Valley bottoms of the Troodos range and adjacent coastal lowlands, including the Akamas, most common in the south, west, and north, and from sea level to *c*. 600 m, though has bred at *c*. 870 m (Ashton-Johnson) and song heard to *c*. 1500 m. Occurs in dense vegetation, often Bramble *Rubus ulmifolius*, with other plants such as Oleander *Nerium oleander*, *Tamarix*, Plane *Platanus orientalis*, Alder *Alnus orientalis* and Golden Oak *Quercus alnifolia*, usually along streams or dry stream beds in forest, scrub and cultivated areas, some also in dense cover in or by reed beds. Breeding proved at Akhelia (R21), Pendayia (NR5), north side Akrotiri Salt Lake (R17), Skouriotissa (R23), Mandria (Troodos) and at 2 locations near the Pedhoulas/Lefka road (Ashton-Johnson). Away from the Troodos range, song in the breeding season at Syrianokhori, Morphou, Kormakiti, Paleomylos valley, and recently at Kyrenia and Nicosia; also at Cape Andreas, where many sing and "certainly nest" (Ashton-Johnson) in the dense *Juniperus phoenicea* maquis in the dry stream beds there. Many also sing in similar juniper maquis at Lara (P. R. Flint). At Cape Andreas, 15 singing birds were counted along *c*. 800 m of track, 24 Apr 1973. Its breeding distribution is apparently extending in the island, song heard at Nicosia, May–Jun 1985, Jun 1986 and May 1987 and 1988; at Kyrenia, May 1985; at Lymbia Dam, 21 Jun 1988; and several in song around Bishops Pool, Akrotiri, 29 Apr 1987 (M. H. Thurston) where none in earlier years. Also now, at least since 1987, nests in and near hotel gardens at Paphos. In the coastal strip Paphos to Lara, singing birds also seemed far more numerous in 1988 than in 1979 (P. R. Flint). Some birds also appear to be moving into drier and flatter habitats than normally used.
    Breeding data. At Akrotiri sings regularly Dec–May, less frequently in Jun, and usually silent Jul–Nov (NR2). Of 3 nests found by Ashton-Johnson in the Troodos range, one was in dead brambles 30 cm over water of stream, one 15 cm up in reedy riparian growth, and one 30 cm up in riparian plants including Fleabane *Inula viscosa* and Rush *Juncus* sp. No published details of eggs. Broods of 4 young

found twice mid May (Ashton-Johnson, R17); fledged young early May (R23) to early Jun.

More widespread in autumn and winter, when occasionally found away from breeding areas, as at Kouklia reservoir, Athalassa, Boghaz and Dhekelia, and an increase at Akrotiri. Well over 100 retraps of birds ringed Akrotiri show breeding population there sedentary, not moving uphill in late summer (*pace* Bourne *et al.*). A census at Akrotiri, early–mid Jan 1972, located 27 birds in the reeds and woodland edge along the north shore of the lake (NR3).

Vaurie ascribed Cyprus birds to *C.c. orientalis*, which is intermediate in size between *C.c cetti* and *C.c albiventris*, but wing lengths of trapped birds (see Appendix 3) are similar to those of *C.c. cetti* (Dement'ev & Gladkov, Williamson 1968). A bird retrapped Akrotiri, 17 Apr 1984, was later attributed to *albiventris* because of its apparent 72 mm wing length (Hallchurch 1984), but this measurement was an error, the bird having been both ringed and previously retrapped with a wing of 63 mm (M. G. Lobb).

262. CISTICOLA JUNCIDIS   RB
Fan-tailed Warbler

Common and widespread resident (*C.j. juncidis*).

Breeding distribution. Low ground and lower hills wherever tall dense herbage occurs, especially barley and wheat, also in tall grass and in reedy vegetation around wetlands. Birds sing over barley in the western Troodos foothills up to *c*. 400 m, song also near Ayios Khrysostomos, Kyrenia range at *c*. 500 m. Few details of numbers, only detailed count: 8 pairs around Akrotiri reed beds, Jun 1971.

Breeding data. Sings from Dec, regularly late Feb to early Aug. Nests in tall grass (Took 1971a), in dead vegetation growing through *Salicornia*, and in open cornfield (Ashton-Johnson). Height above ground of 3 nests 12–30 cm. Eggs, C/5 to C/6, found mid Apr (Took 1971a) to mid May; young mid Apr to early Jun and fledged young till Jul. Wide dispersal after breeding; once 4 near Phikardhou (*c*. 800 m) mid Nov.

263. PRINIA GRACILIS   AV
Graceful Warbler

Accidental visitor, one record: one in an area of grass and reeds by a beach south of Episkopi cliffs, 12 Oct 1987 (W. Pompert *per* C. J. L. Bennett). [A bird seen briefly near Spiro's Beach, Larnaca, 25 Nov 1983, was either this species or Scrub Warbler *Scotocerca inquieta* (NR14).]

264. LOCUSTELLA NAEVIA   AV
Grasshopper Warbler

Accidental visitor, one record: one obtained dead, 22 Sep 1968, skin preserved (R15).

265. LOCUSTELLA FLUVIATILIS   PM
River Warbler

Very scarce passage migrant, 7 trapped Akrotiri, mainly at Bishops Pool: mid Apr, mid Aug, Sep (3) and late Oct (2). In detail: one on 12 Aug 1962 (R9); one on 14 Apr, one on 29 Sep and 2 on 28 Oct 1967 (all R14); one on 8 Sep 1968 (R15); and one on 20 Sep 1970 (R17). In addition to these trapped birds, one was heard singing and seen at Phasouri reed beds, 3 and 7 Apr 1982 (R. Kersley). The 3 birds in autumn 1967 were trapped during an extensive ringing programme, suggesting that the species may be regular in autumn in very small numbers. None were limed at Paralimni in spring 1968 (Horner & Hubbard).

266. LOCUSTELLA LUSCINIOIDES   PM

Savi's Warbler

Scarce to fairly common passage migrant, often in reed beds, mid Mar to Apr and Aug–Oct; also once late Jul and occasional early Nov. Maxima: in spring, 16 limed Paralimni, 11 Mar to 16 Apr 1968 (Horner & Hubbard); and in autumn, 12 trapped Akrotiri, mainly in reed beds, 16 Aug to 28 Oct 1981 (R28). Song heard in reed beds early–mid Apr (R30 & 32).

On plumage colouration, trapped birds are nominate *luscinioides*, though *L.l. fusca* (singles have been obtained Palestine and Egypt – Vaurie) might also occur.

267. ACROCEPHALUS (=LUSCINIOLA) MELANOPOGON   WV

Moustached Warbler

Scarce to fairly common winter visitor (*A.m. melanopogon*) to reed beds. Occurs Oct to mid Mar (once late Mar), mainly mid Nov to mid Feb, maximum 12 Akrotiri, early Jan 1970; maxima elsewhere, 7 Syrianokhori, mid Dec 1972, and 5 Akrounda Creek, early Jan 1988. Singing well at Akrotiri, early Feb 1982. [Apr and Aug sight records may be result of confusion with Sedge Warbler *A. schoenobaenus*.]

268. ACROCEPHALUS SCHOENOBAENUS   PM

Sedge Warbler

Passage migrant in variable numbers, often in reed beds, in some years common, in others scarce. Occasional early Mar, spring passage usually mid Mar to May, peak numbers usually early–mid Apr; maximum of well over 60 singing birds in reeds and scrub at Akrotiri Salt Lake, 16 Apr 1966. Only 30 limed Paralimni, 13 Mar to 8 May 1968 (Horner & Hubbard). In autumn occasional from mid Jul, main passage Aug–Oct, occasional Nov; 2 trapped Bishops Pool, 25 Nov 1973. In most years no clear autumn peak, but in a few years numbers have peaked mid Aug to early Sep, maximum of 36 trapped Akrotiri reed beds, mid–late Aug 1981.

269. ACROCEPHALUS PALUSTRIS   PM

Marsh Warbler

Passage migrant. Exact status unclear owing to confusion with Reed Warbler *A. scirpaceus*. Very few of the records of birds seen or trapped are supported by descriptions. Probably a very scarce migrant in spring: at least 7 sight records Apr, mainly late Apr, and one trapped Akrotiri, 17 Apr 1960. None were limed at Paralimni, spring 1968; birds identified as this species at the time were subsequently found to be *A. scirpaceus* (Horner & Hubbard). Scarce on autumn passage, at least

9 recoveries: early Aug, late Aug (3), Sep and Oct (4). There are also 48 records of birds trapped at Akrotiri, mainly at Bishops Pool, late Aug to early Nov.

10 recoveries of birds ringed in West Germany (5), Belgium (2), Poland, France and Czechoslovakia, 9 of them in autumn and one reported Jan after delay (Appendix 2). A bird ringed as *A. scirpaceus*, Akrotiri, 5 Oct 1980, was retrapped as *A. palustris*, Port Sudan, 14 Aug 1983 (NR14); from correspondence with the ringer and retrapper the bird was probably of the latter species.

270. ACROCEPHALUS SCIRPACEUS   MB PM

Reed Warbler

Locally common migrant breeder (*A.s. fuscus*) (Flint 1972d).

Breeding distribution. Reed beds at Akrotiri/Phasouri and near Morphou; has also bred Akhelia and Kouklia (Paphos). Many probably also breed by the Pendaskhinos river south of Ayios Theodhoros, and by the river at Polis. Only one detailed count: 69 singing ♂♂, Akrotiri reed beds, early Jun 1971.

Breeding data. Arrival from mid Mar, song regular late Mar till at least early Jun. Nests in long grass as well as reeds; also 2 colonies in *Tamarix* bushes at Akrotiri 1957 (A. S. Norris). Eggs, C/2 to C/4, found mid Apr to early Jun; many fledged young late May. Departure from mid–late Aug, last seen Oct or early Nov. 70 ringed Akrotiri retrapped there in subsequent years, one after 9 years (S. Allen).

Fairly common passage migrant. Spring passage mid Mar to early May, autumn passage mid Aug to early Nov. Twice early Mar and once mid Nov. 110 limed Paralimni, spring 1968 (Horner & Hubbard); of 12 examined, 11 were *A.s. fuscus* and one was intermediate between *fuscus* and nominate *scirpaceus*. Probably both races occur on passage.

One recovery of a bird ringed in Greece. One ringed in Cyprus recovered in Sudan (Appendix 2).

271. ACROCEPHALUS ARUNDINACEUS   PM OB

Great Reed Warbler

Usually fairly common passage migrant (*A.a. arundinaceus*), though in some years few recorded. Usually occurs in reed beds. Seen once early Mar, occasional late Mar–early Apr, main spring passage mid–late Apr, sometimes to early May, occasional mid May. Only 12 limed Paralimni, spring 1968 (Horner & Hubbard). Song heard from migrants Apr to early May (P. Boye, R. Frost, S. M. Lister). Autumn passage mid Aug to Oct, occasionally from early Aug and to mid Nov, most frequent early–mid Sep. A presumed autumn migrant was seen catching and eating dragonflies (Murray 1987c).

Breeding. 2 records. At least one pair bred Phasouri reed beds 1982, 2 fledged young there 21 Jul (R29). Bred there again 1985, C/3 found 15 Jun, the nest 3 m above ground in tall reeds (R32). Song heard there summer 1983, 84 and 87. Song also heard Akrotiri reed beds summer 1983, and at the mouth of the river at Polis, early Jun 1985. Birds also present at Akrotiri and Phasouri reed beds late Jul–early Aug 1989 (D. J. Odell).

A.a. griseldis, one trapped Akrotiri reed beds, 21 Jun 1981 (M. G. Lobb); identification confirmed by comparison of the detailed description against 8 skins of *griseldis* in BMNH (P. F. Stewart).

272. HIPPOLAIS PALLIDA   MB PM

Olivaceous Warbler

H.p. elaeica. Very common and widespread migrant breeder, the most numerous and widespread breeding warbler.

Breeding distribution. At all levels wherever there is thick cover – the characteristic warbler of all woods, streams, thickets and gardens (Ashton–Johnson), also occurring in plantations, orchards, groves, scrub and pine forest. Within pine forest breeds along streams in valley bottoms with good cover of deciduous trees, shrubs and brambles.

Breeding data. Occasionally seen Mar, main arrival early or mid Apr, though first on Troodos early May (Mason). Song Apr–Jul, sometimes into early Aug. Nest height 0·35–3 m above ground. Nests usually in shrubs (Ashton-Johnson), such as *Cistus*, thorns, *Tamarix* and brambles *Rubus ulmifolius*; sometimes also in trees – Olive *Olea europaea, Pinus, Eucalyptus* and Golden Oak *Quercus alnifolia*. Nests also found in "forks of dry reed" (R19), in Fleabane *Inula viscosa* and, on Troodos, in *Berberis cretica* (Ashton-Johnson). Sometimes nests at high densities, "at least 6 pairs nesting in a triangle 80 × 80 × 30 yards", Platania, 18 May 1959 (Ashton-Johnson). On lower ground, eggs, C/2 to (mainly) C/4, found May–Jun, young once mid May (NR7) and fledged young once late Jul (R29); on Troodos and Mt. Olympus breeds 2–4 weeks later (Ashton-Johnson); fledged young at Caledonian Falls (Troodos) once early Aug (Took 1971a). Departure mid Jul (Mason) onwards, mainly late Jul to Aug. 6 ringed, Paralimni (2), Akrotiri (2), Troodos and Polemidhia, retrapped where ringed in subsequent summers.

Passage migration obscured by presence of local breeders. Apparently rather scarce in spring, mainly mid Apr to early May; 51 limed Paralimni, spring 1968 (Horner & Hubbard), many of them probably arriving local breeders. More numerous on autumn passage late Jul to Sep (occasional Oct), mainly Aug, when fairly common. [*H.p. opaca*, applied to birds trapped 1975 but without description (Mason), is not acceptable.]

273. HIPPOLAIS OLIVETORUM   PM

Olive-tree Warbler

Scarce passage migrant, most frequent in spring and in the east of the island, where probably often overlooked. 18 records since 1961: Apr to early May (12), late May, and Aug to early Sep (5), usually singly, though 4 on the Karpas, 20 Apr 1972 and 5 Salamis, 21 Apr 1965 (Christensen 1967). Only 3 limed Paralimni, spring 1968 (Horner & Hubbard) and there are no records of trapped birds. [In the past, mentioned by Schrader as a very rare visitor to gardens early Apr.]

274. HIPPOLAIS ICTERINA   PM

Icterine Warbler

Scarce passage migrant, most frequent in spring. Usually only 1–2 reliable records a year, Apr–May (mainly mid Apr to mid May) and late Aug to mid Oct; usually singly, though 3 Cape Andreas, 19 Apr 1973. Only one limed Paralimni, spring 1968 (Horner & Hubbard) and few records of trapped birds. [Some sight records are apparently due to confusion with *Phylloscopus* spp, especially first year Willow Warbler *P. trochilus* in early autumn.]

275. SYLVIA CONSPICILLATA   RB

Spectacled Warbler

Common resident.

Breeding distribution. Garigue and low maquis on arid low ground and hills, also amongst cultivation. Occurs throughout the central plain from the base of the Karpas, Famagusta, Cape Greco and Larnaca, through to Morphou and Cape Kormakiti, extending from the central plain onto the southern slopes of the Kyrenia range, up to c. 500 m (Jeal), and into the northern and eastern foothills of the Troodos range, up to at least c. 210 m (Ashton-Johnson), and probably up to c. 450 m. Around Strovolos occurs in thorny scrub, mainly Christ's Thorn *Paliurus spinachristi*, amidst corn fields, partly bordering small valleys with Prickly Burnet *Poterium spinosum* (H. Bergmann). Believed to be decreasing around Nicosia, probably due to loss of breeding habitat in cultivated areas (NR9). Also breeds commonly on salt flats at Dhekelia (Jeal), Kouklia/Prastio (Jeal, Took 1971a), Larnaca and Akrotiri/Zakaki (Best). Apart from Akrotiri, has also been seen in the coastal southwest in the breeding season below Asprokremmos Dam (displaying – R32), near the Ezousas River (2 adults and 4 fledged young — R34), by Paphos Airport (6 birds – D. J. Odell), near Mavrokolymbos Dam (nesting — R35) and at Polis (a pair – K. Steiof). Northern and southern limits of breeding distribution closely follow 400–450 mm isohyets. Occasional at Skouriotissa, on the north coast and at Cape Andreas, but not known to breed at these locations.

Breeding data. Song and display flight Jan–Feb to Apr, possibly later. In garigue and low maquis typically nests in *Poterium spinosum* (Ashton-Johnson, Took 1971a), also once in Rockrose *Cistus villosus* (P. R. Flint); on salt flats in *Salicornia* (Jeal, Took 1971a, Best), *Tamarix* (Took 1971a) and probably *Suaeda* (D. W. Yalden). Nests have also been found in Fleabane *Inula viscosa* (Ashton-Johnson), and in *Echium* (Jeal). Height of 19 nests, 5–60 cm above ground. Eggs, C/3 to C/5, found Mar to early May; young early Mar (France) to May, and fledged young late Mar to Jul.

Easily overlooked and usually recorded only in ones and twos, but systematic searches and counts show it to be numerous: 113 along c. 1·6 km of embankment Kouklia reservoir, 10 Jun 1971, 48 Akrotiri/Zakaki, Dec 1971 to Jan 1972 (NR2 & 3) and 20 pairs between Akrotiri Bay and the salt lake, 26 Apr 1982 (Best). Not proved to breed until 1958 (Ashton-Johnson), but breeding probably overlooked previously – fairly common on the plain near Trikomo, 1875 (Lilford), and at Akrotiri and between Larnaca and Famagusta, 1887 (Guillemard 1888).

Described as a passage migrant (Vaurie, Williamson 1968, Hüe & Etchécopar), but there are no records of passage and it is not known to breed north of Cyprus. Common in breeding areas throughout the winter, when also some dispersal into non-breeding areas. Of 60 limed Paralimni, spring 1968, a large percentage were fledged juveniles (Horner & Hubbard), indicating that the birds were local breeders and not returning migrants.

Vaurie does not mention the breeding race; there are no plumage differences between 3 skins from Cyprus and skins of *S.c. conspicillata* from Egypt, Palestine and Malta in BMNH (P. F. Stewart), though trapped birds are rather short winged (see Appendix 3) compared with *S.c. conspicillata* (Williamson 1968). Wing/tail ratios of trapped birds show affinities with North African populations of *S.c. conspicillata* (Jeal).

276. SYLVIA CANTILLANS   PM

Subalpine Warbler

Spring passage migrant (*S.c. albistriata*) in variable numbers, sometimes scarce, more usually fairly common in ones and twos, exceptionally very common. Occurs Mar to mid Apr, mainly mid Mar to early Apr, peak numbers usually mid Mar, sometimes late Mar. Occasionally seen late Apr and once early May. Largest passage 1968, when "very large numbers till 24 Mar, groups of 50 not uncommon in bushes bordering Bishops Pool" (R15), and 659 (69%♂♂) limed Paralimni, 10 Mar to 18 Apr 1968 (Horner & Hubbard). No satisfactory autumn records. [One collected 6 Nov 1878 (skin in RSM) is more akin to Sardinian Warbler *Sylvia melanocephala* ♀ (C. J. Mead).]

277. SYLVIA MELANOCEPHALA   WV PM?

Sardinian Warbler

S.m. melanocephala. Winter visitor in variable numbers, usually fairly common or common, frequenting scrub similar to and denser than Cyprus Warbler *S. melanothorax* inhabits, also along river beds and in woodlands. Confined mainly to low ground and the lower hills, usually below 800 m. Once early Aug (skin in BMNH), occasional late Aug to mid Oct, first arrivals usually late Oct or early Nov, peak numbers Dec–Feb, fewer Mar, last seen Apr, occasionally early-mid May. At Akrotiri in 1964 the ratio *S. melanocephala*:*S. melanothorax* was 5:1 on 20 Jan, increasing to 10:1 by 18 Feb after cold weather (R11). Found to be common in maquis in the southwest, mid Feb to early Mar 1985, outnumbering *S. melanothorax* (Hjort *et al.*). Detailed searches in Dec 1971 revealed 32 around Akrotiri Salt Lake and 29 at Tunnel Beach, Episkopi (NR2); and 40 were limed Liveras, 6 Jan 1972 (NR3). 7 ringed, Akrotiri (5), Episkopi and Syrianokhori, retrapped where ringed in subsequent winters, one occurring in 3 winters; one ringed Episkopi, 31 Jan 1981, still there 21 Mar. Little evidence of passage, though some of 25 limed Paralimni, spring 1968 (Horner & Hubbard), may have been migrants. Singing ♂, Baths of Aphrodite, 29 Apr 1988 (W. E. Oddie).

One ringed in Turkey recovered in Cyprus (Appendix 2).

278. SYLVIA MELANOTHORAX   RB MB

Cyprus Warbler

Very common and widespread resident breeder, breeding restricted to Cyprus, some leaving the island in winter, when occurring in Lebanon and Palestine (Vaurie) and northern Sudan (Nikolaus).

Breeding distribution. The Kyrenia range and adjacent coastal lowlands, the Karpas, the Troodos range to *c.* 1400 m and adjacent coastal lowlands. Does not occur where average annual rainfall less than *c.* 340 mm and thus absent from the central plain except for eastern coastal areas (Salamis/Dhekelia). Limits of distribution closely follow 340–350 mm isohyets around edges of the central plain, thus overlapping breeding range of Spectacled Warbler *S. conspicillata (q.v.)*, especially in the northern foothills of the Troodos range and the southern slopes of the Kyrenia range.

Habitat. Primarily low dense scrub, but occurs in a wide variety of habitats wherever there is some low scrub: forest edges, open areas within pine forest, valley bottoms in pine forest, areas of Golden Oak *Quercus alnifolia*, open rocky ground with scattered trees, barren foothills with patches of thorn. *Cistus* scrub especially favoured and density of birds per hectare appears to depend fairly closely on amount of *Cistus* scrub within their territories (Bacon & Bacon). Does not normally occur in reed beds or citrus plantations, but may occur at very low densities in citrus plantations where there is *Cistus* scrub (Bacon & Bacon).

Song. From late Sep, increasing Jan, main song period from late Feb or early Mar to Jun. Usually delivered from a song post, usually a tree or the tops of bushes and shrubs. In high arousal situations song is given in 'butterfly' song flight. (See Bergmann for further details and sonagrams). On termination of song flight, ♂♂ sometimes glide steeply down with wings held up in a deep 'V' (P. R. Flint).

Breeding density. Within favourable habitat 3 singing ♂♂ often heard from one location. 8 pairs between Ayios Theodhoros (Skarinou) and Mazotos, 1 May 1976 (NR7), and 60 birds around Erimi/Pano Kividhes, 16 Apr 1978 (NR9).

Nest Site. Within the Kyrenia range and on the Karpas birds tend to nest in isolated thorn bushes among the *Cistus*, but in the Troodos range nests are more often in the *Cistus* itself (Ashton-Johnson). Nest site may be on level or steeply sloping ground, on a ridge top or in a valley bottom. Nests are usually low down, *c*. 30–60 cm above ground, in the centre of a low bush, usually *Cistus*, Thorny Gorse *Genista sphacelata* or Thorny Broom *Calycotome villosa*; less frequently in Sage *Salvia*, Buckthorn *Rhamnus oleoides*, Lentisk *Pistacia lentiscus, Lithospermum hispidulum* or Prickly Burnet *Poterium spinosum*. Nest once *on* the ground under a bush (Baxendale 1915). A minority of nests are up to *c*. 1·2 m above ground in sapling or stunted trees such as Olive *Olea europaea*, Cypress *Cupressus sempervirens* or Aleppo Pine *Pinus halepensis*. Below Buffavento, where both this species and *S. conspicillata* occur, the former nests only in *Genista sphacelata* and the latter only in *Poterium spinosum* (Took 1971a).

Nest. Occasionally flimsy but usually a substantial deep cup. Usually constructed from grasses, often with soft grey thistle leaves and/or strips of fine grey juniper bark worked in. Some nests are almost entirely of juniper bark. Nests may include juniper bark when there is no juniper nearby and it must have been brought from some distance. Spiders cocoon may be used to hold the nest together and to bind it to the shrub. Nests are usually lined with fine grasses and hairs. "The nest is 2 inches in diameter and the cup about $1\frac{1}{2}$ inches deep, so that the bird sits doubled up like a horseshoe with the tail pointing upwards and tightly closed, hiding its white outer tail feathers" (Ashton-Johnson).

Eggs and Young. In comparison with the very variable eggs of the closely related Sardinian Warbler *S. melanocephala*, the eggs show only a small range of variation. They have a greyish white or pale greenish ground colour, generally speckled with brown or olive green spots over ashy shell marks, sometimes having an indefinite zone at the big end (Ashton-Johnson). McNeile found the ground colour to be pale yellowish-green, many eggs showing underlying blotches of light violet grey, and one egg in the clutch sometimes is lighter in colour than the others.

Clutches have been found 25 Mar (NR14) to 5 Jun (at Halevga – Took 1971a). Usually C/4 or C/5, once C/3. Incubation usually by ♀, but twice recorded by ♂. Possibly double brooded though McNeile unable to prove this. Incubation and fledging periods unknown. Young found 15 Apr to early Jun. On low ground many nests have young by mid–late Apr, fledged young from late Apr, though clutches have been found on low ground till late May. Breeding occurs later in the higher Troodos where many nests have young late May and early Jun. (Details of habitat and breeding generally taken from McNeile and Ashton-Johnson. Extensive further details are given by McNeile.)

Movements. Stated by some authors to move to higher altitudes after breeding. There is no supporting evidence for this, and the pattern of records suggests that no such movement occurs. In winter becomes more widespread on low ground (when some occur on the central plain), but absent above *c.* 1000 m and many leave the island. Although less numerous in winter, still usually common or fairly common then. Some winter numbers: 13 Happy Valley, Episkopi, 24 Nov 1971 and 10 Ligi (Kapoura) 17 Dec 1971 (both NR2); 10 Liveras 6 Jan 1972 (NR3).

Departure from the island mainly late Sep and Oct, returning mainly late Feb and Mar. A weekly survey on Akrotiri peninsula autumn 1962 to spring 1963 revealed an increase in numbers from 21 Feb, many being fresh plumaged ♂♂, and by early Mar birds were generally all over the peninsula (Walker). A survey of 97 limed birds at Paralimni in spring 1968 showed a sharp drop in returning migrants in late Mar with the last birds being limed 13 Apr; ♂♂ slightly preceeded ♀♀ and gonads were small, indicating that birds come into breeding condition after their arrival in Cyprus (Horner & Hubbard).

Retraps of ringed birds show site fidelity: 3 ringed Episkopi golf course, 7 Apr 1980, retrapped there late Feb and late Mar (2) 1981 (M. G. Lobb).

279. SYLVIA RUEPPELLI   PM
Rüppell's Warbler

Fairly common or common passage migrant in spring: occasional early Mar, main passage mid–late Mar to early Apr, peak numbers often mid Mar, sometimes late Mar, exceptionally early Mar – 40 Akrotiri, 6 Mar 1963 (R10); last seen late Apr to mid May, once late May. 451 (65%♂♂) limed Paralimni, spring 1968 (Horner & Hubbard). Singing ♂, Baths of Aphrodite, 4 Apr 1983 (R30). Usually only 1–2 records per autumn, Aug–Nov, with most in Sep. Also occasional singles Dec, Jan or Feb, but not known to overwinter. [No proof for postulated breeding in past (the Bannermanns 1958) and no satisfactory summer records.]

280. SYLVIA NANA   AV
Desert Warbler

Accidental visitor, 3 records: one Akrotiri cliffs, 12 Mar 1958 (R2, B6); one Larnaca, 2 Apr 1961 (R7); one Ayios Yeoryios, Paphos District, 10 Mar 1979 (R26).

281. SYLVIA HORTENSIS   PM
Orphean Warbler

Common passage migrant (*S.h. crassirostris*) in spring: once early Feb (♂ ringed Episkopi, 9 Feb 1964, remained till 4 Mar) and once mid Feb, occasional early Mar, main passage mid-late Mar to early–mid Apr, peak numbers often late Mar, sometimes into early Apr; last seen late Apr, occasionally early–mid May. 1058 limed Paralimni, spring 1968 (Horner & Hubbard). Singing ♂ in dry valley north of Ayios Yeoryios (Paphos), 20 Mar 1986 (I. Hillery). Scarce on return passage Aug to mid Oct, mainly late Aug to mid Sep, usually singly, exceptionally 10 Paralimni, 15 Sep 1974.

One ringed in Cyprus recovered in Lebanon (Appendix 2).

282. SYLVIA NISORIA   PM
Barred Warbler

Passage migrant in variable numbers, usually scarce on both passages but exceptionally fairly common in spring. Most frequent in the east of the island where probably often overlooked. Once seen early Mar, occasional mid Mar to early Apr, spring passage mainly mid Apr to mid May, with peak numbers late Apr or early May. Usually only 1–5 records a year, but in 1968, 56 birds were limed at Paralimni, 9 Apr to 11 May, with 14 each day on 2 and 8 May (Horner & Hubbard). Autumn passage Aug to (once) late Oct (Hubbard 1967a), with most records Sep.

One recovery of a bird ringed in the U.S.S.R. (Appendix 2).

283. SYLVIA CURRUCA   PM
Lesser Whitethroat

Very common passage migrant (*S.c. curruca*) in spring, especially in the east of the island: occasional Jan–Feb, first seen usually early–mid Mar, main passage mid–late Mar to mid–late Apr, peak numbers often early–mid Apr, sometimes from late Mar; last seen early–mid May. 5388 limed Paralimni, spring 1968 (Horner & Hubbard), the highest total of any spp in that survey. Usually less common in autumn: once mid Jul, occasional late Jul to Aug, main passage Sep–Oct, occasional Nov to early Dec, once mid Dec (Christensen 1967).

Wing lengths of birds trapped in spring average 0·7 mm shorter than in autumn (see Appendix 3), possibly due to the presence of British birds (see below), which are shorter winged (Williamson 1968). [*S.c. blythi* was attributed to one trapped at Akrotiri, 18 Oct 1969 (R16), but the description does not preclude nominate *curruca*.]

Of 23 recoveries in Cyprus of birds ringed in Europe (Appendix 2), 17 were recovered in autumn, ringed in Scandinavia (13), Czechoslovakia (2), Poland and the U.S.S.R., and 6 were recovered in spring, ringed in England (3), Germany (2) and Czechoslovakia, suggesting that Scandinavian birds pass through Cyprus only (or mainly) in autumn. The results of British ringing (Mead) indicate birds on autumn passage pass through Italy and the Balkans to Egypt, returning via the Levant and Cyprus in spring; one ringed in Cyprus in spring and recovered in Italy in autumn fits this pattern and may therefore have been of British origin. 2 others ringed in Cyprus were recovered East Germany and Lebanon (Appendix 2).

284. SYLVIA COMMUNIS   PM
Whitethroat

Common passage migrant in spring: occasional late Feb to early Mar, main passage mid–late Mar to Apr, peak numbers often early–mid Apr, sometimes from late Mar or into late Apr; last seen early–mid May, occasionally late May. 692 limed Paralimni, spring 1968 (Horner & Hubbard). Song heard Mar to early Apr. Less common in autumn: once late Jul, main passage mid–late Aug to mid–late Oct, peak numbers late Sep to early Oct; occasional Nov. In 30 minutes observation, Kyrenia range, 7 Oct 1962, 10 separate birds worked their way up through bushes on north side of ridge, flew across open ridge, and started working their way down other side (R9).

Wing lengths of trapped birds (see Appendix 3) are similar to nominate *communis* (Dement'ev & Gladkov, Svensson), though they could include some *S.c. icterops*. [No satisfactory breeding records – that of 1909 (Bucknill 1909–10) lacks adequate detail.]

2 recoveries of birds ringed in the U.S.S.R. within breeding range of nominate *communis* (Appendix 2).

285. SYLVIA BORIN   PM

Garden Warbler

Passage migrant in variable numbers, scarce to fairly common, usually less than 10 records a year. Occasional Mar to early Apr, main spring passage mid–late Apr to mid May; occasional late May, once early Jun and twice late Jun. Usually in ones and twos in spring, exceptionally 20 Bishops Pool, Akrotiri, 24 May 1972. 68 limed Paralimni, spring 1968, with 21 on 12 May (Horner & Hubbard). Once seen mid Aug, autumn passage usually from late Aug or early Sep to mid Oct, once seen early Nov. Usually in ones and twos in autumn, exceptionally "numerous" autumn 1968, when 23 trapped Bishops Pool (R15). Wing lengths of trapped birds (see Appendix 3) suggest nominate *borin* occurs in autumn only, the spring mean being similar to that of the longer winged *S.b. woodwardi* (Vaurie).

2 autumn recoveries of birds ringed in Poland and West Germany, both presumably nominate *borin* (Appendix 2).

286. SYLVIA ATRICAPILLA   PM WV OB?

Blackcap

S.a. atricapilla. Very common passage migrant in spring, abundant in autumn. Spring passage early–mid Mar to mid–late May, peak numbers Apr, sometimes into early May. 3918 (59% ♂♂) limed Paralimni, spring 1968 (Horner & Hubbard). Occasional Jun to early Aug, once oversummering Nicosia (R7). Return migration mid–late Aug to Nov, mainly Sep to early Nov, peak numbers late Sep to Oct; 500 limed in one day, Cape Greco, 29 Sep 1957 (R2), and 1248 caught in one day by a single netter, Paralimni, 28 Sep 1982 (NR13), 2 of pre-migratory mass (25·8 g, 29 g) trapped early Dec.

Winter visitor in variable numbers, occasionally scarce but becoming increasingly common or even very common in favoured areas. Some birds probably present from Oct, main wintering period Nov–Mar. Occurs mainly below 800 m, in gardens, thickets and woodlands, some remaining in Nicosia house gardens for up to 5 months (NR1-3). Maxima, up to 40 Episkopi throughout Jan 1965; 40 Kapoura, 3 Dec 1972; and 100 Baths of Aphrodite, 18 Jan 1982. Also described as "abundant", Macheras and Palekhori, Jan to mid Mar 1976 (NR7), and as "extremely common", Episkopi, Jan–Feb 1981 (R28). Song heard in Nicosia house gardens on sunny winter days (NR10), and sub-song at Episkopi, Nov 1981, increasing to full song by late Dec as the number of birds increased (R28). Wintering birds usually weigh *c.* 17–20 g, some trapped Feb show pre-migratory masses of up to 23·4 g.

[**Breeding**. Reported Kyrenia hills 1909 (Bucknill 1909–10), north side Kyrenia range (D. F. Davidson *in* the Bannermans 1958), and Upper Kyrenia 1973 (R20), all unsubstantiated.]

4 ringed, Akrotiri (2), Episkopi and Strovolos, retrapped where ringed in subsequent winters. 83 recoveries of birds ringed in Czechoslovakia (20), Sweden

(16), Poland (9), the U.S.S.R. (7), Germany (6), Finland (5), Hungary (4), Israel (4), Austria (2), Bulgaria (2), Sudan (2), England, Egypt, Norway, Rumania, Spain and Yugoslavia. 7 ringed in Cyprus recovered in Lebanon (5), Jordan and Italy (Appendix 2). The recoveries of birds ringed in Europe (mean 17°E) conform with the marked "migratory divide" at 10°–11°E (Williamson 1968), the only 3 from west of that had been ringed whilst on autumn migration, and had presumably originated elsewhere. The recoveries also show similar areas of origin for spring and autumn migrants and winter visitors, as do the wing lengths of trapped birds (see Appendix 3), which are similar to those from Sweden, eastern Europe and western U.S.S.R.. The recoveries from Lebanon and Jordan, and of birds ringed in Israel and Egypt, reveal similar spring and autumn migration routes, as does one ringed Polemidhia, 5 Apr 1968, and shot Kykko, Troodos, 15 Sep 1968, on the return passage.
   [*S.a. dammholzi*: one with insufficient detail, 18 Oct 1980 (Hallchurch), though intermediates between *dammholzi* and nominate *atricapilla* probably occur.]

287. PHYLLOSCOPUS INORNATUS   AV
   Yellow-browed Warbler

Accidental visitor, 5 records: one trapped Akrotiri, 6 Nov 1968 (R15); one trapped Akrotiri, 16 Oct 1969 (R16); one Episkopi, 18–29 Oct 1969 (R16); one trapped Akrotiri, 15 Nov 1970 (R17); one Dhekelia, 30 Nov 1990 (K. Heron *per* C. J. L. Bennett). The 1970 bird had a wing formula typical of nominate *inornatus*.

288. PHYLLOSCOPUS FUSCATUS   AV
   Dusky Warbler

Accidental visitor, one record: one trapped Akrotiri, 30 Sep 1967, now a specimen in the United States National Museum (Hubbard 1967a). [The brief description of one Akrotiri, 2 Apr 1980, does not confirm the identification.]

289. PHYLLOSCOPUS BONELLI   PM
   Bonelli's Warbler

Passage migrant (*P.b. orientalis*) in variable numbers in spring, occasionally scarce, more usually fairly common or common: once seen early Mar, occasional mid Mar, main passage late Mar to mid Apr, sometimes into late Apr; last seen late Apr to mid May. Maximum "hundreds" Cape Arnaouti, 21 Apr 1958 (R2). 181 limed Paralimni, spring 1968 (Horner & Hubbard). Once obtained Jul (Madarász 1904b). Very scarce and irregular on autumn passage, late Aug to early Oct.

290. PHYLLOSCOPUS SIBILATRIX   PM
   Wood Warbler

Passage migrant in variable numbers in spring, occasionally scarce, more usually fairly common or common: occasional early–mid Mar, first arrivals usually late Mar or early Apr, main passage mid–late Apr, sometimes into early May; last seen early–mid May, occasionally late May. Maxima, "hundreds" Cape Arnaouti, 21

Apr 1958 (R2), and 30 Baths of Aphrodite, 4 May 1988 (NL88/5). Only 21 limed Paralimni, spring 1968 (Horner & Hubbard). Song heard Phasouri, 28 Apr 1985 (G. van Duin). Much less numerous in autumn, sometimes only 1–2 records, mid Aug to Oct, mostly mid Sep to mid Oct. Once early and once late Nov (Bucknill 1909–10).

One recovery of a bird ringed in the U.S.S.R. (Appendix 2).

291. PHYLLOSCOPUS COLLYBITA   PM WV
Chiffchaff

Very common passage migrant and very common and widespread winter visitor below *c*. 1200 m. Occasional Sep, first (trapped birds) usually arrive early–mid Oct, peak numbers on passage, Nov. Main wintering period from late Nov or early Dec to Feb or early Mar (retrapped birds). Song heard Feb–Apr. Spring passage mainly Mar to early Apr, when often very large influxes on the south coast. Last seen mid–late Apr, twice early May (trapped birds). 4670 limed Paralimni, spring 1968, with 1274 on 4 Apr (Horner & Hubbard).

3 races have been reported: *collybita*, attributed to birds trapped Oct to mid Mar; *abietinus*, attributed to birds trapped Nov to early Apr (call heard late Oct); and *tristis*, trapped mid Nov to early Feb (R10, R17, R19, NR2), but the first 2 races are now considered not reliably separable when handling single birds (Svensson). From trapped birds, sight records (Stewart & Christensen) and calls, *abietinus* seems the commonest race, though many are intermediate between *abietinus* and *collybita; tristis* is the least common, e.g. only one of 69 trapped birds examined 1970–71 (R17, NR2).

60 ringed at Akrotiri and one each at Episkopi and Famagusta were retrapped/recovered where ringed in subsequent winters, 3 individuals occurring in 3 winters. 7 recoveries of birds ringed in West Germany (2), Finland, Israel, Jordan, Poland and Yugoslavia (Appendix 2).

292. PHYLLOSCOPUS TROCHILUS   PM
Willow Warbler

Spring passage migrant in variable numbers, usually scarce, occasionally fairly common or common: twice seen mid Mar, first arrivals usually late Mar, main passage Apr; last seen early–mid May, occasionally late May. 672 limed Paralimni, spring 1968, with 98 on 17 Apr (Horner & Hubbard). Song occasionally heard from spring migrants. Abundant passage migrant in autumn, when the most numerous of all migrants, more so even than Blackcap *S. atricapilla*. Seen once mid and once late Jul and twice early Aug, first arrivals usually mid Aug, main passage usually from late Aug or early Sep to mid Oct, last singles Nov, occasionally early Dec (trapped birds). Several in song Nicosia, Dec 1986. Individuals trapped on low ground once mid Jan and once mid Feb, and song heard once early Feb (W. R. P. Bourne).

Wing lengths of trapped birds (see Appendix 3) average closest to *P.t. trochilus* in autumn, and to *P.t. acredula* in spring. The species is dimorphic throughout its range, an 'olive and yellow' morph dominant in the southwest, and a 'brown and white' morph dominant in the northeast (Williamson 1967). Of 42 trapped autumn 1970, 39 were 'olive and yellow' (last trapped 12 Oct) and only 3 were 'brown and white', including the last 2 trapped, on 3 Nov (R17). If mainly *P.t. acredula* occurs in spring, a higher proportion of 'brown and white' birds might be expected then. Of 38 skins obtained Paralimni, spring 1968, 31 were ascribed to *acredula* (presumably the 'olive and yellow' morph), and only one was listed as *'eversmanni'* – the 'brown and white' morph (Horner & Hubbard).

2 ringed in Cyprus recovered in Egypt and Turkey. 2 autumn recoveries of birds ringed in Finland and the U.S.S.R. within breeding range of *P.t. acredula* (Appendix 2).

293. REGULUS REGULUS WV

Goldcrest

Winter visitor (*R.r. regulus*) in variable numbers, scarce to fairly common, on high and low ground, mainly to pine forest where sometimes widespread. Seen once late Sep, once mid Oct (skin in Tel Aviv University) and occasionally late Oct. Normally occurs Nov–Mar (occasionally to early–mid Apr), maxima 30 Kornos, 3 Jan 1960; 14 Halevga, 19 Mar 1971; and "many" Paphos Forest, 20 Mar 1987 (R34).

294. REGULUS IGNICAPILLUS AV

Firecrest

Accidental visitor (*R.i. ignicapillus*), 2 records: one Kalopanayiotis (Troodos range) at *c.* 800 m, 23 Dec 1957 (B6), and one at *c.* 1200 m, Troodos range, 15 Feb 1962 (R9).

MUSCICAPIDAE

295. MUSCICAPA STRIATA MB PM

Spotted Flycatcher

Locally fairly common migrant breeder (*M.s. neumanni*).
Breeding distribution. Pine forest over *c.* 900 m in the Troodos range, exact numbers and distribution not fully known.
Breeding data. Breeding birds present from mid Apr–early May to Sep. Nests in holes in Troodos Pine *Pinus nigra*, or against its bark, once under eaves of cottage (Ashton-Johnson), and once behind a cafe sign board (R28). Eggs, C/5, found late May and early Jun (Ashton-Johnson); fledged young till late Aug (NR9 & 13).
Common passage migrant in spring: seen once early and twice mid Mar, occasional late Mar, first arrivals usually early–mid Apr, main passage late Apr to mid May; last seen late May, once early Jun (Phasouri). Sometimes very large influxes on the south coast, e.g. 25 Apr to 1 May 1960, when "hundreds, if not thousands", along Garyllis riverbed, Polemidhia (R5). Usually less common in autumn, though passage then more protracted than in spring: twice seen early Aug (Akrotiri and Dhekelia), occasional mid Aug, main passage late Aug to Oct, when sometimes up to 30 at one location; occasional early Nov, twice mid and once late Nov.
One recovery of bird ringed in West Germany within the breeding range of *M.s. striata* (Appendix 2). *M.s. neumanni* probably also occurs on passage. Trapped birds average rather long winged (see Appendix 3) and 6 autumn birds exceed the maximum wing length of both *M.s. neumanni* and *M.s. striata* (Dement'ev & Gladkov).

296. FICEDULA PARVA   PM
Red-breasted Flycatcher

Very scarce and irregular passage migrant (*F.p. parva*) in spring. Only 8 records, mid Apr to early May (including those of the Bannermans 1958 and Christensen 1967). Less scarce and probably regular in autumn, Sep to mid Nov, mainly Oct. Maximum autumn 1967, when several limed Paralimni, 6 Nov, and 9 trapped Akrotiri/Episkopi, 11 Sep to 17 Nov (P. F. Stewart). The small late autumn passage corresponds with those through Malta (Sultana and Gauci) and Tripolitania (Bundy), and supports suggestions that some may winter in tropical Africa (Voous 1960, Moreau 1972).

297. FICEDULA SEMITORQUATA   PM
Semi-collared Flycatcher

Scarce passage migrant in spring, late Mar to early May, mainly Apr; usually singly, occasionally 2 or 3 together. First recorded spring 1938 (Payn). The first recent record, unfortunately not published for some 15 years, was of 9 ♂♂ limed Paralimni, 27 Mar to 27 Apr 1968 (Horner & Hubbard), and apparently subsequently identified as *semitorquata*. In spring 1970 a bird trapped at Akrotiri was photographed and subsequently identified as *semitorquata* (R17). In 1971 and 1972 the species was looked for at Akrotiri, and 2 birds were found in each spring. Since then it has been found regularly in spring when looked for. Prior to these recent records the species was presumably mistaken for Pied Flycatcher *F. hypoleuca*. No certain autumn records (see *Ficedula* spp). Formerly considered to be *F. albicollis semitorquata*, a race of Collared Flycatcher (Vaurie), but accorded specific rank by Voous (1977).

298. FICEDULA ALBICOLLIS   PM
Collared Flycatcher

Spring passage migrant in variable numbers, in some years only a few are seen, but is more usually fairly common: occasional mid Mar, first arrivals usually late Mar or early Apr, main passage occasionally in early Apr (e.g. in 1971, 1980 and 1985), but more usually in mid or late Apr, sometimes to early May; occasionally seen mid May, once late May. Sometimes large influxes on the south coast, maximum "several hundred" at Evdhimou, 19 Apr 1965, with smaller numbers at Akrotiri, Larnaca and elsewhere (R12). Also 100 Baths of Aphrodite, 15 Apr 1987. 186 ♂♂ were limed Paralimni, spring 1968, compared with 83 Pied Flycatcher *F. hypoleuca* ♂♂ and 9 Semi-collared Flycatcher *F. semitorquata* ♂♂ in the same period (Horner & Hubbard). *F. albicollis* often occurs slightly earlier on spring passage than *F. hypoleuca*, occasionally 7–10 days earlier, but in many years the main passages of both species are the same, e.g. in 1968 at Paralimni the peak for both was 24 Apr to 1 May (Horner & Hubbard). The relative numbers of *albicollis* and *hypoleuca* vary considerably from spring to spring, in some years (e.g. 1969, 1976 and 1981) the former is more numerous than the latter, in others (e.g. 1967, 1975 and 1979) the reverse is the case, and in others again both pass in roughly equal numbers. *Ficedula* ♂♂ tend to occur earlier than ♀♀ (B2, R17, Horner & Hubbard); in 1967 ♀♀ greatly outnumbered ♂♂ (Stagg 1967), but in 1968 both sexes passed in equal numbers (Horner & Hubbard). These variations in the relative numbers of the species and sexes may be caused by variations in the occurrence of easterly winds which bring birds from the Levant to Cyprus. No certain autumn records, but see *Ficedula* spp. Trapped birds average rather long winged (see Appendix 3) and 4 ♂♂ exceed the maximum wing length given by Svensson.

299. FICEDULA HYPOLEUCA   PM
       Pied Flycatcher

Spring passage migrant in variable numbers, in some years only a few are seen, but is more usually fairly common: occasional mid Mar, first arrivals usually late Mar or early Apr, main passage mid–late Apr, sometimes to early May; last seen early–mid May, occasionally late May and once early Jun. Sometimes in large influxes: "hundreds" Cape Arnaouti, 21 Apr 1958 (R2), and "hundreds" Akrotiri, late Apr to early May 1967 (R14). (See also Collared Flycatcher *F. albicollis*). Only 5 certain autumn records: 2 trapped Troodos, 13 Sep 1966; ♂ Episkopi, 17 Oct 1968; ♂ Troodos, 11 Sep 1975; one trapped Strovolos, 9 Sep 1978; and one Salamis, 29 Oct 1990. (See also *Ficedula* spp.)

   Both the mean and range of wing lengths of birds trapped in spring (see Appendix 3) are close to those of *F.h. sibirica* of western Siberia (Vaurie), and support the suggestion that Siberian birds travel on a great-circle route in spring (Moreau 1961). Some spring ♂♂ also show the brown-grey plumage of *sibirica* (Stagg 1967).

   The marked northeasterly movement of one ringed in Nigeria and recovered in Cyprus in spring suggests it was of Siberian origin (Appendix 2).

       FICEDULA spp

Ficedula flycatchers are scarce but regular on autumn passage. The majority are recorded as *Ficedula* sp, some are specifically identified as Collared Flycatcher *F. albicollis* or more often as Pied Flycatcher *F. hypoleuca* but these records are generally not supported by descriptions. Once seen late Jul and once early Aug, occasional from mid–late Aug, most frequent mid Sep to early Oct; occasional mid Oct, once late Oct. Usually in ones and twos, occasionally more, maxima 11 Paralimni, 22 Sep 1970 (R17), and 20 Kritou Marottou and 8 Polis, 1 Oct 1980 (NR11). Often recorded from the higher Troodos, suggesting that, in autumn, birds are overflying the island at altitude.

TIMALIIDAE

300. PANURUS BIARMICUS   WV
       Bearded Tit

Irregular winter visitor, mainly to reed beds, mid Oct to mid Mar, mainly Nov–Feb. Sometimes fairly common, maximum 41 trapped Akrotiri Salt Lake, Dec 1972. 8 limed Paralimni, 15 Oct 1974 and occasional birds at Bishops Pool, Nov, suggest autumn movement through the island. Also 3 apparent migrants at Phasouri reed beds, 17 Apr 1985.

   One collected Paralimni, 8 Dec 1941 (skin in RSM) identified as nominate *biarmicus* (the Bannermans 1958). On distribution *P.b. russicus* seems of more likely occurrence.

   One ringed Akrotiri, 19 Dec 1972, recovered Limassol, 10 Jan 1976.

PARIDAE

301. PARUS ATER   RB
Coal Tit

Common resident (*P.a. cypriotes*, an endemic race).
Breeding distribution. Above *c*. 400 m in pine forest of the Troodos range, possibly down to *c*. 200 m on northern slopes.
Breeding data. Nests usually in a hole in the ground under a slab of rock, often under a small pine or in a sloping bank of stones (Ashton-Johnson), once under the roof of a hut (NL89/4). Eggs, C/5, found early–mid May (Jourdain 1929a, Ashton-Johnson); young early Apr (the Bannermans 1958) to May, many fledged young late May. Pullus ringed Pano Platres, 1 May 1957, recovered there, 30 Oct 1960.

A small movement to lower hills in autumn and winter, occasionally to adjacent coastal lowlands, but common on Mt. Troodos all year, even in bad weather (Mason). Occasionally reported from the Kyrenia range and the north coast, usually in spring or autumn, and at Nicosia in mid-winter. Some of these records apparently due to confusion with immature *P. major aphrodite*, though Riddell believed he saw nominate *ater* near Kyrenia late Mar 1927, and occasional immigration is a possibility.

P.a. cypriotes differs very distinctly from nominate *ater*, by having a brown back, more black on the head reaching farther back to invade the upper mantle, and by being very dark below, rufous brown on the flanks and lower abdomen (Vaurie).

302. PARUS MAJOR   RB
Great Tit

Common resident (*P.m. aphrodite*).
Breeding distribution. Broadleaved wooded areas, especially on low ground and the lower hills, less common in montane pine forest.
Breeding data. On low ground nests in holes in a wide variety of trees, especially Carob *Ceratonia siliqua*, Hawthorn *Crataegus azarolus* and Olive *Olea europaea*, and in stone walls and holes in posts; in the mountains nests under wooden eaves and corrugated iron roofs, in holes in culverts and in cracks in Plane *Platanus orientalis* and Troodos Pine *Pinus nigra* (mainly Ashton-Johnson). On low ground, eggs, C/5 to C/9, from mid Feb (NR13) but commonest late Mar (Ashton-Johnson); young occasional Feb (NR6, NL88/2), more usually Mar–May (Ashton-Johnson). On Troodos (at *c*. 1700 m) eggs once late May (Ashton-Johnson).

Although first described from Cyprus, *aphrodite* is not an endemic race, and also occurs in the Balearics, Greece and Crete (Vaurie). Juveniles are very dull, almost lacking in colour, and have given rise to occasional reports of Sombre Tit *P. lugubris*.

2 ringed Troodos, 23 Sep 1968, recovered there 5 Nov 1968 and 22 Mar 1969.

TICHODROMADIDAE

303. TICHODROMA MURARIA   WV
Wallcreeper

Winter visitor (*T.m. muraria*), probably fairly common, to mountain rock faces, coastal cliffs, road cuttings and large stone buildings such as castles and monasteries. Occurs widely in suitable habitat, though only 3 records from the Troodos range, where rock faces are relatively few. Most frequent in the Kyrenia range and on relatively well watched and accessible sea cliffs at Episkopi, where regular in winter, remaining for up to 5 months. In view of extensive suitable habitat, probably much overlooked and more frequent than records suggest. Occurs late Oct to Mar (once early Sep and once early Apr), usually singly or in pairs, maximum 4 Tunnel Beach, Episkopi, 20 Nov 1971. One moving SSW along the coast at Cape Andreas, 31 Oct 1971, probably newly arrived.

CERTHIIDAE

304. CERTHIA BRACHYDACTYLA   RB

Short-toed Treecreeper

Common resident (*C.b. dorotheae*, an endemic race).
   Breeding distribution. Pine forests of the Troodos range, mainly above *c.* 900 m, though within the Paphos Forest song and family parties down to *c.* 450 m (Flint 1980). Distribution requires further study.
   Breeding data. Song at least mid Feb to Jun. Nests found in a hole in a wall (Bucknill 1911), under eaves of huts and in cracks or holes in Troodos Pine *Pinus nigra* and *Juniperus* spp (Ashton-Johnson). A foundation of pine needles for nest seems characteristic for this race (Ashton-Johnson). Height of 11 nests, 1–10 m above ground (Ashton-Johnson, Mason). Eggs, C/5, once late May; young mid–late May (Ashton-Johnson) and early Jul (Bucknill 1911), fledged young late May onwards.
   C.b. dorotheae is only a moderately well differentiated race, being very similar to nominate *brachydactyla*, but very slightly greyer above, especially on the rump, a little purer white below and slightly paler, more greyish on the flanks (Vaurie). The song, however, is remarkably short and simple when compared with continental songs from Germany and France (Bergmann).
   One ringed Troodos, 13 Sep 1966, retrapped there 12 Jul 1969; another ringed Troodos, 22 Jun 1970, retrapped there 5 Nov 1970.

REMIZIDAE

305. REMIZ PENDULINUS   WV OB?

Penduline Tit

Scarce to fairly common winter visitor to reed beds, mainly at Akrotiri/Phasouri and Syrianokhori, from Oct (occasionally from Aug or Sep) to Apr; once early May. Maxima *c.* 60 Akrotiri, Jan to mid Feb 1972; and (unusually late) 50 Akrotiri, 8 May 1983. In 1982 birds, including fledged juveniles, were present Akrotiri/Phasouri from mid Jul onwards (R29). It is not known if these were local breeders or immigrants. One bird seen then showed characters of either *R.p. caspius* or *R.p. menzbieri* (T. A. Box, M. G. Lobb).
   19 trapped birds examined Akrotiri, winter 1971–72, showed no plumage differences from nominate *pendulinus* (P. R. Flint) and wing lengths of trapped birds (see Appendix 3) are also similar to *pendulinus* (Vaurie, Dement'ev *et al.*, BMNH skins).

ORIOLIDAE

306. ORIOLUS ORIOLUS   PM MB

Golden Oriole

O.o. oriolus. Fairly common passage migrant in spring: once seen mid Mar (Morris 1946b), occasional late Mar to early Apr, main passage mid Apr to mid May; occasional late May, once early Jun. Maxima 100 Cape Andreas, 23 Apr 1973, and 80 Akamas, 23 Apr 1978. Less common on autumn passage, Sep (occasional Aug and Oct).

Breeding. Scarce and local migrant breeder in deciduous woodland of the Troodos range, breeding recorded only twice – R. R. Waterer (*in* the Bannermans 1958) "found its nest near Platania Forest Station", and on 25 May 1959, nest found with C/4 in Plane *Platanus orientalis* in a wooded valley above Platania at *c*.1100 m (Ashton-Johnson). Has also occurred in the breeding season at Saittas at *c*. 800 m, 3 pairs with ♂♂ singing, 30 Jun and 7 Jul 1957; at Ayios Avikon, near Milikouri at *c*. 800 m; at Kalokhorio Dam at *c*. 550 m; near Phasoula at *c*. 150 m. Mating and regular song Thermia, near Kyrenia, 24 Apr to 11 May 1971, until both birds shot (R18), and song there early Jul 1980.

LANIIDAE

307. LANIUS COLLURIO   PM OB?

Red-backed Shrike

Passage migrant in variable numbers in spring, usually common, sometimes in large influxes. Occasional late Mar to early Apr, main passage mid–late Apr to early–mid May; occasional late May. Maximum 100+ Lachi area, 5 May 1988. In the past "hundreds" on the Karpas, 19 Apr 1912 (Bucknill 1913a). 484 were limed Paralimni, 7 Apr to 12 May 1968 (Horner & Hubbard). Fairly common in autumn, with birds (mainly juveniles) more widespread. First arrivals mid–late Aug (once each mid Jul, late Jul and early Aug), main passage Sep to early Oct; last seen late Oct, occasionally Nov.

No proof of breeding though possible occasionally – ♀ building nest Kantara, 1 May 1953 (the Bannermans 1958). On Troodos, one early Jun 1887 (Guillemard 1888) and 3 recent records there, mid Jun, late Jun and early Jul, but there is no evidence of breeding and no records of young seen or adults collected there 1908–9 (*pace* the Bannermans 1971, Stewart & Christensen).

3 recoveries of birds ringed in Poland, West Germany and Yugoslavia (Appendix 2).

[*L. isabellinus* Isabelline Shrike. A ♀ *L. isabellinus* was collected Stavrovouni, 8 Nov 1902 (Madarász 1904b), but no description is available. One, with bright chestnut tail, Akrotiri, 12 Sep 1964 (R12), possibly *L.i. phoenicuroides* or a hybrid between that and *L. collurio*. Another with chestnut tail, Akrotiri, 23 Sep 1980 (*per* Mrs J. Whiter), but upperparts similar to *L. collurio*. Individuals Akrotiri, 19 Oct 1957 (R2) and 22 Sep 1959 (R4), "pale sandy but otherwise typical" of *L. collurio*.]

308. LANIUS MINOR   PM

Lesser Grey Shrike

Spring passage migrant in variable numbers, usually scarce and occasionally very scarce. It is also occasionally fairly common and in a few years there have been large influxes on the Karpas, indicating that most birds probably pass to the east of the island in spring. Once seen mid Mar, first arrivals usually late Mar to mid Apr, main passage usually late Apr to early May; last seen mid–late May, twice mid Jun. Recent maxima: "very numerous" Cape Andreas, 5 May 1971; and 52 between Yialousa and Cape Andreas, 29 Apr 1972. In the past, "hundreds" between Rizokarpaso and Cape Andreas, 19 Apr 1912 (Bucknill 1913a). Only 7 limed Paralimni, 2–8 May 1968 (Horner & Hubbard). Much more numerous in autumn, when very common and widespread, some briefly taking up territories (Bourne *et al.*). Once mid Jul (trapped), occasional late Jul, otherwise first seen early–mid Aug, main passage usually mid–late Aug to mid Sep; last seen late Sep or Oct, once early Dec. Also a melanistic bird Akrotiri, 28 Oct to 15 Dec 1962.

309. LANIUS EXCUBITOR   AV

Great Grey Shrike

Accidental visitor, one record: one Larnaca airport, 1 Apr 1989 (M. Sainsbury *per* C. J. L. Bennett). From 2 colour slides the bird shows characters of the race *L.e. elegans*, which breeds in North Africa from Mauritania, through southern Tunisia and Libya to Egypt, the Sinai peninsula and southern Palestine (Vaurie). The race *elegans* is believed to be non-migratory, but there is some evidence that local winter movements occur in Egypt (Goodman & Meininger), and the Cyprus record perhaps resulted from a bird over-shooting when returning to its breeding grounds.

[Some 10 records (one spring, 9 autumn) 1956–71, none adequately separated from Lesser Grey Shrike *L. minor*. In the past mentioned by Schrader (1891). This species is not a passage migrant through the eastern Mediterranean, European birds wintering only as far south as the northern shores of that sea (Vaurie), and were they ever to occur in Cyprus it would most likely be in winter rather than during the migrations. See also Bourne 1959a:10 and 1960b.]

310. LANIUS SENATOR   PM OB

Woodchat Shrike

Passage migrant in variable numbers in spring, occasionally scarce, more usually fairly common. Once seen early Mar, occasional mid–late Mar, main passage Apr, peak numbers usually in the second half of the month; last seen May. Usually in ones and twos, sometimes up to 10–15 at one location; there are no records of large influxes. Only 2 limed Paralimni, spring 1968 (Horner & Hubbard). Prior to the mid 1970s it was irregular and very scarce on autumn passage, Aug to early Oct, but since then it has become regular and less scarce in autumn. Exceptional were 10 Paralimni, 18 Sep 1976 (NR7), and *c.* 20 Pomos/Polis/Akamas, 27 Aug to 2 Sep 1978 (NR9).

Breeding. 2 records. Adult feeding 2 fledged young near the Phasouri end of M1 road, 15 Jul 1980; habitat stubble field with small bushes, Fig *Ficus carica* and line of Olives *Olea europaea* (*per* Mrs J. Whiter). A pair bred Paphos 1988, nest building 15 May, feeding young 3 Jun and 2 young fledged 20 Jun; nest situated in a small Almond *Prunus dulcis* in an old orchard next to a house and a busy road (NL88/5 & 6). In addition, there are several recent records of possible or probable breeding: a pair with an empty nest, Macheras, 24 Jun 1980 (NR11); adults feeding juveniles at Polis/Akamas late Aug to early Sep 1980 and 1981 (NR11 & 12); a pair Parekklisha, Jul 1983 (R30); and juveniles at Kouklia (Paphos) and Drousha, Jul 1984 (NR15). Also recent (1978–89) Jun–Jul records from several other areas of the western Troodos coastal lowlands: Evdhimou, Episkopi, Kathikas, Anavargos, Khlorakas and Peyia. It is probable that the species is now a regular breeder in small numbers. ["Very young birds on Troodos in June" in the past (G. F. Wilson *in* the Bannermans 1958) were probably Masked Shrike *L. nubicus*.]

Nominate *senator* collected once (the Bannermans 1958, skin in RSM); on distribution *L.s. niloticus* may also occur.

311. LANIUS NUBICUS   MB PM

Masked Shrike

Very common migrant breeder.

Breeding distribution. Wooded areas of both mountain ranges, usually above 200–400 m, locally to sea level on the north coast and on the Troodos coastal lowlands. Has also recently bred on low ground at Strovolos (1976–NR7), and up to 4 pairs have bred in the riverbed area of Nicosia since 1985 (R32–R34), with others present at Athalassa.

Breeding data. Seen once early and once late Feb, occasional early Mar, first arrivals usually mid Mar, widespread by early Apr. Nests in Aleppo Pine *P. halepensis* and Troodos Pine *P. nigra* in pine forest, and in a wide variety of broadleaved trees. Nest, height 1·5–9 m above ground (many over 5 m), usually far out on a lateral branch, but sometimes against the trunk (R33), and once in the centre of a bush (R19). Clutch size C/4 to C/7. A detailed description of the nest and eggs is given by Ashton-Johnson. On low ground eggs found once early Apr (NR6) to May; young once late Apr (R33) with many early–mid May; fledged young once early May (R33), many mid May with others till Jun, and once Aug (R22). On Troodos fresh eggs are generally found in the latter half of May and early Jun (Ashton-Johnson), with many fledged young from late Jun (Mason). The incubation period is *c*. 14 days, possibly less, and may start before the clutch is complete, resulting in a brood of different sized young (Aloneftis, Bourne 1985). At Skouriotissa in 1976 a C/6 hatched over a 3 day period, 7–10 Jun, but all the young fledged together on 22 Jun (Aloneftis). At Nicosia in 1986 young fledged in 11–12 days (R33).

Ashton-Johnson found the breeding season to be very protracted, and this confirmed by many later observers. The species is stated to be double brooded (Witherby *et al.*) and in the first edition we considered this to be the probable reason for the protracted breeding season. However there are no records of 2 successful broods from Cyprus, and the main reason for the lengthy breeding season may be repeat laying after heavy predation of first clutches and broods. Of 13 nests at Skouriotissa in 1976, 10 were predated, probably mainly by large lizards. In all the cases of failed breeding the nests later disappeared, and in 2 cases the birds were seen dismantling the old nest and using the material to build a new one (R23). In 1985, 3 young fledged successfully from a nest at Episkopi, 20 May, and a week later the nest had disappeared, suggesting that the adults may have rebuilt it elsewhere for a second brood (Murray 1985, R32). This raises the possibility that some adults with successful early broods (fledging in May), may in fact be double brooded, and a follow-up study on this is needed.

A movement of mainly juveniles to low ground late Jun onwards, mainly late Jul to Aug, when some take up territories, but birds also remain numerous in the mountains till late Aug: still 50 on Troodos, 28 Aug 1972 (NR3), and frequent with many juveniles in the Paphos Forest, Aug 1984 (NR15). Murray (1987b) observed a juvenile closely associating with man to obtain disturbed insects. Departure mainly mid Aug to early–mid Sep, few remaining after mid Sep, last seen Oct, occasionally Nov.

Arrival and departure of migrant breeders tends to obscure passage, though passage migrants are sometimes common at northern capes mid–late Apr; maximum "very large numbers" Cape Andreas, 15 Apr 1968, with over 40 counted from one point (R15). 113 limed Paralimni, 17 Mar to 12 May 1968 (Horner & Hubbard), probably both passage birds and arriving breeders. "Many" on the Karpas, 9 Sep 1972 (R19) were probably passage birds.

One ringed Akrotiri 29 Aug 1971, retrapped there 11 and 20 Aug 1972. One ringed in Cyprus recovered in Lebanon (Appendix 2).

CORVIDAE

312. GARRULUS GLANDARIUS   RB

Jay

Common resident (*G.g glaszneri*, an endemic race).

Breeding distribution. Wooded areas of the Troodos range, mainly above *c*. 900 m, though in the Paphos Forest down to *c*. 500 m. Occurs in pine forest and in areas of Cyprus Cedar *Cedrus libanotica* and Golden Oak *Quercus alnifolia*.

Breeding data. Nests in *pinus*; lichen seems almost a characteristic feature of nests of this race (Ashton-Johnson). Height of 3 nests, 4·9, 5·5 and 18·3 m above ground (Ashton-Johnson). Eggs, C/4 to C/6, found May to early Jun (Ashton-Johnson, Bucknill 1909–10); fledged young late May to early Jul. Maximum post-breeding count: 50 Troodos-Kykko-Cedar Valley-Panayia, including a flock of 16 at Cedar Valley, 6 Sep 1989 (NL89/9). Seen feeding in snow on Troodos, Dec, but generally fewer there mid-winter, when birds occur down to 200 m in the Paphos Forest (R28). Occasional individuals also on the Troodos coastal lowlands, mainly Mar and Aug–Oct. Away from the Troodos range: 2 Akanthou Pass, 2 May 1948 (McNeile); one Nicosia, 17 Oct 1961; and one Cape Andreas, 23 Apr 1973 (Stagg 1974); all possibly vagrants from the north.

G.g. glaszneri is a dark race differing from all other races in the nominate *glandarius* group by having a reddish, not whitish, forecrown and by having a smaller bill (Vaurie).

One ringed Troodos, 9 Nov 1970, shot there 3 Apr 1971.

313. PICA PICA   RB WV?

Magpie

Very common resident (*P.p. pica*).

Breeding distribution. Up to 1200–1500 m in lightly wooded areas and more open country with scattered trees, particularly common in cultivation near villages. Most numerous in the north of the island, from Kormakiti to the Karpas. Scarce on the Mesaoria. Small flocks occur all year, some remaining for months at rubbish tips, maximum 60 Pergamos rubbish tip, 13 Feb 1983.

Breeding data. Nests in a wide variety of broadleaved and coniferous trees, Carob *Ceratonia siliqua* particularly favoured. Height of 8 nests, 3·6–10·6 m above ground (Ashton-Johnson). Eggs, C/5 to C/9 , found Apr to mid May; young mid Apr to early May (once early Jul). Parasitised by Great Spotted Cuckoo *Clamator glandarius (q.v.)*.

158   Corvidae

Apparently is also a winter visitor from the north, possibly not uncommon. At Cape Andreas, 23 Apr to 1 May 1972, daily numbers fluctuated markedly from 6 to 50; yet a few miles down the Karpas, birds were paired for breeding and variation in numbers was minimal. Similar pattern noted at Cape Andreas Apr 1973, where on 6 and 10 Apr groups made attempts to move out to sea towards Turkey. 3 attempts successful, unspecified numbers climbing to *c.* 900 m and moving steadily NNW until lost from view in excellent visibility. Successful departures made when winds were light and variable, other attempts quickly abandoned when slightest freshening of wind (Stagg 1974). Size and regularity of this movement require investigation, since the species is normally sedentary (Voous 1960, Vaurie, Hüe & Etchécopar) except in northern regions of the U.S.S.R. (Dement'ev & Gladkov), though recent Aug and Oct records from Lebanon (Benson) suggest southward movement also in that area.

314. CORVUS MONEDULA   RB WV
Jackdaw

C.m. soemmerringii. Locally very common resident.

Breeding distribution. Cliffs and rock faces below *c.* 900 m, possibly a few up to *c.* 1700 m. Probably most numerous within the Kyrenia range, and on coastal and near coastal cliffs in the southwest and west Troodos coastal lowlands, but occurs widely in suitable habitat. Also recorded breeding on the Karpas (Ashton-Johnson, R34), on Yeronisos Island (R29), and in the southeast near Dhekelia. Has also bred in buildings or walls in Kyrenia, Famagusta and Nicosia. In Famagusta formerly bred abundantly in the old city walls (Lilford, Jourdain 1929b, Ashton-Johnson), its present status there is not known.

Breeding data. Usually colonial, largest colonies documented, *c.* 400 pairs on coastal cliffs from Curium to Cape Aspro in 1970, but probably equally large colonies elsewhere. Isolated pairs also nest in holes in trees. Since 1987 several pairs have bred in air conditioners on high rise buildings in Nicosia. Eggs, C/4 to C/7, found Apr to early May; fledged young May (mainly Bucknill 1909–10, Jourdain 1929a, Ashton-Johnson).

Flocks of up to 1000 form after breeding and in winter, roosts noted Polemidhia and in pines at Myrtou. Flocks from the Kyrenia range regularly visit adjacent lowlands to feed. Probably a not uncommon winter visitor: over 100 north at Cape Andreas, Apr 1973 (Stagg 1974).

The resident birds were formerly considered, along with those from elsewhere in the Middle East, to be of the race *C.m. pontocaspius* (Kleiner); but this was united with *C.m. soemmerringii* by Vaurie. Birds both lacking collars and with exceptionally white collars have been reported (Stagg 1974, R33). Bucknill (1910) observed that "In many specimens the nuchal collar is extremely white, but this is by no means invariably the case, and is partially a sign of age. In any case one can always see birds with almost every grade of colour".

315. CORVUS FRUGILEGUS   WV
Rook

Scarce and irregular visitor (*C.f. frugilegus*) mainly in winter. 11 recent records mainly Oct–May, though has been recorded in every month. Usually singly or less than 10 together, maximum 50 Kolossi, 9 Feb 1958. Some birds apparently remain for weeks or months. In the past, G. F. Wilson saw it only in severe winters, and R. R. Waterer never saw one in 22 years (both *in* the Bannermans 1958); Bucknill (1909–10), over 2 or 3 winters, found it "common" mid Nov to mid Mar, with 100s in fields near Nicosia. Mentioned by Guillemard (1888) and one collected Nov 1878 (Lilford).

316. CORVUS CORONE   RB
Hooded Crow

Common and widespread resident (*C.c. sardonius*).

Breeding distribution. Below *c.* 1000 m, scarcer up to *c.* 1500 m, and absent from pine forest.

Breeding data. Nests in a variety of trees, often *Eucalyptus* sp or Aleppo Pine *Pinus halepensis*. Height of 8 nests, 4–9 m above ground (Ashton-Johnson), also once 12 m (NL88/5). Eggs, C/3 to C/6 (mainly C/5), found Apr–May (mainly Bucknill 1909–10, the Bannermans 1958, Ashton-Johnson).

Post-breeding flocks of 10s (occasionally 100s) form Jun onwards, usually on low ground in winter. Roosts of up to 150 noted Morphou and Polemidhia. In the past, Stochove (*in* Cobham) found that, in 1631, in the gardens in Nicosia, "the number of crows is incredible, the trees are black with them .. at dawn their croaking makes it impossible to sleep" (probably this and/or Raven *C. corax* involved). This abundance was probably due to protection, as the local Turkish population would not have the birds killed.

One, showing characters of the nominate *corone* group of races, probably *C.c orientalis*, at Akrotiri 26 Mar 1980 (Allen *et al.*).

The resident birds were formerly considered to be an endemic race *C.c. pallescens*, but this was united with *C.c. sardonius* by Vaurie, along with birds from elsewhere in the Mediterranean region.

317. CORVUS CORAX   RB
Raven

Scarce to fairly common resident, decreasing and now less numerous than in 1950s.

Breeding distribution. Formerly "exceedingly common" (Lilford) and widespread on low ground. Now mainly confined to open and rocky areas of mountains, and to coastal cliffs.

Breeding data. Nests on cliffs and rock faces, less frequently in trees; nested Famagusta walls 1929 (Jourdain 1929a). Has nested commonly in sides of steep, flat-topped, hills on the Mesaoria (Bucknill 1909–10, Ashton-Johnson), and some probably still do so. Eggs, C/4 late Feb, C/7 early Mar (Ashton-Johnson) and C/6 mid Mar (Bucknill 1909–10); young late Mar to early May.

Birds gather to soar in thermals and display at Amiandos Mine/Troodos/Mt. Olympus all year (this behaviour described by Hurrell), peak numbers Jul–Sep: up to 200 there 1960, now usually in 10s, though 200 Troodos, 29 Sep 1987. Occasional wandering flocks, of 10s or less, occur anywhere, mainly after breeding and in winter, when more frequent on low ground, some foraging at town rubbish tips.

The subspecific status of the population requires further study, the birds do not appear to be separable from nominate *corax*, but it is possible that the population is intermediate between *corax* and *subcorax* (Vaurie). Lilford's specimens "vary considerably in dimensions, are very stout-billed, and have all some umber-brown feathers in the wings, showing affinity to the races *C. umbrinus* and *C. tingitanus*".

STURNIDAE

318. STURNUS VULGARIS   WV PM
Starling

Very common winter visitor, mainly to open low ground, especially the Mesaoria. Occasional Jul to early Oct, first arrivals usually mid–late Oct, main influx early–mid Nov. Roosts of 1000s form Nicosia; up to half a million, Nov to early Dec 1970. Main departure early–mid Feb, few after late Feb, last singles in Apr, exceptionally into May–Jun. Passages of flocks of up to 200 at Cape Gata and Cape Andreas early and mid Nov. Only one record of spring passage: a flock in from sea at Cape Andreas, 19 Mar 1954 (the Bannermans 1958).

13 recoveries of birds ringed in the U.S.S.R., 11 ringed within the breeding range of nominate *vulgaris*, one within the range of *S.v. tauricus*, and one without details (Appendix 2). On distribution *S.v. purpurascens* probably also occurs.

319. STURNUS ROSEUS   PM
Rose-coloured Starling

Very scarce and irregular passage migrant May and Aug (once Jul); all autumn records are of juveniles. 6 recent records: one Kormakiti, 22 May 1966 (R13); 2 Cape Andreas, 18 May 1971 (NR2); 12 Cape Andreas, 12 May 1974 (NR5); 2 Akrotiri, 20 Aug 1975 (NR6); 8 near Phrenaros, 17 May 1979 (Kephalas 1989); 4 near Polis, 20 Aug 1982 (R29). In the past: a small flock 6 Jul 1876 (Schrader); 8 near Paphos, 20 May 1909 and 12 on 22 May (Bucknill 1909–10); one shot from flock of 4 or 5 near Limassol, 18 Aug 1945 (skin in NRS). Seigneur de Villamont (*in* Cobham), who visited Cyprus in 1589, relates an (apocryphal) story concerning the destruction of locusts by an irruption of flocks of this species in some previous year, though at the time of his visit the species was once more scarce or absent.

PASSERIDAE

320. PASSER DOMESTICUS   RB PM WV?
House Sparrow

Locally abundant resident (*P.d. biblicus*).

Breeding distribution. Mainly around towns, villages, houses and cultivation; also in isolated colonies in both open and wooded country far from human habitation. Breeds at all altitudes, though numbers on Troodos/Mt. Olympus considerably reduced after autumn (Mason).

Breeding data. Nests in a wide variety of natural and man-made sites, in the country usually in holes in banks and cuttings, and in trees, particularly *Eucalyptus* sp and *Pinus* sp, in colonies of up to 100 pairs. Also nests in sea caves (NL88/5). Tree colonies often shared with Spanish Sparrow *P. hispaniolensis (q.v.)*, but no direct evidence of hybridization (see below). In open agricultural areas also builds nests on tops of electricity or telegraph poles. Nest building and mating Jan onwards; eggs, C/3 to C/8, found late Mar to May; young mid Mar to early Jul. Post-breeding and winter flocks mainly Jun–Feb, though some flocking all year; *c.* 1000 roosting Moni

early–mid Aug 1980, fewer later. 5 ringed, Xeros (2) and Akrotiri (3), recovered/
retrapped where ringed in subsequent years.

Apparent hybrid trapped Akrotiri, 24 Oct 1980 (Hallchurch), was probably
melanistic *P. domesticus* (J. D. Summers-Smith). A bird resembling "Italian"
Sparrow *P.d. italiae* at Anarita, 26 Nov 1983 (R30), and "hybrids" at Paphos
lighthouse, 15–28 Oct 1989 (NL89/10). In view of the dates some of these birds may
have been immigrants.

2 records of passage, both from Cape Andreas: on 19 Apr 1972 small parties of
5–10 moving steadily northeast towards tip of Cape, and at the tip *c.* 30 flew
northeast out to sea until lost to sight (J. R. Neighbour); on 23 Sep 1972, *c.* 2000 flew
east out to sea with *P. hispaniolensis* (NR3) and there were also many exhausted
birds there, probably newly arrived migrants. Of 357 limed Paralimni, spring 1968,
59% were fledged juveniles, indicating that the birds were local breeders and not
migrants (Horner & Hubbard 1982), as was suggested by the Bannermans (1971). In
early–mid Oct 1969 recently arrived flocks of 100s of *P. hispaniolensis* in vineyards at
Akrotiri contained fair numbers of *P. domesticus* (P. R. Flint, P. F. Stewart), though
possibly some of the latter were local birds which had joined the flocks. Observation
of the flocks of *P. hispaniolensis* (*q.v.*) on autumn passage through the Karvounas
Pass, should reveal if, and in what proportion, these flocks contain *P. domesticus.*
Not known to be migratory in the Near East (Dement'ev & Gladkov, Hüe &
Etchécopar, Vaurie) nor to be a winter visitor to Egypt or Sinai (Etchécopar & Hüe,
Ghabbour), but is often overlooked or ignored and its movements clearly require
more study. Although not recorded as migrating from Turkey, of interest were
"several thousands", 24 Sep 1968, at Göksu Delta on the Turkish south coast —
only *c.* 90 km north of Cyprus (Vittery & Squire).

321. PASSER HISPANIOLENSIS   RB PM WV

Spanish Sparrow

Locally fairly common to common resident, increasing in numbers and colonising
new areas.

Breeding distribution. Isolated colonies throughout most of island, in wooded
areas, including pine forest, and in plantations and stands of trees in open country
and around villages. In the Troodos range breeds up to at least 1300 m, and juveniles
seen at *c.* 1600 m.

Breeding data. Nests in a variety of broadleaved and coniferous trees,
Eucalyptus favoured on low ground, and Aleppo Pine *P. halepensis* in pine forest.
Colony size usually 10–75 pairs, though over 100 pairs increasingly common and
250–300 pairs at Salamis in 1959 in stand of Stone Pine *P. pinea* (Ashton-Johnson),
with a similar number near Kolossi, Apr 1982. Colonies often shared with House
Sparrow *P. domesticus* (*q.v.*). Eggs, C/4 to C/6, found late Mar to early May
(Ashton-Johnson); young once early Aug at Agros, *c.* 1250 m (NR7).

Very common passage migrant in flocks in autumn: occasional early–mid Sep,
peak numbers early–mid Oct (sometimes from late Sep), with fewer into Nov.
Flocks seen to depart east from Cape Andreas and south from Akrotiri. A
traditional route of migrating flocks is up the valley from Xeros, to Evrykhou,
Kakopetria and south through the Karvounas Pass; in late Sep to Oct 1974, up to
5000 moved through the Karvounas Pass every morning, and *c.*15,000 were killed
there on limesticks (NR5). Some flocks also pass west around the Troodos range. Of
a west–east evening coasting movement of flocks of 150–200 *Passer* sp at Episkopi
late Sep to early Oct 1981 (maximum 3000 in 53 minutes on 9 Oct), the few flocks

which settled briefly were *P. hispaniolensis* (M. G. Lobb). Common but usually in smaller flocks on spring passage, mainly late Mar to early May, though 60 were moving northeast Cape Andreas, 31 May 1971. Passage flocks are very common on the Akamas in spring: up to 20,000 there, 25 Apr 1979 (NR10); and *c.* 1000 (in flocks of 10–50) departed north from Cape Arnaouti, 15 Apr 1988, with many other flocks in scrub behind the cape (P. R. Flint). Fairly common and widespread winter visitor Oct to Mar–Apr, mainly to low ground, usually in flocks of 10s, occasionally in 100s.

322. PASSER MOABITICUS   RB or MB

Dead Sea Sparrow

P.m. moabiticus. Resident or migrant breeder.

Breeding distribution. Along the northern edge of Akrotiri Salt Lake. Probably first bred there in 1976 if not earlier. In 1976 and 1977 several nests (similar to those described below) were found in the northwestern corner of the lake, and in 1977 an egg typical for the species was found (R. Foers). The first birds were recorded in 1980 when 17 (including 8 juveniles) were trapped at Akrotiri reed beds, 6 Jul to 9 Nov, and 2 nests containing 3 dead young found (Lobb 1981, R27). In 1982 a survey from 27 Apr to 4 May located 14 nests along the northwestern edge of the lake and 2 nests in the northeastern corner (Jenkins 1986a). A further survey in mid–late Apr 1985 located 3 colonies totalling 35 nests: 22 nests in the northwestern corner of the lake, 4 nests 100–500 m east of these, and a further 9 nests in the bay in the northeastern corner of the lake. Most of these nests were there from previous years, over 25 were in good condition and could have been used for breeding in 1984. The number of birds seen represented a breeding population of probably 20–30 pairs (J. D. Summers-Smith). In 1983 a pair also bred at Zakaki (R30); in mid Apr 1984, up to 5 were in *Tamarix* by a small pond at Phasouri beach (R31); and on 18 Apr 1987, 3 were at Phasouri reed beds (R34) — these 3 locations are all within 2–3 km of the Akrotiri Salt Lake colonies.

Breeding data. ♂♂ in song noted early Jan, late Feb, Apr and mid Jul. Nest building, recorded only by ♂♂, late Feb, late Apr and late May. All nests found in *Tamarix* bushes (not *Juniperus*, as stated in the first edition), mainly growing in clumps in water (10–60 cm deep) with emergent vegetation, between the reed beds and the open water of the lake. Birds show a preference for nesting in dead bushes. Height of nests 1–3 m above ground. Nests are well spaced, the closest being *c.* 5 m apart. Nests are built of *Tamarix* twigs with reed panicles and *Tamarix* seed heads incorporated, and sometimes lined with fluffy reed tops. They have an entrance hole at the top and a spiral shaft leading down to the egg chamber. Dimensions of one nest: width 220 mm, height 220 mm, inside depth 160 mm, entrance diameter 40 mm. One new nest was built on top of an old one, resulting in a massive structure. The nests are well built and remain substantially intact for several years. Eggs, usually C/4, once C/3 (incomplete) and once C/5, found late Apr, late May and late Jun. Broods of 4 young twice late May (newly hatched) and once late Jun. (Breeding details J. D. Summers-Smith, Lobb 1981, Jenkins 1986a, *per* C. J. L. Bennett, R28, 30, 33 & 34).

Birds are usually present at or near their breeding colonies Apr to Oct–Nov. In 1985 no birds were seen at the main colony on 17 Apr, but by 28 Apr ♂♂ were present at 6 nests (J. D. Summers-Smith). Usually absent or not recorded Dec–Mar, though 9 birds overwintered Akrotiri Salt Lake from late Dec 1983 into the following breeding season. During the winter birds may migrate, as elsewhere in the Middle East (Cramp 1971a), or they may move locally, as in Israel (Paz). Away from the

Akrotiri area, 20 were at Polis, 2 Sep 1982, and 6 at Skarinou, 8 Nov 1986. These may have been wandering birds from Akrotiri (or elsewhere), or immigrants. There is evidence of range extension in the Middle East (Cramp 1971b), and the recent breeding in Cyprus appears to be a continuation of this. In the Middle East the species breeds mainly in *Tamarix*, but also in other trees and shrubs (sometimes within plantations), and usually within *c.* 100 m of fresh water (Cramp 1971b, Paz). There is much similar habitat in Cyprus and there are probably other undiscovered colonies in the island.

One ringed 7 Sep 1980, retrapped 1 Nov 1981; one ringed 14 Sep 1980, retrapped 28 Oct 1981; and one ringed 24 Oct 1980, retrapped 11 Jul 1982. All at Akrotiri reed beds (M. G. Lobb).

323. PASSER MONTANUS   WV
Tree Sparrow

Scarce (regular?) winter visitor to low ground and lower hills, mid Oct to mid Apr, mainly before mid-winter. Usually singly, but 50 Upper Kyrenia, 22 Nov 1971 with fewer Dec (R18), and 10 there 25 Oct 1972, increasing to 40 by 29 Nov, 1–8 remaining Dec (R19). 2 have been trapped among large flocks of Spanish Sparrow *P. hispaniolensis.*

324. PETRONIA PETRONIA   AV
Rock Sparrow

Accidental visitor, 2 records: one found dead near Pissouri, 13 Nov 1982 (now a skin in RSM) shows characters of the race *P.p. exigua*; another seen caged at Limassol market, 23 Nov 1982, was said to have been recently limed at Yermasoyia (both F. J. Walker, R29). [As *Fringilla petronia*, included in the list of Sibthorp (1787), but with no details.] The species is a fairly common resident or partial migrant in Turkey (Beaman), and may occur more frequently than the above records indicate.

FRINGILLIDAE

325. FRINGILLA COELEBS   RB PM WV
Chaffinch

F.c. coelebs. Common resident.
Breeding distribution. Pine forests (and orchards) of the Troodos range above *c.* 600 m, locally down to 300–450 m in northern valleys. Not known to breed outside the Troodos range, though song Kormakitis Forest once late May, and Karkas (Kyrenia range), once early Jun.
Breeding data. Song at least Apr–Jun. Nests usually in *Pinus*. Breeding little studied: eggs, C/3 to C/4, found May to early Jun; fledged young once mid May (mainly Ashton-Johnson). Some winter Troodos/Mt. Olympus, though numbers considerably reduced there late Oct (Mason), indicating movement to lower ground. 2 ringed Troodos retrapped there in subsequent summers.

Very common passage migrant. Spring passage mid Feb to mid Apr (occasional singles to mid May), peak numbers mid Feb to mid Mar, when birds fly in off the sea at the south coast (R10), and marked (mainly afternoon) passage west and northwest at Akrotiri, maximum *c.* 5000 moving west there in 2·5 hours, 11 Mar

1971. Also 3000 west at Curium, 22 Jan 1985, either immigrants or local movement. Autumn passage mainly Oct to mid Nov, maximum 800 over Akrotiri in 4 hours, 7 Oct 1968. Very common and widespread winter visitor (♀♀ often predominating) late Oct to Feb (fewer Mar). Mean wing lengths of residents are similar to those of migrants and winter visitors.

One ringed Akrotiri, 19 Nov 1972, still there 11 Mar 1973. One ringed in Cyprus recovered in the U.S.S.R. (Appendix 2).

Formerly considered to be an endemic race *F.c. cypriotis* (Harrison), but this was united with nominate *coelebs* by Vaurie. Cyprus birds do not have a rain call dialect of their own, the pure tone element between 4 and 5 kHz is essentially the same as heard in Greece (Bergmann).

326. FRINGILLA MONTIFRINGILLA   WV

Brambling

Scarce winter visitor to low and high ground late Oct to mid Mar, mainly Nov–Feb, often amongst flocks of Chaffinches *F. coelebs*. Usually singly or up to 10 together, maximum 50 near Nicosia, 23 Feb 1964. Also seen twice late Mar, once early Apr (A. J. Stagg) and once late Apr.

327. SERINUS PUSILLUS   AV

Red-fronted Serin

Accidental visitor, one limed Vasilia (? date) 1973 (NR4). [One taken 1968, possibly an escape (Stewart & Christensen); others with inadequate detail Cape Andreas, 10 Apr 1971, and Nicosia Airport, 31 Dec 1978.] The species is a fairly common resident in southern Turkey, with some movement to the south coast in winter (Beaman), and might be expected to occur more frequently.

328. SERINUS SERINUS   RB WV PM

Serin

Locally common resident.

Breeding distribution. The Troodos range, mainly above 600 m, to near sea level in northern valleys, and locally onto adjacent low ground and coastal areas. Also 2 breeding records in the Kyrenia range, at Aghirda and Kantara, 1974. First known to breed on low ground, at Phasouri plantations, in 1969 (suspected 1963), and common throughout the plantations by 1971, at least 100 pairs (P. R. Flint). During 1970s also found breeding in the lower hills, and on low ground at Athalassa, Lakatamia, Morphou and Pendayia, probably also at Kormakiti and Akhelia. Also a pair Nicosia Presidential Palace, summer 1980. Although some low ground breeding probably overlooked in the past, these records appear to represent a genuine altitudinal extension of the breeding range. Breeds in open pine forest and woodland, in orchards and plantations, and in gardens and villages.

Breeding data. Song (at Phasouri) late Feb to Aug. Nests in a variety of coniferous and broadleaved trees – around cultivation, particularly in Cypress *Cupressus sempervirens* windbreaks. Height of 7 nests, *c.* 3–10 m above ground. Eggs, C/3 and C/4 found mid Jun to early Jul; fledged young late Apr onwards. Few residents remain above 1000 m in the Troodos range, Nov–Feb.

Common winter visitor to low ground, in flocks of 10s or 100s, occurring around towns and villages, and in open park-like areas and sports fields. First arrivals usually late Oct, peak numbers late Nov to Feb, fewer Mar, last early Apr. 2 ringed, Nicosia and Episkopi, retrapped/recovered where ringed in subsequent winters, one after 6 years (R17). 2 ringed Episkopi, recovered Limassol (19 km east) in subsequent winters.

Departure of winter visitors (or passage?), up to 10 daily, at northern capes late Mar to early Apr, stragglers to mid May. Only definite passage record, "several" south at Akrotiri, late Oct to early Nov 1957.

329. CARDUELIS CHLORIS   RB WV PM
Greenfinch

Common and widespread resident, having colonised the island very rapidly during 1960s and 1970s.

Breeding distribution. Jourdain (1930) thought "some probably breed Paphos", song and display there late Mar 1958, but no evidence that any remained after early Apr (R2). "Small numbers" Akrotiri all year 1962, and breeding proved there and at Phasouri 1963 (R10). By 1967/68 "abundant resident" in irrigated areas around Phasouri and Polemidhia (R14 & 15). In 1971/72 breeding in many areas on high and low ground, including Troodos and Nicosia, and by mid 1970s common and widespread. Occurs in woodland, including pine forest, and in cultivated areas, towns and villages.

Breeding data. Song at least late Feb to Jun. Nests in wide variety of trees, often *Eucalyptus* or Aleppo Pine *P. halepensis*. Eggs, C/4 and C/5, found May to mid Jul; fledged young late Apr to early Aug. Post-breeding flocks mid May onwards, in 100s Aug–Sep. Few above *c.* 800 m in winter, scarce Troodos after mid Sep, none there Nov–Dec (Mason). 12 ringed/retrapped Akrotiri, showing that breeders there are resident and sedentary.

Common winter visitor to low ground in flocks of 10s: first arrivals late Oct to early Nov, peak numbers usually late Nov to Feb, fewer Mar. Common passage migrant. "Small movement off sea" after 20 Feb 1963 (R10), flocks of 10s on south coast late Mar to Apr, very common in flocks Cape Andreas late Mar, fewer Apr. Passage out to sea Cape Andreas late Oct–Nov 1971, maximum 860 moving northeast, 31 Oct (Flint 1972e).

330. CARDUELIS CARDUELIS   RB WV PM
Goldfinch

Very common and widespread resident (*C.c. niediecki*).

Breeding distribution. Most numerous on low ground, but almost ubiquitous, wherever trees occur.

Breeding data. Nests in a wide variety of trees, often *Eucalyptus, Acacia,* Aleppo Pine *P. halepensis* and various fruit trees. Nest height, *c.* 2–10 m above ground, "usually high up" (Ashton-Johnson). Eggs, usually C/4 or C/5, once C/6 (the Bannermans 1958), found late Mar to early Jun; fledged young once late Mar (R31) to Jul (seen at both Troodos and Nicosia late Jul). Post-breeding flocks of 10s and 100s Jun onwards. Absent or very scarce on Troodos mid Nov to early Mar, most descending below *c.* 1200 m. 36 local retraps/recoveries show that breeders on low ground are resident and more or less sedentary, though a juvenile ringed Cyprus and recovered Egypt (Appendix 2) indicates some movement off the island.

Common winter visitor, peak numbers Nov–Feb, when, with residents, abundant on low ground. Departure (and passage?) at northern capes mid Feb to early Apr (many late Mar), few till mid May. Passage out to sea Akrotiri, 3 Nov 1957 (R2), and at Cape Andreas, late Oct–Nov 1971, maximum 17 moving east 31 Oct (Flint 1972e).

Probably several races occur on passage and in winter, both *brevirostris* and *loudoni* being mentioned by Hartert (1903–1923), and one ringed in Yugoslavia (Appendix 2) was (probably) either *carduelis* or *balcanica*.

331. CARDUELIS SPINUS   WV
Siskin

Winter visitor in variable numbers, occasionally scarce, more usually fairly common in 10s, occasionally common in 100s. Occurs Nov to early Apr, mainly Dec–Mar, usually in pinewood areas on high and low ground. Also occasional mid-late Oct and mid-late Apr. 'Siskin years' are listed by Bourne *et al.* and by the Bannermans (1971), and "extensive flocks may winter" (Waterer), but there is only one documented irruption of large flocks — in the winter of 1961–62: *c.* 200 St. Hilarion, 28 Dec 1961 (R8), 100s there and Troodos until late Mar (*c.* 300 Troodos 17 Mar), and *c.* 200 in area of Presidential Palace, Nicosia, 20 Mar to 2 Apr (R9).

2 recoveries of birds ringed in Hungary and the U.S.S.R. (Appendix 2).

332. CARDUELIS (=ACANTHIS) CANNABINA   RB WV PM
Linnet

Fairly common and widespread resident though of patchy distribution and rather scarce in much apparently suitable habitat.

Breeding distribution. Occurs at all altitudes, in open areas with scrub or bushes, including cultivation and gardens; most numerous in uncultivated areas of hills and mountains, but not proved to breed above *c.* 1450 m, though a few present Troodos/Mt. Olympus in summer.

Breeding data. Nests in wide variety of bushes and small scrubby trees, nest height 0·3–2·5 m above ground. Eggs, C/4 and C/5, found Apr to early Jul, once late Jul; young Apr–Jul, and fledged young twice early Apr (Horner & Hubbard). Post-breeding flocks mainly Jul onwards. Few above *c.* 800 m in winter. One ringed Polemidhia, 30 Jul 1968, still there 8 Dec.

Very common winter visitor to open low ground Nov–Mar, usually in flocks of 10s or 100s, occasionally in 1000s. Departure and passage flocks very common at northern capes mid Feb to Apr, probably on passage into May. Common on passage Oct to mid Nov, 10s moving out to sea Cape Gata and Cape Andreas.

Vaurie listed the resident birds as *C.c. cannabina*, but the Bannermans (1971) and Stewart & Christensen believed them to be *C.c. bella*. Probably both races occur on passage or in winter.

333. CARDUELIS (=ACANTHIS) FLAMMEA   AV
Redpoll

Occasional winter visitor, 5 records: one of the nominate race collected Argates, 13 Jan 1966 and one caught near Lefkara, 26 Nov 1966 (both R13); one caught near Limassol, 4 Jan 1968 (R15); 2 ♂♂ limed Lythrodhonda (date ?) 1971 (NR2); 2 limed near Yermasoyia, late Jan 1974 (NR5). No sight records, is probably overlooked.

334. LOXIA CURVIROSTRA   RB WV?

Crossbill

Fairly common resident (*L.c. guillemardi*, an endemic race).
Breeding distribution. In Troodos Pine *P. nigra* forest on Troodos above *c*. 1500 m.
Breeding data. Little studied, no published details of eggs, nests or young. Apparently breeds very early, coinciding with the ripening of *P. nigra* seed in early spring, though some breeding throughout most of year. Song at least Dec–Jan, and once late Mar, also several in full song once mid Aug and once late Aug. Fledged young mid Mar, mid Apr, Jun, mid Jul, mid Sep (Bucknill 1909–10), late Sep and mid Oct (R34), and early Nov (R2), probably also mid Feb. Flocks of 10s, sometimes 100–200, form Jun–Sep, dispersing by early Oct. Occasional small flocks, up to 8, in Aleppo Pine *P. halepensis* down to *c*. 600 m in the Troodos range, mainly Dec–Mar, once 6 at Stavros, mid Jul.
7 records of singles and flocks in coastal areas Sep–Dec, maximum 40 in pines at Kormakiti, 22 Nov 1970. In view of the restricted range and sedentary nature of the residents, these records perhaps refer to immigrants of the nominate race, which has occurred in Syria and the Lebanon (Hüe & Etchécopar).
The race *guillemardi* is variable in colour but red ♂♂ are very rare and paler than in nominate *curvirostra*, nearly all ♂♂ are washed very heavily with yellow or orange yellow above and below; the bill is much larger and thicker than in *curvirostra* (Vaurie).

335. BUCANETES GITHAGINEUS
(= RHODOPECHYS GITHAGINEA)   PM

Trumpeter Finch

Very scarce and irregular passage migrant, 7 records: Mar–Apr (6) and early Dec. In detail: one limed Paralimni, 27 Apr 1969 (*per* P. F. Stewart); ♂ Cape Andreas, 26 Mar and 10 Apr 1971 (NR2, R18); ♂ Nicosia, 24 Apr 1974 (R21); ♂ Ayia Napa, 9 Mar 1980 (*per* Mrs. J. Whiter); ♂ Episkopi, 16 Apr 1987, and ♀ Ladies Mile, Akrotiri, 5 Dec 1987 (both R34); ♂ Evretou Dam, 28 Apr 1988 (W. E. Oddie).

336. CARPODACUS ERYTHRINUS   AV

Scarlet Rosefinch

Accidental visitor, 4 records: immature ♀ collected Bishops Pool, Akrotiri, 19 Sep 1969 (skin in RSM); others (not adult ♂♂) trapped there, 10 Nov 1969 (R16) and 23 May 1970 (R17); one seen Akrounda Creek, 21 Dec 1982 (R29, *per* C. J. L. Bennett). The species is migratory, breeding throughout much of eastern Europe and Asia, including northern Turkey (Vaurie), and probably occurs more frequently than these records suggest.

337. COCCOTHRAUSTES COCCOTHRAUSTES   WV

Hawfinch

Scarce (occasionally fairly common) winter visitor (*C.c. coccothraustes*) to wooded areas on high and low ground, sometimes also around towns and villages. Has occurred late Oct to mid May, but mainly Nov to early Mar. The Apr to mid May records are mainly from Troodos. Also 9 Troodos once early Sep. Usually less than 10 together, occasionally in flocks of up to 60, sometimes with other finches. A "horde" in hard weather late Jan to Mar 1911 (Bucknill 1911). A flock fed for several weeks on fruits of Nettle Tree *Celtis australis,* and, for 2–3 winters, flocks at Platania fed on fruits of Terebinth *Pistacia terebinthus* (R. R. Waterer *in* the Bannermans 1958). Feeding also observed on *Cotoneaster* sp berries and in *Pinus* sp.

One recovery of a bird ringed in Yugoslavia (Appendix 2).

EMBERIZIDAE

338. EMBERIZA LEUCOCEPHALOS   AV

Pine Bunting

Accidential visitor, 3 records: 2 (one ♂) limed Troodos, late Sep 1972 (NR3); 2 (one ♂) Troodos, 4 Nov 1975 (NR6); 14 near Stavrovouni, 25 Jan 1976, with one there 1 Feb (NR7).

339. EMBERIZA CITRINELLA   WV

Yellowhammer

Scarce (regular ?) winter visitor, mainly to open woodland and orchard areas in the Troodos range, occasionally to low ground. Occurs mainly Dec–Feb; also seen once each late Sep, Nov and Mar, twice Apr and once May. Usually singly or a few together, maximum 25 Platres, 24 Jan 1958 (R2). Up to 9 wintered Perapedhi/ Mandria, Dec 1981 to Feb 1982 (R28 & 29), and 3 there, Dec 1984 (R31). 2 collected Kellaki, 18 Feb 1955 (skins in Tel Aviv University) pre-date previous earliest published record.

340. EMBERIZA CIA   PM WV?

Rock Bunting

Very scarce and irregular passage migrant (and winter visitor ?), 6 records: mid Jan and late Mar to Apr (5). In detail: 8 above Ayios Khrysostomos, Kyrenia range, 15 Jan 1958 (R2, B6); ♂ Episkopi, 23 Apr 1963 (R10); ♂ Yermasoyia, 5 Apr 1971, and ♂ Kakopetria, 22 Apr 1971 (both NR2); ♂ Cape Andreas, 6 Apr 1973 (NR4), and another there, 24 Mar 1974 (NR5). In view of its status in Turkey, as a widespread and fairly common resident and partial migrant (Beaman), it is surprising that it does not occur in Cyprus more frequently in winter. [Vaurie includes Cyprus within breeding range of nominate race, but no evidence of breeding exists. Doubtfully reported as a rare visitor, arriving 12 Mar and staying till Sep (Schrader). Not collected by Schrader and the race occurring is unknown (*pace* the Bannermans 1958).]

341. EMBERIZA CINERACEA   PM

Cinereous Bunting

Very scarce (regular ?) passage migrant (*E.c. cineracea*) in spring, probably overlooked. Since 1974, 11 records (including those of R. Frost and M. E. J. Gore) of 1–2 birds at Cape Andreas, Amathus/Akrotiri/Episkopi area, and Paphos/Coral Bay, late Mar to Apr, some remaining 2–3 days. In the past, 3 records of 1–2 birds, early–mid Apr 1929 (W. B. Alexander *in* the Bannermans 1958, Jourdain 1929a). All records mention ♂♂, some with ♀♀ or immatures, descriptions fitting the nominate race.

342. EMBERIZA HORTULANA   PM OB?
Ortolan Bunting

Usually fairly common or common passage migrant in spring in flocks of 10s, mid–late Mar to early May, peak numbers mid–late Apr, maximum 200 at the Akamas, 14 Apr 1988. Also seen once early Mar, and twice mid and once late May. In autumn, usually only a few records of small numbers, maximum 20 together, on passage late Aug to mid Sep (occasional early–mid Aug, twice late Sep and twice Oct). 3 summer records: a pair Platres, 1 Jul 1967; ♀ Ayios Khrysostomos, 24 Jun 1969; and ♂ Episkopi, 10 Jul 1982. [C/4 taken Kyrenia range, *c.* 11 Jun 1914 identified as *E. hortulana* by F. C. R. Jourdain (Baxendale 1915), but later Jourdain (1929b) stated that the record needed confirmation.]

343. EMBERIZA CAESIA   MB PM
Cretzschmar's Bunting

Common migrant breeder.

Breeding distribution. Hills and mountains mainly above 150–400 m, locally onto adjacent low ground. Occurs on open, rocky (usually steep) slopes with low scattered scrub and a few trees, also on similar slopes within open pine forest.

Breeding data. First arrivals early–mid Mar (twice late Feb), common by late Mar or early Apr. Song at least Apr–Jun, once late Aug. Bergmann found no dialectal peculiarities in the song when compared with continental populations. Nests on the ground, often partly or completely sheltered by a small shrub (often *Cistus*), or concealed among debris of twigs and pine needles, but some nests are open and exposed. [Records of nests in sapling pines (the Bannermans 1958) should refer to Cyprus Warbler *Sylvia melanothorax* (McNeile).] Eggs, C/4 and C/5, found mid Apr to May, once early Jun (Müller), incubation once by ♂ (R20); young late Apr to early Jun, once late Jun (Troodos), fledged young once early May. [Records of nests with young at Kakopetria (the Bannermans 1958, 1971) should be dated 9–18 *May* 1954, not Apr (McNeile).] (Breeding details mainly from McNeile, Ashton-Johnson, Took 1971a). Main departure mid Aug to mid Sep, occasionally 1–2 stay to mid Nov. One ringed Mitsero, 5 May 1958, recovered near there Mar 1960.

Fairly common or common on passage on low ground and at northern capes, mainly mid–late Mar to early–mid Apr, usually in flocks of 10s, maximum 180 Akrotiri, 14 Mar 1968. Less common on low ground in autumn, when any passage is obscured by departure of local breeders.

344. EMBERIZA AUREOLA   AV
Yellow-breasted Bunting

Accidental visitor, one record: one limed Ayios Amvrosios, east of Kyrenia, 20 May 1974 (NR5). [The description of one seen Paramali, 3 Jun 1980, does not confirm the identification.]

345. EMBERIZA SCHOENICLUS   WV

Reed Bunting

Common winter visitor to reed beds: occasional mid Sep to mid Oct, first arrivals
usually late Oct, peak numbers late Nov to mid Feb, usually last seen mid–late Mar,
occasionally Apr. Maximum 166 along north shore Akrotiri Salt Lake, early Jan
1972. In the past, "hundreds" in hard weather at Fresh Water Lake, winter 1910–11
(Bucknill 1911).

Of 85 trapped birds examined Akrotiri Salt Lake in winter 1970–71 and
1971–72, 67 had thick bills of the *intermedia* group of races, 10 had thin bills
of the *schoeniclus* group, and 8 had bills intermediate between the 2 groups; one
bird of the *schoeniclus* group was very pale, perhaps *E.s. pallidior*; of the 85 birds,
only 17 were ♂♂ (P. R. Flint). Specimens obtained winter 1910–11 sent to
"Dr Hartert and Mr Nicoll, who identified them as *E.s. canneti*" (= *intermedia*)
(Bucknill 1911).

346. EMBERIZA MELANOCEPHALA   MB PM

Black-headed Bunting

Common (locally very common) migrant breeder.

Breeding distribution. The Troodos range up to *c*. 1300 m and adjacent
coastal lowlands; also the north coast, the Kyrenia range, the Karpas and south to
Trikomo and Salamis area (once south to Dherinia – NR15). Within the Kyrenia
range and on the Karpas birds are most numerous in small valleys and basins in
the hills where there is maquis with trees. One such area well described by
J. A. McGeoch (*in* the Bannermans 1958) — "At least 10 ♂♂ were within half a mile
of the area, a basin in the hills with a base of pasture; the sides being in ascending
order, scrub, low bushes, mixed forest, pine forest with rocky areas, dwindling out to
cliffs. Each ♂ seemed to have a narrow strip of about 20 yards from the pasture up to
the rocks, giving each pair a similar strip of mixed territories". Within the Troodos
range birds occur in maquis with trees and in cultivation, the highest densities there
being in vineyard areas with trees, particularly in parts of the south and west
Troodos and the Paphos district; vineyard areas with no trees hold relatively few
birds (Flint 1980).

Breeding data. Occasional singles Mar, first arrivals usually early–mid Apr,
sometimes late Apr, common by late Apr or early May, with some arrival into mid
May; ♂♂ much more in evidence than ♀♀. ♂♂ arrive in Cyprus in breeding condition
(Horner & Hubbard). Song Apr–Jun. Nests low down, at *c*. 12–75 cm above
ground, in *Cistus*, grapevine or low herbage (Ashton-Johnson, Took 1971a). Eggs,
C/3 to C/6, mainly mid–late May, once early May (the Bannermans 1958). ♀ once
added material to nest after clutch complete (R19). Incubation period once recorded
as 10 days (J. M. E. Took *in* R17). Young mid May to mid Jun, once mid Jul.
Departure unobtrusive, apparently mainly Jul, a few records Aug–Sep, twice Oct
and once mid Nov.

Fairly common passage migrant mid–late Apr to early May, though usually
scarce Akrotiri, presumably because birds enter the island from the east. No obvious
autumn passage.

2 recoveries of birds ringed in India and Yugoslavia (Appendix 2).

347. MILIARIA (=EMBERIZA) CALANDRA   RB PM WV

Corn Bunting

Common and widespread resident (*M.c. calandra*).

Breeding distribution. Up to *c*. 1500 m in open cultivation, especially cereals, vineyards and vegetables (in the Troodos range usually in barley and vineyards), and in rough open country (including salt flats) with low scrub, herbage and grasses.

Breeding data. Song mainly Jan–Jun, though some song all year. Nests on the ground or low down in grasses, thistles or other herbage, or in low bushes such as Prickly Burnet *Poterium spinosum* or *Salicornia*. Eggs, C/3 to C/6, found late Mar to early Jun on low ground; fledged young once mid Apr and once late Jul.

Post-breeding flocks of 10s and 100s occur Jun onwards, during the heat of summer and early autumn usually near fresh water (reservoirs, dams, etc.). 100s were at Akhna Dam, Jul 1988, but heavy and persistent liming decimated the numbers (NL88/7–8). During Jul–Sep birds become apparently less numerous on low ground, especially on the Mesaoria, and perhaps some move to cooler parts of the island or migrate. In winter birds in song in the Troodos range to at least 600 m.

Common passage migrant mid Feb to early May (mainly Mar to mid Apr), and Oct–Nov. Winter visitor in variable numbers to low ground, sometimes in flocks of 100s.

One ringed Nicosia, 6 Jan 1959, recovered there 19 Mar 1959.

APPENDIX 1

OMITTED SPECIES

Species omitted from the systematic list for the reasons given. A number of other species have also been reported from Cyprus, the records of which were never published, either because the birds were obvious escapes, or because supporting evidence was inadequate or lacking. These unpublished records are excluded from the list below.

Red-throated Diver *Gavia stellata*. One off Limassol, 27 Apr 1958, is not confirmed by the brief description (Bourne 1959a).

Great Shearwater *Puffinus gravis*. Included as *P. major* Faber in the list of Unger & Kotschy (1865), perhaps in error for Manx Shearwater *P. puffinus* which they do not mention.

Bean Goose *Anser fabalis*. One obtained near Famagusta, Dec 1904, and one seen near Morphou, 7 Dec 1908 (Bucknill 1909–10), both unsubstantiated.

Brent Goose *Branta bernicla*. One shot Kyrenia, Dec 1908 (Bucknill 1909–10); no description and skin not retained.

Black-winged Kite *Elanus caeruleus*. One Pissouri, 20 Nov 1960, withdrawn by observer. One Kouklia, 13 Apr 1972, is not confirmed by the description. Others Phrenaros, 21 Sep and Athalassa, 30 Sep 1974, both unsubstantiated.

Tawny Eagle *Aquila rapax*. One Akrotiri, 6 Oct 1957, and singles at Lefkoniko and Akrotiri, 18 Sep 1960. The description of the 1957 bird better fits Spotted Eagle *A. clanga* and the 1960 birds were more likely Imperial Eagles *A. heliaca* (Stewart & Christensen).

Lanner *Falco biarmicus*. One Cape Greco, 24 Sep 1968, and one Cape Andreas, 28 Mar 1970, both withdrawn by observers. Some 13 other sight records 1958–1973, all with inadequate detail. One shot near Famagusta, 1 Feb 1914 (Baxendale 1915); no description and skin not retained.

Caspian Snowcock *Tetraogallus caspius*. One Phrenaros, 24 Dec 1977 (Kephalas 1989), description too brief to confirm the identification.

Sand Partridge *Ammoperdix heyi*. Unsuccessfully introduced 1937 at Ayia Napa and Pyroi (G. F. Wilson *in* the Bannermans 1958).

Grey Partridge *Perdix perdix*. Unsuccessfully introduced Kolossi 1883 (Bucknill 1909–10).

Pheasant *Phasianus colchicus*. Unsuccessfully introduced at Aghirda *c.* 1880, at two locations 1910 (Bucknill 1909–10) and at Athalassa and Kouklia (Paphos) 1952 (D. F. Davidson). Large introduction Morphou area *c.* 1968, a few surviving there 1972. Introduced Cape Greco 1971.

Lesser Sand Plover *Charadrius mongolus*. 8 records 1958–1984, all Mar to mid Apr, 4 of them of single birds, the others of flocks of 4, 7, 8 and 10 birds. In every case the descriptions equally (and usually better) fit Greater Sand Plover *C. leschenaultii*, which we believe the birds were. The race of Greater Sand Plover which occurs in Cyprus, *C. l. columbinus*, has a relatively small bill and can show extensive rufous on the breast and flanks (this confirmed by our examination of skins in BMNH), thus resembling typical field guide illustrations of *C. mongolus*. The descriptions mentioned above generally rely only on the bill size and/or the breast band width, and not on other important characters such as overall size, and the relative sizes of the head, body and legs. The status given by Cramp & Simmons and Hollom *et al.*

suggests that *C. mongolus* is a vagrant to the eastern Mediterranean — however the Syrian records are old (1904), and require confirmation, and our inquiries into the Turkish and Israeli records indicate that they may well have been *C. leschenaultii* (M. Beaman, Hovel 1987 and *in litt.*). *C. mongolus* could of course occur as a vagrant to Cyprus, but as yet there are no adequately documented records.

Black-headed Lapwing *Hoplopterus tectus*. "Said to have occurred in Cyprus" (Vaurie 1965).

Lesser Crested Tern *Sterna bengalensis*. One, with inadequate detail, Larnaca, 24 Apr 1963.

Chestnut-bellied Sandgrouse *Pterocles exustus*. "Probably found in the island" (Cobham *in* Bucknill 1909–10).

Barbary Dove *Streptopelia roseogrisea*. Introduced Nicosia c. 1963 (NR4), present status not known.

Emerald Dove *Chalcophaps indica*. One limed Dec 1957, a probable escape (Stewart & Christensen).

Hawk Owl *Surnia ulula*. One Akrotiri, 6 Apr 1963, possibly this species (Stewart & Christensen).

Tawny Owl *Strix aluco*. 2 full grown young run over near Lefkoniko, 30 Apr 1966, were attributed to this species but not conclusively identified (R13). Feathers from these birds can not be identified as coming from this species. 10 other records 1952–1984, only 2 of them supported by descriptions, which in both cases could fit other owl species. On distribution (Cramp 1985) it could well occur as an occasional visitor, or even as an occasional or scarce breeder, but as yet there are no adequately documented records.

Tengmalm's Owl *Aegolius funereus*. One Akrotiri, 24 Aug 1957, probably this species (Stewart & Christensen).

Egyptian Nightjar *Caprimulgus aegyptius*. One near Nicosia, 18–19 Apr 1957, is not confirmed by the description (Stewart & Christensen). One Kophinou, 20 Apr 1984 (NR15), description not published.

White-rumped Swift/Little Swift *Apus caffer/affinis*. 3 Petra tou Romiou, 8 Apr 1968, are not confirmed by the description (Stewart & Christensen). Unconfirmed report of *A. affinis* breeding 1981 (*per* S. Cramp).

Green Woodpecker *Picus viridis*. One Evdhimou, 24 Sep 1977; investigation of the record suggests Golden Oriole *O. oriolus* was the species involved.

Woodpecker *Picus* species. Included in the list of Unger & Kotschy (1865), but with no details.

Bar-tailed Desert Lark *Ammomanes cincturus*. One Larnaca, 28 Oct 1976, description brief and not correct in all details.

Pechora Pipit *Anthus gustavi*. One near Patriki, Mar 1954, the description lacked adequate detail (Stewart & Christensen).

Yellow-vented Bulbul *Pycnonotus (barbatus) xanthopygos*. One, believed an escape, obtained Larnaca, 1876–8 (Schrader 1891). One Larnaca, Apr 1887 (Guillemard 1888). Bucknill (1909–10) found it a "regular visitor in spring" with 3 together in his garden at Nicosia, 30 Apr to 18 May 1909. Seen in Nicosia "a few times" (Waterer) and "presumably a Bulbul" at Athalassa, 9 Apr 1929 (Jourdain 1929b). A sedentary species unlikely to occur except as a vagrant and these records (all unsubstantiated) may refer to escaped or released cage birds.

Red-tailed Wheatear *Oenanthe xanthoprymna*. One Mt. Olympus, 1 Sep 1975, is not confirmed by the description.

Mourning Wheatear *Oenanthe lugens.* See *O. finschii* in the Systematic List.

Aquatic Warbler *Acrocephalus paludicola.* One Curium Marsh, 4 Apr 1958; description too brief to confirm the identification.

Blyth's Reed Warbler *Acrocephalus dumetorum.* One trapped Akrotiri, 14 Aug 1962. The detailed description can be matched exactly with the eastern race of Reed Warbler *A. scirpaceus fuscus* which is a numerous breeding species at Akrotiri and it seems virtually certain that that was the species involved.

Melodious Warbler *Hippolais polyglotta.* 3 trapped Troodos, 28 Aug 1977, and one limed Platres, 4 Sep 1977 (NR8). Descriptions not published and confusion with other species is a possibility.

Green Warbler/Greenish Warbler *Phylloscopus nitidus/trochiloides.* One trapped Akrotiri, 22 Aug 1973 (NR4). The ringer has corrected a transcription error in his original description and it is now clear that the bird was of one of these two species (which are considered conspecific by some authors).

Blue Tit *Parus caeruleus.* One Bellapais, 17–20 Feb 1990 (R. A. Streatfeild). The observer was familiar with the species but did not realise it was a rarity and thus took no description. In the past, erroneously listed as resident by Schrader (1891), and one (unsubstantiated) between Stavrovouni and Tokhni, 5 Mar 1887 (Guillemard 1888). On distribution (Hollom *et al.*) it could well occur as a vagrant, but as yet there are no documented records.

Rock Nuthatch *Sitta neumayer.* As *S. syriaca* included in the list of Unger & Kotschy (1865), perhaps in error for Short-toed Treecreeper *Certhia brachydactyla* which they do not mention.

Isabelline Shrike *Lanius isabellinus.* See Red-backed Shrike *L. collurio* in the Systematic List.

Azure-winged Magpie *Cyanopica cyana.* 2 records (1960 and 1961), both presumably escapes.

Alpine Chough *Pyrrhocorax graculus.* 2 birds seen near Pentadaktylos, 12 Apr 1987 (NL87/4), were probably of this species.

Two-barred Crossbill *Loxia leucoptera.* One Mt. Olympus, 24 Feb 1965, withdrawn by observer.

Cirl Bunting *Emberiza cirlus.* One Troodos, 8 Nov 1957, description inconclusive (Bourne 1959a).

Little Bunting *Emberiza pusilla.* One Limassol, 20 Oct 1957, the description lacks adequate detail (Stewart & Christensen).

Dupont's Lark *Chersophilus duponti.* One on the coast below Mavrokolymbos Dam, 12 Apr 1988 (*Oriolus* 54(4): 182–183), the photographs do not confirm the identification.

APPENDIX 2

RINGING AND RECOVERIES

Rings supplied by the British Trust for Ornithology (BTO) and inscribed INFORM BRITISH MUSEUM LONDON SW7 were used in Cyprus from 1957 to 1970. Of the 17,475 birds ringed, there have been 118 recoveries within the island and 35 overseas. Local rings inscribed CYPRUS ORN SOC were introduced in 1970 and up to 1984 (the most recent year's figures available) 13,861 birds had been ringed. The low recovery rate since the introduction of the new Cyprus rings (only 9 published recoveries, 6 within the island) suggests at least that the rings' inscriptions are unsatisfactory as a return address. The many retraps of birds from both the BTO and Cyprus schemes have, nevertheless, been valuable in proving re-wintering and re-summering and in revealing the sedentary nature of some resident species. These retraps and local recoveries are summarised under species in the systematic list.

The greatest benefit from trapping birds for ringing has been the opportunity to examine and identify them in the hand. From plumage and biometric data it has been possible with many species to determine their geographic race and hence their area of origin. The migration dates and status of species such as Chiffchaff, Willow Warbler, Reed and Marsh Warbler, Savi's and River Warbler, Nightingale and Thrush Nightingale, have been determined with certainty largely as a result of ringing operations.

Details of foreign ringed birds recovered in Cyprus were originally collected through the Department of Agriculture in Nicosia, at first by H. M. Morris, the Government Entomologist, and after 1951 by D. F. Davidson, the Conservator of Forests. After the formation of COS (1957), the society was notified of the list of recoveries kept by the Department of Agriculture and the society also traced details of foreign recoveries which had been reported direct to the original ringing schemes. Other recoveries were located by W. Rydzewski following a survey of the literature. A list of all known recoveries was compiled by W. R. P. Bourne and W. Rydzewski, and published by Rydzewski (1960) and also by COS (1957) in Bulletin 6. Since then recoveries of foreign ringed birds have been published regularly by COS (1957), and since 1970 by COS (1970) also. In 1980 a list of recoveries was compiled and privately circulated by R. Foers; this list including many previously unpublished recoveries extracted from the files of COS (1970) or obtained from private individuals.

Of the several million birds killed in Cyprus each year probably several 10s at least carry rings, yet recovery details of only some 5 to 9 foreign ringed birds are usually obtained each year. It seems probable that details of many recoveries are being lost as a result of lack of regular publicity and organised collection. In the past, several attempts have been made to realise an improved recovery rate of foreign ringed birds. A circular sent to local police stations in 1939 was still bringing in good results up to the beginning of the emergency 15 years later. From 1960 to 1962 COS (1957) conducted a ring reward scheme which was given good publicity in the local press and rewards were paid to a number of people who sent in rings. Details of 6 recoveries were also obtained by reading the local Greek press. During 1963–65 cards in Greek and Turkish were distributed around the island requesting people to forward rings to their District Offices, and in 1966 an appeal for recovery of rings was circulated by the Ministry of Education, on behalf of COS (1957), to all school children and a 5 shilling reward was offered. The annual recovery rate reached a peak between 1968 and 1971, since when it has declined considerably.

The following list includes details of Cyprus ringed birds recovered outside the island and of foreign ringed birds recovered within the island. Local recoveries are omitted, but the total number of recoveries is stated in brackets after the scientific name of each species. Ringing details are given on the first line and recovery data on the second. They are preceded by the ring origin and number and any known details of age (see below), sex (M or F) and manner of recovery (see below). Co-ordinates are given in degrees and minutes. References are given as explained at the beginning of the Systematic List. Details of some recoveries have been corrected after examination of the original records at the BTO office, Tring.

Key to symbols and terms:

Age	Manner of Recovery
1 = Pullus, young bird ringed in the nest	+ = Shot
2 = Full grown, year of hatching unknown	X = Found dead
3 = Hatched during current calendar year	V = Trapped or caught and released with ring
4 = Hatched before current calendar year	( ) = Trapped or caught and not released
	L = Limed

Night Heron *Nycticorax nycticorax* (5)

Budapest	1	14.6.29	Kisbalaton 46°40'N, 17°15'E **Hungary**	
54164	+	18.5.30	Nicosia 35°10'N, 33°23'E	(B.6)
Budapest	1	10.6.53	Kisbalaton 46°40'N, 17°15'E **Hungary**	
170438	+	13.9.53	Cyprus	(B.6)
Radolfzell	1	6.6.63	Marchegg, Ganserndorf 48°17'N, 16°55'E **Austria**	
G 39357	X	9.4.67	Cape Andreas 35°41'N, 34°35'E	(R.14)
Zagreb	1	30.6.69	Drenov Bok/Krapje, Hrvatska 45°18'N, 16°50'E **Yugoslavia**	
C 231153	+	15.4.71	Akrotiri Salt Lake 34°35'N, 32°57'E	(NR.2)
Tel Aviv	4	9.7.74	Hula Lack Reserve 33°05'N, 35°37'E **Israel**	
G 6520	+	4.9.76	Psevdhas 34°58'N, 33°26'E Larnaca	(Foers 1980)

Purple Heron *Ardea purpurea* (1)

| Radolfzell | 1 | 23.6.64 | Illmitz, Burgenland 47°46'N, 16°48'E **Austria** | |
| B 58906 | + | 25.4.71 | Akrotiri 34°35'N, 32°57'E | (R.18) |

White Stork *Ciconia ciconia* (4)

Helgoland	1	8.7.37	Wathlingen b. Celle 52°33'N, 10°10'E **W Germany**	
222913	+	28.9.37	Xylophagou 34°58'N, 33°51'E Larnaca	(B.6)
Rossitten	1	6.39	Gr. Eschenbruch, E Prussia 54°35'N, 21°24'E **USSR**	
BB 13065	( )	8.10.39	Ayios Andronicos 35°20'N, 33°52'E Famagusta	(B.6)
Helgoland	1	10.6.39	Elsfleth 54°14'N, 08°27'E **W Germany**	
225241	+	c. 19.11.39	Avgolidha 35°21'N, 33°58'E Famagusta	(B.6)
Radolfzell	1	16.7.55	Wechingen 48°54'N, 10°37'E **W Germany**	
BB 5470		13.9.55	Dhromolaxia 34°52'N, 33°35'E Larnaca	(B.6)

Glossy Ibis *Plegadis falcinellus* (1)

| Moskwa | 1 | 3.6.54 | Kizil Agach, Azerbaydzhan 39°00'N, 48°50'E **USSR** | |
| D 51458 | | 30.3.61 | Morphou Bay 35°10'N, 32°55'E | (B.12) |

Greater Flamingo *Phoenicopterus ruber* (8)

Tehran	1	7.8.72	Ashk Island, Lake Rezaiyeh 37°25'N, 45°30'E **Iran**	
LL 2665		3.73	Larnaca 34°55'N, 33°38'E	(Foers 1980)
Tehran	1	4.8.77	Ashk Island, Lake Rezaiyeh 37°25'N, 45°30'E **Iran**	
LL 11477	+	2.78	Akrotiri Salt Lake 34°38'N, 33°00'E	(NR.9)

Sightings of birds ringed as juveniles at the Carmargue, Et Fangassier, B du Rhone, **S France**
Ringed on 20.7.77

| AKY | | 21.1.89 | Akrotiri Salt Lake 34°38'N, 33°00'E | (Johnson) |

Ringed on 24.7.84

| 434 | | 21.1.89 | Akrotiri Salt Lake 34°38'N, 33°00'E | (Johnson) |
| 457 | | 26.1.89 | Akrotiri Salt Lake 34°38'N, 33°00'E | (Johnson) |

Ringed on 22.7.87

| AKJX | | 19.1.89 | Larnaca Salt Lake 34°55'N, 33°38'E | (Johnson) |
| AJCD | | 27.1.89 | Akrotiri Salt Lake 34°38'N, 33°00'E | (Johnson) |

Sighting of a bird ringed as a juvenile **Spain**
No details.

| K/01 | | 1.89 | Akrotiri or Larnaca Salt Lake | (Johnson) |

Teal *Anas crecca* (3)

| Moskwa | 4 | 28.7.48 | Astrakhan Reserve 46°12'N, 48°55'E **USSR** | |
| E 75556 | | 2.49 | Livadhia 34°57'N, 33°38'E Larnaca | (B.6) |

Teal *Anas crecca* (3) (*Continued*)
Brit Mus	2M	22.11.59	Akrotiri 34°36′N, 32°58′E	
2032002	+	6.3.60	Ardabil 38°15′N, 48°22′E **Iran**	(B.12)

Pintail *Anas acuta* (1)
Moskwa	4	4.8.49	Astrakhan Reserve 46°12′N, 48°55′E **USSR**	
E 133007	+	17.3.51	Ktima 34°46′N, 32°25′E Paphos	(B.6)

Shoveler *Anas clypeata* (1)
Moskwa	4M	8.8.40	Astrakhan Reserve 46°12′N, 48°55′E **USSR**	
E 74278		29.4.54	Kalokhorio 34°55′N, 33°32′E Larnaca	(B.6)

Honey Buzzard *Pernis apivorus* (1)
Written Label*		12.9.29	Aseevka, Kuznetsk, probably 53°11′N, 46°26′E **USSR**	
	+	10.10.29	Karavas 35°20′N, 33°11′E Kyrenia	(B.6)

*"1929, 11 September. This hawk was caught by Nicholas Timofee and after one day and night was let go. Village Aseevka, district Kuznetsk, USSR, T.N." (Rydzewski 1958).

Black Kite *Milvus migrans* (1)
Rossitten	3	11.6.38	Grabow 53°00′N, 14°23′E (Germany) **Poland**	
C 63775	+	21.9.38	Famagusta 35°07′N, 33°57′E	(B.6)

Marsh Harrier *Circus aeruginosus* (1)
Paris	4F	1.4.68	El Haouaria, Cap Bon 37°03′N, 11°00′E **Tunisia**	
DWO 4254		23.3.69	Larnaca 34°55′N, 33°38′E	(R.16)

Eleonora's Falcon *Falco eleonorae* (11)
Brit Mus	1	22.9.62	Cape Gata, Akrotiri 34°34′N, 33°01′E	
3091453	X	30.11.62	Ankazobe 18°20′S, 47°07′E **Madagascar**	(B.13)
Brit Mus	1	15.9.67	Cape Gata, Akrotiri 34°34′N, 33°01′E	
3104491	+	9.69	Mersa Matruh 31°21′N, 27°15′E **Egypt**	(R.17)
	1	9.82	Paximadhi, Crete 35°00′N, 24°35′E **Greece**	
	+	20.10.83	Akamas 35°05′N, 32°18′E Paphos	(NR.14)

Little Ringed Plover *Charadrius dubius* (1)
Brit Mus	3	27.9.67	Akrotiri 34°36′N, 32°58′E	
BE 82554	+	15.3.71	Lanciano, R Sangro 42°13′N, 14°23′E **Italy**	(R.18)

Sanderling *Calidris alba* (2)
Brit Mus	4	26.9.67	Akrotiri 34°36′N, 32°58′E	
BE 78134	+	14.5.69	Nr Sousse 35°50′N, 10°38′E **Tunisia**	(Foers 1980)

Ruff *Philomachus pugnax* (2)
Norway	4	4.8.68	Vadsaya 70°04′N, 29°45′E **Norway**	
7100571	X	21.3.71	Argaka 35°04′N, 32°30′E Paphos	(NR.3)

Greenshank *Tringa nebularia* (1)
Pretoria		21.3.71	Swartcops Estuary 33°52′S, 25°36′E **South Africa**	
412916	+	10.5.72	Avlona 35°10′N, 33°07′E Nicosia	(NR.5)

Green Sandpiper *Tringa ochropus* (1)
Helsinki	3	21.7.68	Vuojaari, Uusimaa 60°13′N, 25°10′E **Finland**	
A 102117	X	27.3.71	Famagusta 35°07′N, 33°57′E	(NR.3)

Mediterranean Gull *Larus melanocephalus* (2)
Moskwa	3	3.7.48	Orlov Id, Black Sea 46°17′N, 31°45′E **USSR**	
E 127972	+	1.8.48	Larnaca 34°55′N, 33°39′E	(B.6)
Moskwa	3	29.6.50	Orlov Id, Black Sea 46°17′N, 31°45′E **USSR**	
E 190262		25.3.51	North Coast at 34°30′E	(B.6)

Black-headed Gull *Larus ridibundus* (2)
Moskwa	1	6.6.48	Lake Kievo 56°02′N, 37°30′E **USSR**	
E 133993		29.12.48	Zakaki 34°39′N, 33°00′E Limassol	(B.6)
Moskwa	3	12.6.59	Ivanou Region, Sokolskoe 59°10′N, 43°10′E **USSR**	
M 46172		2.12.59	Limassol 34°41′N, 33°05′E	(B.11 & 12)

Slender-billed Gull *Larus genei* (15)
All ringed with Moskwa rings as juveniles at the Black Sea Reserve, Orlov Island 46°17′N, 31°45′E **USSR**
Ringed on 10.7.47
E 105372	+	12.61	Limassol 34°40′N, 33°00′E	(B.15)

Ringed on 3.7.49
E 149423		18.10.49	Zyggi 34°43′N, 33°20′E Larnaca	(B.6)
E 170336		10.10.52	Xeros 35°08′N, 32°50′E Nicosia	(B.6)

Ringed on 26.6.50
E 161861		29.10.50	Salamis 35°10′N, 33°54′E Famagusta	(B.6)
E 200241		20.2.51	Engomi 35°09′N, 33°52′E Famagusta	(B.6)

Ringed on 16–18.6.52
E 205063		6.1.53	Limassol 34°41′N, 33°05′E	(B.6)
E 205357		11.52	Larnaca 34°55′N, 33°39′E	(B.6)
E 228386		14.1.53	Limassol 34°41′N, 33°05′E	(B.6)

Slender-billed Gull *Larus genei* (15) (*Continued*)
E 228623	27.12.52	Larnaca 34°55′N, 33°39′E	(B.6)
Ringed on 24.6.53			
E 273208	16.11.53	Xerovounos 35°08′N, 32°44′E Nicosia	(B.6)
Ringed on 22.6.54			
E 331615	19.11.54	Larnaca 34°55′N, 33°39′E	(B.6)
E 334319	24.11.54	Ayia Irini 35°18′N, 32°58′E Kyrenia	(B.6)
E 334469	24.3.55	Syrianokhori 35°13′N, 32°57′E Nicosia	(B.6)
Ringed on 22.6.55			
E 275646	11.12.55	Xeros 35°08′N, 32°50′E Nicosia	(B.6)
E 380862	5.1.56	Larnaca 34°55′N, 33°39′E	(B.6)

Lesser Black-backed Gull *Larus fuscus* (2)
Copenhagen	3	27.6.38	Christianso, Bornholm Id, 55°21′N, 15°12′E **Denmark**
M 7462	+	30.3.41	Limassol 34°41′N, 33°05′E	(B.6)
		9.7.77	Dulum Laani 65°22′N, 24°50′E **Finland**
	+	11.5.83	Maroni 34°45′N, 33°22′E Larnaca	(NR.14)

Sandwich Tern *Sterna sandvicensis* (2)
Moskwa	1	23.6.52	Orlov Id, Black Sea 46°17′N, 31°45′E **USSR**
F 133144		2.53	Cyprus	(B.6)
Moskwa	1	5.7.52	Orlov Id, Black Sea 46°17′N, 31°45′E **USSR**
F 163244		19.2.53	Larnaca 34°55′N, 33°39′E	(B.6)

Turtle Dove *Streptopelia turtur* (6)
Brit Mus	3	20.9.67	Akrotiri 34°35′N, 32°57′E
DS 51003	+	11.8.68	Gulyaypole, Ukraine 47°39′N, 36°15′E **USSR**	(Foers 1980)
Brit Mus	4	19.4.69	Akrotiri 34°35′N, 32°57′E
DS 44111	+	14.9.69	Siros Island, Cyclades 37°25′N, 24°55′E **Greece**	(R.17)
Brit Mus	2	15.9.70	Akrotiri 34°35′N, 32°57′E
DS 51530	+	18.9.76	Nr Novonikolayevka, Ukraine 47°57′N, 35°55′E **USSR**
				(Foers 1980)

Nightjar *Caprimulgus europaeus* (1)
Brit Mus	4M	25.9.67	Akrotiri 34°35′N, 32°57′E
CS 71066		6.3.69	Mkolani, Iringa District 07°45′S, 35°40′E **Tanzania** (G. Backhurst)

Bee-eater *Merops apiaster* (7)
Sofia	4	14.6.33	Sindel 43°07′N, 27°36′E **Bulgaria**
D 8771	( )	24.9.34	Larnaca 34°55′N, 33°39′E	(B.6)
Moskwa	3	21.7.34	Yerki 48°53′N, 30°43′E **USSR**
F 14988		25.9.34	Larnaca 34°55′N, 33°39′E	(B.6)
Sofia	1	9.7.35	Kuzina 43°17′N, 25°38′E **Bulgaria**
E 22929	( )	21.9.35	Pakhna 34°46′N, 32°48′E Limassol	(B.6)
Moskwa		3.8.40	Kanev 49°44′N, 31°02′E **USSR**
F 20719		26.9.40	Ormidhia 34°59′N, 33°47′E Larnaca	(B.6 & 12)
TAU		8.5.68	Eilat 29°33′N, 34°57′E **Israel**
C 2179		.68	Paralimni 35°02′N, 33°59′E Famagusta	(R.15)
Moskwa	4	7.8.74	Kasimov, Ryazan Region 54°58′N, 41°28′E **USSR**
P 402220	+	28.9.75	Larnaca 34°58′N, 33°33′E	(NR.6)
Moskwa	4F	10.8.74	Kasimov, Ryazan Region 54°58′N, 41°28′E **USSR**
P 407430	+	28.9.75	Larnaca 34°58′N, 33°33′E	(NR.6)

Roller *Coracias garrulus* (1)
Riga	1	16.7.38	Nauleni, Latvia 55°58′N, 27°40′E **USSR**
112152		26.9.38	Ormidhia 34°59′N, 33°47′E Larnaca	(B.6)

Woodlark *Lullula arborea* (1)
Budapest	4	2.5.48	Budaors 47°26′N, 18°59′E **Hungary**
141632	+	27.2.57	Lefkara 34°51′N, 33°19′E Larnaca	(B.6)

Sand Martin *Riparia riparia* (3)
Brit Mus	4	27.9.67	Akrotiri 34°35′N, 32°57′E
HK 88108	V	2.8.70	Nr Chernikov, Ukraine 51°30′N, 31°20′E **USSR**	(R.18)
Brit Mus	2	1.4.68	Malamfatori, Lake Chad 13°33′N, 13°23′E **Nigeria**
HR 35621	L	9.69	Paralimni 35°02′N, 33°59′E Famagusta	(R.17)
Brit Mus	3	2.10.68	Akrotiri 34°35′N, 32°57′E
HK 62237	X	15.8.69	Nr Liski, Voronezh 51°00′N, 39°30′E **USSR**	(R.16)

Swallow *Hirundo rustica* (8)
Brit Mus	2	29.9.57	Salamis 35°10′N, 33°55′E Famagusta
E 11240		25.5.58	Novo Nikolaevka, Zaporoze 47°58′N, 35°44′E **USSR**
				(B.6)

Swallow *Hirundo rustica* (8) (*Continued*)

Brit Mus	3	22.7.67	Akrotiri 34°35′N, 32°57′E	
HB 56537	( )	18.2.71	Ha'il 27°31′N, 41°45′E **Saudi Arabia**	(R.18)

Yellow Wagtail *Motacilla flava* (1)

Brit Mus	3	7.10.63	Episkopi 34°40′N, 32°53′E	
AE 55768		28.9.64	Mersin, Silifke 36°22′N, 33°56′E **Turkey**	(B.16)

White Wagtail *Motacilla alba* (8)

Stockholm	4	9.9.38	Ottenby, Oland 56°12′N, 16°24′E **Sweden**	
ZO 1073	+	3.11.38	Larnaca 34°55′N, 33°39′E	(B.6)
Stockholm	4	1.9.50	Ottenby, Oland 56°12′N, 16°24′E **Sweden**	
ZOD 1252	( )	22.10.50	At sea between Famagusta and Port Said	(B.6)
Stockholm	1	9.7.52	Via 61°49′N, 17°23′E **Sweden**	
ZAH 6133		12.4.53	Limassol 34°41′N, 33°05′E	(B.6)
Stockholm	3	6.8.60	Katrineholm 59°00′N, 16°12′E **Sweden**	
		Handed in		
2011525	L	7.3.74	Yeroskipos 34°45′N, 32°27′E Paphos	(Foers 1980)
Stockholm	3	1.7.61	Stallarolmen, Malaren 59°30′N, 17°30′E **Sweden**	
2025467		27.2.63	Cyprus	(B.14)
Brit Mus	4	3.4.68	Paralimni 35°02′N, 33°59′E Famagusta	
HK 64014	X	4.68	Roznov Pod Radh 49°28′N, 18°09′E **Czechoslovakia**(R.15)
Helsinki	3	8.9.68	Suomanoja, Espoo 60°09′N, 24°44′E **Finland**	
K 546711	X	14.11.68	Xeros 35°08′N, 32°50′E Nicosia	(R.16)
Helsinki	4	2.9.70	Kangasala 61°27′N, 24°02′E **Finland**	
K 710324		4.3.71	Morphou 35°15′N, 32°55′E	(R.18)

Robin *Erithacus rubecula* (15)

Stockholm	2	5.10.50	Ottenby, Oland 56°12′N, 16°24′E **Sweden**	
ZOD 4681	V	19.12.50	Rizokarpaso 35°36′N, 34°24′E Karpas	(B.6)
Helsinki	2	8.10.61	Kirkkonummi 59°56′N, 24°23′E **Finland**	
K 131760		12.61	Lefkara 34°51′N, 33°19′E Larnaca	(B.15)
Brit Mus	2	9.11.67	Akrotiri 34°35′N, 32°57′E	
HK 88382	+	21.11.72	Nr Beirut 33°50′N, 35°30′E **Lebanon**	(Foers 1980)
Helsinki	2	24.9.68	Sappi, Luvia 61°24′N, 21°21′E **Finland**	
K 488260	+	31.12.68	West Cyprus *c*.35°00′N, 34°00′E	(Foers 1980)
Helsinki	4	10.5.70	Jurmo Korppae, Turku 59°50′N, 21°37′E **Finland**	
K 654721	L	16.3.71	Halevga 35°16′N, 33°32′E Kyrenia	(NR.3)
Moskwa		27.9.79	Cherkassy Region, Nr Kanev 49°44′N, 31°26′E **USSR**	
XA 153842		15.1.80	Ora 34°55′N, 33°38′E Larnaca	(NR.11)

Nightingale *Luscinia megarhynchos* (1)

Brit Mus	3	13.10.68	Akrotiri 34°35′N, 32°57′E	
HK 62824	V	24.3.69	Eilat 29°34′N, 34°57′E **Israel**	(R.16)

Black Redstart *Phoenicurus ochrurus* (7)

Rossitten		2.10.36	Lossen 50°48′N, 17°35′E (Germany) **Poland**	
G 453846		5.11.37	Moni 34°44′N, 33°12′E Limassol	(B.6)
Varsovia	3	8.8.37	Dublany 49°54′N, 24°05′E (Poland) **USSR**	
G 59485	+	22.11.37	Geunyeli 35°12′N, 33°18′E Nicosia	(B.6)
Prague	4	8.10.64	Halda, Nr Vyprachtice 49°58′N, 16°38′E **Czechoslovakia**	
Z 316737	L	8.2.65	Leonarisso 35°27′N, 34°09′E Karpas	(R.12)
Prague	1	9.7.65	Dubnica 48°58′N, 18°10′E **Czechoslovakia**	
M 404255	+	9.11.65	Paphos 34°45′N, 32°25′E	(Foers 1980)
Varsovia	2F	19.9.65	Wapnica, Wolin 53°52′N, 14°26′E **Poland**	
H 141945	X	early 1.66	Kyrenia 35°20′N, 33°20′E	(R.13)
Praha	1	30.6.71	Zastava, Brno 49°11′N, 16°22′E **Czechoslovakia**	
M 623448	+	27.11.71	Dheftera 35°05′N, 33°17′E Nicosia	(Foers 1980)
		2.8.80	Praded, Bruntal 50°03′N, 17°15′E **Czechoslovakia**	
		12.1.81	Maroni 34°45′N, 33°22′E Larnaca	(NR.13)

Redstart *Phoenicurus phoenicurus* (3)

Helgoland	3	14.7.64	Mechlenburg Rieps 53°47′N, 10°52′E **E Germany**	
0194775	V	1.65	Episkopi 34°40′N, 32°52′E	(R.12)
Brit Mus	4M	25.4.70	Akrotiri 34°35′N, 32°57′E	
JA 17772	+	20.5.71	Nr Novouzensk, (Saratov) 50°27′N, 48°09′E **USSR** (R.18)
Tel Aviv	4F	30.4.70	Eilat 29°33′N, 34°57′E **Israel**	
A 28768	L	15.5.70	Paralimni 35°02′N, 33°59′E Famagusta	(Foers 1980)

Blackbird *Turdus merula* (7)

Moskwa	2	10.10.54	Azov Sivash Reserve 46°07'N, 35°08'E **USSR**	
F 63745		2.12.55	Kakopetria 34°59'N, 32°54'E Nicosia	(B.6)
Moskwa	2F	14.4.57	Biruchii Id, Sea of Azov 45°15'N, 35°30'E **USSR**	
F 230166		11.58	Lythrodhonda 34°57'N, 33°18'E Nicosia	(B.6)
Moskwa	3M	25.5.68	Ryazan Shatsk 54°00'N, 41°45'E **USSR**	
P 200782	+	5.1.72	Nicosia 35°10'N, 33°20'E	(Foers 1980)
Washington		12.11.69	Bahig 30°56'N, 29°35'E **Egypt**	
	+	5.11.72	Kakopetria 34°59'N, 32°34'E Nicosia	(R.19)

Fieldfare *Turdus pilaris* (3)

Moskwa		7.6.53	Nr Voronezh 51°40'N, 39°13'E **USSR**	
F 178211		2.61	Limassol 34°40'N, 33°03'E	(B.12)
Radolfzell	2	31.12.60	Mannheim–Sandhofen 49°33'N, 08°28'E **W Germany**	
G 177269	+	c. 7.1.62	Nr Lefkara 34°50'N, 33°20'E Larnaca	(B.12)
		18.5.81	BZEZ (Bauska Bystrica) 48°48'N, 19°39'E **Czechoslovakia**	
	+	15.12.81	Troodos 34°55'N, 32°55'E	(NR.12)

Song Thrush *Turdus philomelos* (22)

Moskwa		7.10.54	Azov Sivash Reserve 46°07'N, 35°08'E **USSR**	
F 63729		9.1.55	Apostolos Andreas 35°39'N, 34°35'E Karpas	(B.6)
Brit Mus	4	12.2.61	Nicosia 35°10'N, 33°22'E	
V 23508	+	1.1.62	Nr Delphi 38°29'N, 22°30'E **Greece**	(B.12)
Moskwa	2	2.10.68	Tatarskaya, ASSR, Leninogorsk 54°37'N, 52°31'E **USSR**	
P 117558	X	20.12.71	Nicosia 35°10'N, 33°22'E	(NR.3)
		20.10.80	Zmeingi Id, Black Sea 45°11'N, 30°14'E **USSR**	
	+	15.10.81	Mathiatis 34°58'N, 33°15'E Nicosia	(NR.12)
		20.10.80	Zmeingi Id, Black Sea 45°11'N, 30°14'E **USSR**	
	+	12.9.83	Paralimni 35°02'N, 33°59'E Famagusta	(NR.14)
Rumania		No details		
5923	+	25.10.83	Lythrodhonda 34°57'N, 33°18'E Nicosia	(NR.14)

Redwing *Turdus iliacus* (5)

Brit Mus	3	1.11.52	Gibraltar Point 53°06'N, 00°12'E **England**	
PR 300	X	13.2.54	Kyrenia 35°20'N, 33°20'E	(B.6)
Helsinki	3	11.10.77	Luvia, Turin Ja Porin 61°29'N, 21°21'E **Finland**	
P 336386	+	15.12.77	Lythrodhonda 34°57'N, 33°18'E Nicosia	(R.25)
Helgoland		27.10.78	Helgoland Schlesning, Holstein 54°11'N, 07°55'E **W Germany**	
807466786		1.2.80	Limassol 34°40'N, 33°03'E	(NR.11)
GBT	2	19.1.85	Bray, Wicklow 53°12'N, 06°07'W **S Ireland**	
RX 20652	X	22.12.85	Lefkara Dam 34°52'N, 33°18'E Larnaca	(R.32)

Marsh Warbler *Acrocephalus palustris* (11)

Bruxelles	1	21.6.52	Ieper 50°51'N, 02°53'E **Belgium**	
4B 6471	X	10.52	Famagusta 35°07'N, 33°57'E	(B.6)
Helgoland	2	9.7.61	Nr Marburg, Hessen 50°46'N, 08°49'E **W Germany**	
80127136	+	c. 30.10.61	Cyprus	(B.12)
Radolfzell	2	28.7.62	Bretzenheim 49°53'N, 07°54'E **W Germany**	
H 806811	L	10.1.66	(reported after delay) Famagusta 35°07'N, 33°57'E	(R.13)
Radolfzell		28.7.63	Lengfeld, Wurzburg 49°48'N, 09°59'E **W Germany**	
H 825365	L	22.8.63	Famagusta 35°07'N, 33°57'E	(Foers 1980)
Varsovia	3	22.7.64	Zaporow, Nr Slupca 52°17'N, 17°52'E **Poland**	
H 146062		24.8.64	Famagusta 35°07'N, 33°57'E	(R.12)
Bruxelles	1	20.6.66	Maaseik, Limburg 51°06'N, 05°48'E **Belgium**	
11A 9682	L	10.70	Paralimni 35°02'N, 33°59'E Famagusta	(NR.3)
Paris	2	6.7.72	Willems, Nord 50°38'N, 03°14'E **France**	
1637631	L	21.8.73	Perapedhi 34°51'N, 32°52'E Limassol	(NR.4)
Radolfzell		24.7.72	Egelsee, Thurgau 48°01'N, 10°03'E **W Germany**	
A 92192	+	1.9.73	Paralimni 35°02'N, 33°59'E Famagusta	(R.23)
Radolfzell		17.8.77	Kauerlach, Mittelfranken 49°09'N, 11°18'E **W Germany**	
BP 46874	X	8.10.77	Nicosia 35°10'N, 33°22'E	(Foers 1980)
010 06677		5.10.80	Akrotiri 34°35'N, 32°57'E	
	V	14.8.83	Khor Arba'at 19°48'N, 37°03'E **Sudan**	(NR.14)
Praha		16.7.82	Ishy Horka, Chrudim 49°53'N, 15°55'E **Czechoslovakia**	
M 915144	V	8.8.82	Akrotiri 34°35'N, 32°57'E	(M. Lobb)

Reed Warbler *Acrocephalus scirpaceus* (3)

Brit Mus	4	22.8.77	Lake Koronia, Macedonia 40°40'N, 23°13'E **Greece**	
KJ 95493	L	20.10.77	Anophotia 35°00'N, 33°50'E Larnaca	(Foers 1980)

Reed Warbler *Acrocephalus scirpaceus* (3) (*Continued*)
010 06507   17.8.80   Akrotiri 34°35′N, 32°57′E
                 12.9.83   Khartoum 15°33′N, 32°35′E **Sudan**   (NR.14)

Acrocephalus scirpaceus/palustris (1)
Radolfzell   2   21.7.69   Waghausel, Bruchsal 49°15′N, 08°31′E **W Germany**
BA 25725   +   11.9.69   Limassol 34°40′N, 33°03′E   (Foers 1980)

Sardinian Warbler *Sylvia melanocephala* (2)
Bruxelles   3F   12.8.73   Koccali 41°03′N, 30°54′E **Turkey**
A 995251   L   12.3.74   Lapithos 35°20′N, 33°10′E Kyrenia   (NR.5)

Orphean Warbler *Sylvia hortensis* (1)
Brit Mus   2M   13.4.68   Paralimni 35°02′N, 33°59′E Famagusta
BE 78676   31.3.69   El Koura, Nr Beirut 33°50′N, 35°30′E **Lebanon**   (Foers 1980)

Barred Warbler *Sylvia nisoria* (1)
                 26.7.79   Leningrad Region, Nr Gambaritsy 61°30′N, 32°55′E **USSR**
         L   18.9.81   Ayia Napa 34°58′N, 34°00′E Famagusta   (NR.12)

Lesser Whitethroat *Sylvia curruca* (27)
Copenhagen   3   10.8.53   Amager 55°33′N, 12°36′E **Denmark**
985500   *c.* 22.9.53   Sotira 35°02′N, 33°57′E Famagusta   (B.6)
Radolfzell   15.9.59   Memmingen, Allgau 47°59′N, 10°11′E **W Germany**
K 181141   22.3.60   Nr Famagusta 35°07′N, 33°57′E   (Foers 1980)
Praha   3.6.60   Albrechtice 49°55′N, 16°39′E **Czechoslovakia**
N 59486   3.10.60   Maroni 34°45′N, 33°22′E Larnaca   (B.11)
Stockholm   24.8.60   Ottenby, Oland 56°12′N, 16°24′E **Sweden**
2001651   3.11.60   Mazotos 34°47′N, 33°30′E Larnaca   (B.9)
Helsinki   4   10.7.61   Rukkoila, Hauho 61°13′N, 24°37′E **Finland**
K 93631   *c.* 18.9.61   Cyprus   (B.12)
Stockholm   2   21.8.63   Ottenby, Oland 56°12′N, 16°24′E **Sweden**
1144646   L   30.9.67   Paralimni 35°02′N, 33°59′E Famagusta   (R.14)
Brit Mus   15.8.64   Chichester 50°48′N, 00°48′W **England**
P 41780   L   3.4.68   Paralimni 35°02′N, 33°59′E Famagusta   (R.15)
Stockholm   3   12.9.65   Getteron, Varberg 57°08′N, 12°13′E **Sweden**
2218839   L   10.66   Nr Famagusta 35°07′N, 33°57′E   (Foers 1980)
Praha   23.4.67   Zleby, Kutna Hora 49°53′N, 15°29′E **Czechoslovakia**
M 523186   L   20.3.68   Paralimni 35°02′N, 33°59′E Famagusta   (R.15)
Stockholm   4   30.5.67   Orskar, Uppland 60°31′N, 18°24′E **Sweden**
2274981   L   Autumn 69   Paralimni 35°02′N, 33°59′E Famagusta   (NR.4)
Stockholm   2   10.9.67   Hartso-Enskar, Balinge 58°41′N, 17°29′E **Sweden**
1339202   L   24.10.68   Mazotos Village 34°48′N, 33°29′E Larnaca   (R.15)
Brit Mus   1.4.68   Paralimni 35°02′N, 33°59′E Famagusta
HK 63970   28.8.68   Schio, Vicenza 45°43′N, 11°21′E **Italy**   (NR.7)
Brit Mus   4   21.4.68   Brightlingsea, Essex 51°49′N, 01°02′E **England**
HR 77264   6.5.69   Xylophagou 34°57′N, 33°52′E Larnaca   (R.16)
Brit Mus   4   6.4.69   Cape Andreas 35°40′N, 34°36′E Karpas
HS 92205   X   17.9.69   Vielau/Zwickau 50°41′N, 12°33′E **E Germany**   (R.16)
Stockholm   4   28.5.69   Enskar, Balinge 58°41′N, 17°29′E **Sweden**
1419915   L   Autumn 69   Paralimni 35°02′N, 33°59′E Famagusta   (Foers 1980)
Helsinki   4   20.8.69   Tauvo, Siikajoki (Oulu) 64°49′N, 24°34′E **Finland**
K 580954   ( )   10.10.71   Ayia Napa 34°59′N, 34°00′E Famagusta   (NR.3)
Brit Mus   4   11.4.70   Akrotiri 34°35′N, 32°57′E
JA 17686   +   4.4.71   Aleih, Nr Beirut 33°47′N, 35°37′E **Lebanon**   (R.18)
Helsinki   2   7.8.70   Vanhankaupunginlahti 60°12′N, 25°00′E **Finland**
K 720241   L   15.8.72   Lefkara 34°50′N, 33°18′E Larnaca   (NR.3)
No trace   1   16.8.70   Vienenburg, Brunswick 51°57′N, 10°34′E **W Germany**
          +   28.4.71   Larnaca 34°55′N, 33°38′E   (R.18)
Stockholm   4   27.5.73   Utklippan, Blekinge 55°57′N, 15°42′E **Sweden**
1672784   L   2.10.73   Asgata 34°46′N, 33°13′E Limassol   (NR.4)
Stockholm   20.5.76   Utklippan, Blekinge 55°57′N, 15°42′E **Sweden**
         L   4.10.81   Larnaca 34°54′N, 33°39′E   (NR.12)
Praha   3   10.9.77   Horky, Svitavy 49°55′N, 16°15′E **Czechoslovakia**
M 769555   L   20.10.77   Anaphotia 35°00′N, 33°50′E Larnaca   (Foers 1980)
Helsinki   4.9.80   Kirkkonumni, Uusimaa 59°56′N, 24°24′E **Finland**
J 668675   14.10.81   Livadhia, 34°56′N, 33°39′E Larnaca   (R.28)
                 1.8.81   Nyskie Lake, Nysa, Opole 50°27′N, 17°16′E **Poland**
         L   26.9.83   Asgata 34°47′N, 33°15′E Limassol   (NR.14)

Lesser Whitethroat *Sylvia curruca* (27) (*Continued*)

Brit Mus	3	20.8.81	Stock, Essex 51°40′N, 00°26′E **England**	
A 909723	+	30.5.82	Paralimni 35°02′N, 33°59′E Famagusta	(P. F. Stewart)
Moskwa		25.6.85	Kaliningrad O Rybachy 55°08′N, 20°42′E **USSR**	
0257127		85	Lefkara 34°51′N, 33°19′E Larnaca	(R.32)

Whitethroat *Sylvia communis* (2)

Riga		12.7.43	Kuldiga, Latvia 56°58′N, 21°58′E **USSR**	
134391		9.11.43	Pyrga 34°55′N, 33°25′E Larnaca	(R.12)
		7.9.81	Kaliningrad O Rybachy 55°08′N, 20°42′E **USSR**	
	L	7.10.82	Paralimni 35°02′N, 33°59′E Famagusta	(NR.13)

Garden Warbler *Sylvia borin* (2)

Helgoland	3	27.6.33	Dalbersdorf 51°12′N, 17°44′E (Germany) **Poland**	
898140	+	26.8.33	Larnaca 34°55′N, 33°39′E	(B.6)
Helgoland	1	30.5.34	Burg 52°17′N, 11°52′E **W Germany**	
8085637	( )	16.10.34	Famagusta 35°07′N, 33°57′E	(B.6)

Blackcap *Sylvia atricapilla* (92)

Budapest	1	3.6.29	Nagylozs 47°33′N, 16°43′E **Hungary**	
49434	+	18.9.30	Hadjichtori 34°54′N, 32°56′E Limassol	(B.6)
Stockholm	3	1.8.31	Ulriksdal 59°23′N, 18°00′E **Sweden**	
C 3871	( )	5.11.32	Ayios Theodoros 34°48′N, 33°24′E Larnaca	(B.6)
Helgoland	4	30.8.32	Gimmel 51°13′N, 17°35′E (Germany) **Poland**	
869093	X	10.9.32	Paralimni 35°02′N, 33°59′E Famagusta	(B.6)
Helgoland	1	6.6.33	Barzdorf 51°00′N, 16°28′E (Germany) **Poland**	
8022101	( ) pre	22.9.34	Athna 35°04′N, 33°47′E Famagusta	(B.6)
Lotos	3	27.6.33	Troppau 49°57′N, 17°54′E **Czechoslovakia**	
H 3929		10.10.34	Nicosia 35°10′N, 33°23′E	(B.6)
Rossitten	3	10.10.33	Ulmenhorst, Rossitten 55°09′N, 20°52′E (Germany) **USSR**	
G 237308		10.10.34	Khirokitia 34°47′N, 33°22′E Larnaca	(B.6)
Helgoland	4	14.9.34	Heligoland 54°11′N, 07°55′E **W Germany**	
9032860	+	1.10.37	Ayios Theodoros 35°21′N, 34°02′E Famagusta	(B.6)
Praha	4	10.9.36	Pikovice n/Saz 49°53′N, 14°26′E **Czechoslovakia**	
E 8873	X	18.10.38	Maroni 34°45′N, 33°21′E Larnaca	(B.6)
Goteborg	3	10.6.37	Ekeby 56°01′N, 12°58′E **Sweden**	
A 13322	( )	4.10.37	Kophinou 34°50′N, 33°24′E Larnaca	(B.6)
Rossitten	3	12.9.37	Ulmenhorst, Rossitten 55°09′N, 20°52′E (Germany) **USSR**	
G 404492	+	c. 19.10.37	Dhali 35°01′N, 33°25′E Nicosia	(B.6)
Rossitten	4	19.9.37	Ulmenhorst, Rossitten 55°09′N, 20°52′E (Germany) **USSR**	
G 404709	+	6.11.37	Ayios Theodoros 34°48′N, 33°24′E Larnaca	(B.6)
Praha	3	21.6.41	Dubi Bustehrad 50°10′N, 14°09′E **Czechoslovakia**	
M 20071	+	31.10.41	Anglisidhes 34°50′N, 33°28′E Larnaca	(B.6)
Praha	1	2.6.42	Vrapice 50°10′N, 14°10′E **Czechoslovakia**	
M 33261	+	6.10.43	Ayios Theodoros 34°48′N, 33°24′E Larnaca	(B.6)
Praha	4	27.7.43	Turnov 50°36′N, 15°10′E **Czechoslovakia**	
M 64929	+	1.10.46	Anaphotia 34°48′N, 33°28′E Larnaca	(B.6)
Goteborg	3	6.6.45	Henriksdorp 55°58′N, 13°38′E **Sweden**	
A 44375	( )	25.10.45	Kornos 34°56′N, 33°24′E Larnaca	(B.6)
Praha	1	31.7.48	Zlin 49°13′N, 17°46′E **Czechoslovakia**	
M 143374		c. 1.10.48	Mazotos 34°48′N, 33°29′E Larnaca	(B.6)
Cairo	4M	8.4.51	Fayid 30°17′N, 32°19′E **Egypt**	
C 674		11.10.51	Dherynia 35°03′N, 33°57′E Famagusta	(B.6)
Praha	4F	17.8.51	Caslav 49°56′N, 15°20′E **Czechoslovakia**	
M 183206		c. 22.10.51	Limassol 34°41′N, 33°05′E	(B.6)
Praha	1	2.6.52	Pilsen 49°45′N, 13°23′E **Czechoslovakia**	
M 215929	+	10.52	Nr Famagusta 35°07′N, 33°57′E	(B.6)
Moskwa	1	23.6.52	Moscow 55°45′N, 37°42′E **USSR**	
216596		10.52	Famagusta 35°07′N, 33°57′E	(B.15)
Praha		26.7.52	Bela Rohovladova 50°06′N, 15°36′E **Czechoslovakia**	
Z 84636		10.52	Nr Famagusta 35°07′N, 33°57′E	(B.6)
Praha		10.8.53	Litvinov 50°35′N, 13°36′E **Czechoslovakia**	
M 170567		1.10.53	Perochorio, Nr Dhali c.35°00′N, 33°23′E Nicosia	(B.12)

Blackcap *Sylvia atricapilla* (92) (*Continued*)

Madartani		3.6.57	Janoshegy, Nr Budapest, **Hungary**	
66560		14.4.59	Kato Paphos 34°42′N, 32°24′E	(B.12)
Varsovia	1	9.6.57	Rydzyna 51°48′N, 16°11′E **Poland**	
G 551358	( )	16.9.57	Livadhia 34°57′N, 33°38′E Larnaca	(B.6)
Praha		28.8.59	Pilsen 49°45′N, 13°23′E **Czechoslovakia**	
M 286299		5.5.60	Yialousa 35°31′N, 34°12′E Famagusta	(B.12)
Moskwa	3	17.7.60	Rybatschi, Kaliningrad 55°11′N, 20°49′E **USSR**	
X 908622	L	5.10.60	Paralimni 35°02′N, 33°59′E Famagusta	(B.12)
Budapest	4F	7.8.60	Nr Piliscsaba 47°38′N, 18°50′E **Hungary**	
111256		26.9.60	Avgorou 35°01′N, 33°50′E Famagusta	(B.9)
Praha	1	2.7.61	Zleby, Caslav 49°54′N, 15°30′E **Czechoslovakia**	
M 399114		*c.* 30.10.61	Nr Famagusta 35°07′N, 33°57′E	(B.12)
Radolfzell	1	23.6.62	Hartenstein, Karl Marx Stadt 50°40′N, 12°41′E **E Germany**	
H 793923	L	13.9.63	Paralimni 35°02′N, 33°59′E Famagusta	(Foers 1980)
Varsovia	2F	21.8.62	Mierzigu Wislana (Gdansk) 54°19′N, 19°14′E **Poland**	
H 32547	L	1.9.64	Khirokitia 34°47′N, 33°21′E Limassol	(R.12)
Helsinki	4M	20.5.63	Jurmo, Korpo 59°50′N, 21°37′E **Finland**	
P 93329	L	1.66	Nicosia 35°10′N, 33°22′E	(R.12)
Helsinki		20.5.63	Jurmo, Korpo 59°50′N, 21°37′E **Finland**	
P 93529	+	15.4.72	Nicosia 35°11′N, 33°23′E	(NR.4)
Stockholm	3	10.8.63	Ytterby (Bohuslan) 57°52′N, 11°55′E **Sweden**	
2121435	L	*c.* 10.1.64	Ayios Omvrosis, Nr Kividhes 34°46′N, 32°51′E Limassol	(B.16)
Stockholm	3M	17.9.63	Ottenby, Oland 56°12′N, 16°24′E **Sweden**	
2117955	+	11.63	Paralimni 35°02′N, 33°59′E Famagusta	(B.14)
Helsinki	4F	29.5.64	Jurmo, Korpo 59°50′N, 21°37′E **Finland**	
P 110336	L	*c.* 24.10.64	Paralimni 35°02′N, 33°59′E Famagusta	(R.12)
Hiddensee	1	18.6.64	Leutzsch, Leipzig 51°20′N, 12°18′E **E Germany**	
80017344	L	*c.* 24.10.64	Paralimni 35°02′N, 33°59′E Famagusta	(R.12)
Stockholm	4M	4.8.64	Kvismaren, Norrbyas 59°11′N, 15°24′E **Sweden**	
2167462	L	17.10.65	Alaminos 34°48′N, 33°26′E Larnaca	(R.12)
Brit Mus	2F	16.2.65	Episkopi 34°40′N, 32°55′E Limassol	
AN 26927	+	6.9.70	Salerno 40°41′N, 14°46′E **Italy**	(Foers 1980)
Praha	3	3.8.65	Halda, Usti nad Orlici 49°58′N, 16°38′E **Czechoslovakia**	
M 502237	+	15.2.72	Nicosia 35°10′N, 33°20′E	(NR.5)
Praha	2M	24.8.65	Novy Dvur, Nr Pisek 49°16′N, 14°12′E **Czechoslovakia**	
M 503343		24.9.68	Cyprus	(R.16)
Moskwa	4	29.8.65	Nr Rybatschi, Kaliningrad 55°11′N, 20°49′E **USSR**	
S 209897		*c.* 9.67	Paralimni 35°02′N, 33°59′E Famagusta	(R.16)
Stockholm	4M	11.9.65	Skanor (Skane) 55°25′N, 12°50′E **Sweden**	
2199381	L	15.11.65	Nr Larnaca 34°55′N, 33°39′E	(R.12)
Stockholm	4M	16.9.65	Fasterbo, Skane 55°23′N, 12°50′E **Sweden**	
2212574	L	16.11.65	Maroni 34°55′N, 33°40′E Larnaca	(Foers 1980)
Varsovia	4M	20.8.66	Nowy Pasleka 54°26′N, 19°45′E **Poland**	
H 137343	L	3.10.66	Alaminos 34°48′N, 33°26′E Larnaca	(R.14)
Stockholm		8.9.66	Enskar, Balinge 58°41′N, 17°29′E **Sweden**	
2194316		4.68	Paralimni 35°02′N, 33°59′E Famagusta	(R.15)
Helsinki	2M	1.9.67	Pasila, Nr Helsinki 60°12′N, 24°56′E **Finland**	
P 192101	L	9.68	Paralimni 35°02′N, 33°59′E Famagusta	(R.16)
Stockholm		2.9.67	Lake Landsjou, Skarstad 57°52′N, 14°19′E **Sweden**	
2276883		8.6.68	Paralimni 35°02′N, 33°59′E Famagusta	(R.15)
Brit Mus	4M	2.4.68	Paralimni 35°02′N, 33°59′E Famagusta	
HK 63989	( )	28.8.68	Beirut 33°52′N, 35°28′E **Lebanon**	(R.15)
Brit Mus	4M	6.4.68	Polemidhia 34°41′N, 33°00′E Limassol	
HK 61542	+	20.9.68	Ramallah 31°54′N, 35°12′E **Jordan**	(R.15)
Brit Mus	4M	8.4.68	Paralimni 35°02′N, 33°59′E Famagusta	
HK 64109	+	25.8.73	Nr Al Mukhtara 33°39′N, 35°35′E **Lebanon**	(Foers 1980)
Tel Aviv	4M	23.4.68	Eilat 29°33′N, 34°57′E **Israel**	
A 6747	L	10.69	Paralimni 35°02′N, 33°59′E Famagusta	(Foers 1980)
Tel Aviv		24.4.68	Eilat 29°33′N, 34°57′E **Israel**	
A 8558		9.68	Paralimni 35°02′N, 33°59′E Famagusta	(P. F. Stewart)

Blackcap *Sylvia atricapilla* (92) (*Continued*)

Brit Mus	2F	24.4.68	Paralimni 35°02′N, 33°59′E Famagusta	
HK 64686	+	Autumn 69	Ayn Sekka (Share Jdid) c. 34°20′N, 36°30′E **Lebanon**(R.17)	
Radolfzell		28.4.68	Marchegg, Ganserndorf 48°17′N, 16°55′E **Austria**	
HA 51464	L	Autumn 69	Paralimni 35°02′N, 33°59′E Famagusta	(Foers 1980)
Tel Aviv		29.4.68	Eilat 29°33′N, 34°57′E **Israel**	
A 9422		6.10.69	Anaphotia 34°49′N, 33°28′E Larnaca	(P. F. Stewart)
Radolfzell	2M	18.5.68	Waldsassen, Oberpfalz 50°00′N, 12°18′E **W Germany**	
K 134618	L	9.68	Paralimni 35°02′N, 33°59′E Famagusta	(Foers 1980)
Helsinki	2F	21.8.68	Tauvo, Siikajoki (Oulu) 64°49′N, 24°35′E **Finland**	
P 223798	L	11.10.68	Psematismenos 34°46′N, 33°21′E Larnaca	(R.16)
Stockholm	3	24.8.68	Ottenby, Oland 56°12′N, 16°24′E **Sweden**	
2229076		c. 10.11.68	Zyyi 34°43′N, 33°21′E Larnaca	(R.16)
Varsovia	3	25.8.68	Suchatowka, Nr Torun 52°54′N, 18°30′E **Poland**	
H 187875	+	18.10.68	Louvaras 34°50′N, 33°02′E Limassol	(R.17)
Stockholm	2M	11.9.68	Hartso-Enskar, Balinge 58°41′N, 17°29′E **Sweden**	
2315169	L	27.10.68	Paralimni 35°02′N, 33°59′E Famagusta	(R.16)
Stockholm	2F	22.9.68	Skanor, Skane 55°25′N, 12°50′E **Sweden**	
2295165	L	4.70	Paralimni 35°02′N, 33°59′E Famagusta	(NR.4)
Brit Mus	4F	2.10.68	Akrotiri, 34°36′N, 32°56′E	
HK 62244	+	14.5.71	Nr Beirut 33°41′N, 35°31′E **Lebanon**	(R.18)
Varsovia	3M	16.9.69	Mierzeja Wislana, Gdansk 54°21′N, 19°19′E **Poland**	
HA 115602	L	9.70	Paralimni 35°02′N, 33°59′E Famagusta	(NR.2)
Brit Mus	3M	30.10.69	Akrotiri 34°35′N, 32°57′E	
HX 78926	+	8.73	Merjayoun 33°18′N, 35°33′E **Lebanon**	(Foers 1980)
Praha	1	14.6.70	Usti nad Orlici 49°58′N, 16°24′E **Czechoslovakia**	
M 608412	X	20.9.71	Lefkara 34°51′N, 33°19′E Larnaca	(NR.4)
Praha	2M	25.7.70	Zleby, Kutna Hora 49°53′N, 15°29′E **Czechoslovakia**	
M 611812	L	5.10.77	Anaphotia 35°00′N, 33°50′E Larnaca	(Foers 1980)
Praha	2M	13.8.70	Bila Hora, Pilsen 49°46′N, 13°24′E **Czechoslovakia**	
M 592875	+	10.10.76	Psevdhas, 34°58′N, 33°26′E Larnaca	(Foers 1980)
Varsovia	3M	10.9.70	Mierzeja Wislana, Gdansk 54°21′N, 19°19′E **Poland**	
HA 153993	L early 10.70		Paralimni 35°02′N, 33°59′E Famagusta	(NR.2)
Praha	3	18.8.71	Zimrovice, Opava 49°51′N, 17°51′E **Czechoslovakia**	
M 634703	L	24.9.72	Paralimni 35°02′N, 33°59′E Famagusta	(Foers 1980)
Radolfzell	4	13.9.71	Ebenthal, Klagenfurt 46°36′N, 14°22′E **Austria**	
CD 56171		7.12.71	Akanthou 35°22′N, 33°45′E Famagusta	(R.18)
Rumania	2M	29.9.71	Cluj Jud 46°50′N, 23°37′E **Rumania**	
R 25278	X	2.10.72	Aglantzia 35°10′N, 33°25′E Nicosia	(NR.3)
Varsovia	4F	9.7.72	Ojcow-Ziota Gora 50°12′N, 19°50′E **Poland**	
G 576515	L	24.9.72	Paralimni 35°02′N, 33°59′E Famagusta	(NR.3)
Stockholm	4F	14.9.72	Farlov, Skane 56°04′N, 14°05′E **Sweden**	
2406849	L	28.4.74	Paralimni 35°02′N, 33°59′E Famagusta	(Foers 1980)
Praha		11.5.73	Zliv, Ceske Budejovice, Praha 49°04′N, 14°22′E **Czechoslovakia**	
		9.74	Paralimni 35°02′N, 33°59′E Famagusta	(NR.13)
Stockholm	2F	8.9.75	Hammaron, Varmland 59°15′N, 13°30′E **Sweden**	
2500253	L	20.10.75	Ayia Napa 34°59′N, 34°00′E Famagusta	(NR.6)
Tel Aviv	4F	1.5.76	Nr Shimron 32°38′N, 35°13′E **Israel**	
A 46130	L	8.9.76	Zoopiya 34°51′N, 33°01′E Limassol	(Foers 1980)
Brit Mus	2F	16.9.76	Redcar 54°39′N, 01°08′W **England**	
KH 63282	X	21.3.78	Pallouriotissa 35°11′N, 33°26′E Nicosia	(R.25)
Hiddensee		29.9.78	Kloster, Hid 54°36′N, 13°07′E **E Germany**	
80516656	L	2.12.78	Lazania 35°00′N, 33°00′E Nicosia	(NR.9)
Stockholm		23.9.79	Eggegrund, Gastrikland 60°44′N, 17°33′E **Sweden**	
2681558	L	20.10.81	Pyrga 34°56′N, 33°30′E Larnaca	(NR.12)
Nairobi	3	17.10.80	Erkowit, Red Sea 18°49′N, 37°01′E **Sudan**	
J 160061		14.11.82	Nicosia 35°10′N, 33°20′E	(G. Backhurst)
		28.8.81	Vransko Jesero, Dalmacija 43°56′N, 15°31′E **Yugoslavia**	
	V	24.9.83	Xylophagou 34°58′N, 33°51′E Larnaca	(NR.14)
Sofia	3	15.9.81	Petrisch 41°28′N, 23°17′E **Bulgaria**	
1–62616		9.81	Ormidhia 34°59′N, 33°47′E Larnaca	(P. F. Stewart)

Blackcap *Sylvia atricapilla* (92) (*Continued*)
Sofia		14.4.82	Rupite, Petritsch 41°28′N, 23°17′E **Bulgaria**	
	L	31.5.82	Monagrouli 34°45′N, 33°14′E Limassol	(NR.13)
		29.5.82	Molen, Brunlanes, Vestfold 58°58′N, 09°49′E **Norway**	
	L	23.10.82	Dhali 35°02′N, 33°26′E Nicosia	(NR.13)
		7.6.82	Groszdybraw Bantzen DDR 51°11′N, 14°26′E **E Germany**	
	L	23.10.82	Lythrodhonda 34°57′N, 33°18′E Nicosia	(NR.13)
Budapest	3	26.8.82	Zagyvarona, Budapest 47°05′N, 16°37′E **Hungary**	
		31.10.82	Dhali 35°02′N, 33°26′E Nicosia	(NR.13)
Moskwa		2.8.83	Cherkassy Kavensky Reserve, Ukraine 49°48′N, 31°23′E **USSR**	
XC 062155	+	26.9.84	Argaka 35°04′N, 32°30′E Paphos	(NR.15)
		3.9.83	San Pedro Pescadro, Gerona 42°11′N, 03°05′E **Spain**	
	+	2.10.83	Trimiklini 34°49′N, 32°57′E Limassol	(NR.14)
Prague	No details			
M 898376	L	1.10.84	Livadhia 34°57′N, 33°38′E Larnaca	(NR.15)
Nairobi		1.5.84	Sanganeb Is., Red Sea 19°44′N, 37°26′E **Sudan**	
A 48207		20.9.85	Paralimni 35°02′N, 33°59′E Famagusta	(G. Backhurst)

Wood Warbler *Phylloscopus sibilatrix* (1)
Moskwa		3.6.79	Rybatschi, Kaliningrad 55°08′N, 20°42′E **USSR**	
	L	25.8.83	Trimiklini 34°49′N, 32°57′E Limassol	(NR.14)

Chiffchaff *Phylloscopus collybita* (11)
Rossitten	3	15.7.35	Munsterberg 50°37′N, 17°02′E (Germany) **Poland**	
G 354566		4.12.35	Kophinou 34°50′N, 33°24′E Larnaca	(B.6)
Brit Mus	4	24.4.66	Azraq 31°50′N, 36°50′E **Jordan**	
HC 27525		8.4.68	Paralimni 35°02′N, 33°59′E Famagusta	(R.15)
Hiddensee	2	14.8.76	Ziegenhals, Furstenwalde 52°22′N, 13°41′E **W Germany**	
90726821	L	10.12.76	Konia 34°47′N, 31°28′E Paphos	(Foers 1980)
Avivuniu		1.3.80	Eilat 29°34′N, 34°57′E **Israel**	
Z 17111	L	21.3.80	Paralimni 35°02′N, 33°59′E Famagusta	(NR.11)
Radolfzell		28.9.83	Illmit 2, Ber, Neusiedl, Burgenland 47°46′N, 16°48′E **W Germany**	
BT 65623	L	12.3.84	Larnaca 31°55′N, 33°38′E	(NR.15)
Zagreb		21.10.83	Presevo, Srbija 42°16′N, 21°40′E **Yugoslavia**	
E 25811	L	19.1.84	Paralimni 35°02′N, 33°59′E Famagusta	(NR.15)
Finland	No details			
C 73797	L	17.9.84	Nicosia 35°10′N, 33°22′E	(NR.15)

Willow Warbler *Phylloscopus trochilus* (5)
Brit Mus	2	8.9.67	Akrotiri 34°35′N, 32°57′E	
PC 1699	+	23.11.68	Nr Istanbul 41°00′N, 29°00′E **Turkey**	(R.15)
Brit Mus	2	15.9.70	Akrotiri 34°35′N, 32°57′E	
189161		20.10.72	El Hauwariya 30°58′N, 29°41′E **Egypt**	(R.19)
Helsinki	2	4.8.77	Espoo, Uudenmaan 60°12′N, 24°49′E **Finland**	
R 61453	L	18.9.77	Stroumbi 34°53′N, 32°29′E Paphos	(Foers 1980)
Moskwa	2	21.8.78	Rybatschi, Kaliningrad 55°11′N, 20°49′E **USSR**	
S 910413	L	25.9.78	Paphos 34°45′N, 32°24′E	(Foers 1980)

Spotted Flycatcher *Muscicapa striata* (1)
Helgoland		17.9.59	Heligoland 54°11′N, 07°55′E **W Germany**	
9837132		30.10.59	Episkopi 34°40′N, 32°44′E Limassol	(B.11)

Pied Flycatcher *Ficedula hypoleuca* (1)
Jos Museum	2	9.10.66	Mallam Fatori, Lake Chad 13°33′N, 13°23′E **Nigeria**	
26642	L	Spring 67	Paralimni 35°02′N, 33°59′E Famagusta	(R.15)

Red-backed Shrike *Lanius collurio* (4)
Rossitten	1	Summer 39	Barzdorf 51°00′N, 16°24′E (Germany) **Poland**	
F 359777		14.9.39	Tavros 35°22′N, 34°04′E Famagusta	(B.6)
Ljubljana		16.7.39	Svetje Medvode 46°08′N, 14°22′E **Yugoslavia**	
20000		c. 3.5.40	Paralimni 35°02′N, 33°59′E Famagusta	(B.6)
Radolfzell	4	17.7.65	Dagenfeld, Gmund 48°44′N, 08°53′E **W Germany**	
G 282066	L	9.67	Paralimni 35°02′N, 33°59′E Famagusta	(R.15)

Masked Shrike *Lanius nubicus* (1)
Brit Mus	2	30.6.63	Troodos 34°56′N, 32°53′E	
41688R	()	13.4.64	Akbiyeh, Nr Sidon 33°30′N, 35°16′E **Lebanon**	(B.15)

Starling *Sturnus vulgaris* (13)
Moskwa	3	28.5.49	Oksky Reserve 54°45′N, 40°50′E **USSR**	
F 75814		6.12.49	Pergamos 35°02′N, 33°43′E Famagusta	(B.6)

Starling *Sturnus vulgaris* (13) (*Continued*)

Moskwa	3	31.5.49	Oksky Reserve 54°45′N, 40°50′E **USSR**	
F 75870		29.11.49	Yeroskipos 34°45′N, 32°27′E Paphos	(B.6)
Moskwa	3	27.5.50	Oksky Reserve 54°45′N, 40°50′E **USSR**	
F 80248		6.11.50	Mandria 34°43′N, 32°32′E Paphos	(B.6)
Moskwa	3	25.5.53	Oksky Reserve 54°45′N, 40°50′E **USSR**	
F 129647		9.11.53	Ktima 34°45′N, 32°25′E Paphos	(B.6)
Moskwa	3	3.6.57	Zakharove, Ryazan 54°23′N, 39°17′E **USSR**	
F 353949		8.12.59	Ayia Napa 34°59′N, 34°00′E Famagusta	(B.15)
Moskwa		6.60	Alushta, Crimea 44°40′N, 34°25′E **USSR**	
F 244937		10.12.60	Kiti 35°50′N, 33°35′E Larnaca	(B.12)
Moskwa	1	28.5.61	Kamenka (Penza) 53°10′N, 44°50′E **USSR**	
F 715709		12.11.61	Paphos 33°45′N, 32°25′E	(B.15)
Moskwa	4F	24.5.70	Oksky Reserve 54°45′N, 40°50′E **USSR**	
313598	X	11.2.71	Nr Nicosia 35°11′N, 33°26′E	(NR.3)
Moskwa	3	16.5.72	Oksky Reserve 54°45′N, 40°50′E **USSR**	
335338	X	15.12.72	Ayios Theodhoros 35°22′N, 34°02′E Famagusta	(NR.3)
Moskwa		1.4.73	Shatsk, Ryazan 54°00′N, 41°45′E **USSR**	
P 209601	+	20.12.73	Kythrea 35°15′N, 33°30′E Kyrenia	(NR.5)
Moskwa		No details		
P 205981		10.12.73	Tseri 35°13′N, 33°28′E Nicosia	(P. F. Stewart)
Moskwa	2	18.4.77	Oksky Reserve 54°45′N, 40°50′E **USSR**	
P 301210	X	*c.* 15.1.78	Pyrga 34°50′N, 33°30′E Larnaca	(Foers 1980)
Moskwa		20.6.80	Vologda Okatuiskiy Khokhlovo 59°15′N, 37°11′E **USSR**	
518346	+	17.1.84	Limassol 34°40′N, 32°42′E	(NR.15)

Chaffinch *Fringilla coelebs* (2)

Brit Mus	4F	29.1.59	Nicosia 35°13′N, 33°22′E	
E 11512	( )	2.4.60	Vulkaneshty, Moldavia 45°41′N, 28°23′E **USSR**	(B.11)

Goldfinch *Carduelis carduelis* (10)

Zagreb	3	12.10.48	Split 43°30′N, 16°27′E **Yugoslavia**	
A 135727	V	28.1.49	Limassol 34°41′N, 33°05′E	(B.6)
Brit Mus	3	27.4.68	Akrotiri 34°35′N, 32°57′E	
HK 61572		6.12.68	Alexandria 31°13′N, 29°55′E **Egypt**	(Foers 1980)

Siskin *Carduelis spinus* (2)

Madartani		8.10.55	Harma Shatarhagy, Nr Budapest 47°30′N, 19°00′E **Hungary**	
51166		10.10.59	Spilia 34°58′N, 32°57′E Troodos	(B.12)
Moskwa		30.6.65	Rybatschi, Kaliningrad 55°11′N, 20°49′E **USSR**	
S 201301		30.10.65	Kaminaria 34°56′N, 32°47′E Troodos	(R.12)

Hawfinch *Coccothraustes coccothraustes* (1)

Zagreb	2F	8.10.72	Mali, Losinj 44°32′N, 14°29′E **Yugoslavia**	
A 386503	+	5.1.75	Nr Evrykhou, Morphou 35°11′N, 32°59′E Nicosia	(R.25)

Black-headed Bunting *Emberiza melanocephala* (2)

Zagreb	3	23.6.56	Gata 43°28′N, 16°42′E **Yugoslavia**	
5930	( )	20.4.57	Famagusta 35°07′N, 33°57′E	(B.6)
No details		Winter 64	Kutch Area of **India**	
		Summer 65	Cyprus	(McClure 1974)

APPENDIX 3

THE MEAN WING AND MASS MEASUREMENTS OF SELECTED SPECIES TAKEN IN CYPRUS 1960–1990

Species		Wing (mm)			Mass (g)		
		Sample	Mean	Range	Sample	Mean	Range
Little Ringed Plover	Spring	5	120·5	118–119(127)	5	32·2	30·6–33
Charadrius dubius	Autumn	15	114·7	109–121	12	36·7	30–47
Ringed Plover	Autumn	54	125·1	110–132	51	47·1	34–72·1
Charadrius hiaticula							
Little Stint	Spring	3	95·6	94–97	3	20·3	19·2–22
Calidris minuta	Autumn	113	97·5	82–112	112	25·6	18·6–33
Curlew Sandpiper	Autumn	12	128·7	123–134	12	61·9	47·3–79
Calidris ferruginea							
Dunlin	Autumn	48	115·9	100–125	48	46·2	29·4–59
Calidris alpina							
Wood Sandpiper	Spring	8	130·4	124–137	8	55·0	51·1–63·5
Tringa glareola	Autumn	15	120·8	100–131	12	66·6	52–86
Common Sandpiper		29	110·5	103–115	28	47·9	34–67
Actitis (= Tringa) hypoleucos							
Turtle Dove	Spring	13	169·2	161–178	6	140·0	102–175
Streptopelia turtur	Autumn	33	171·0	160–183	33	150·7	89·7–175
Scops Owl	Mar–Apr	54	154·8	143–168	43	69·5	57·1–93
Otus scops	Sep	4	161·7	160–165	4	98·6	90·3–104·1
Nightjar	Sep–May	7	183·1	163–200	7	62·3	49·8–77·6
Caprimulgus europaeus							
Pallid Swift	Summer	9	173·4	167–178	9	38·0	33·4–42
Apus pallidus							
Kingfisher		74	74·8	71–80	73	33·3	23·5–43·5
Alcedo atthis							
Hoopoe		38	144·1	131–155	38	67·0	39·5–80·9
Upupa epops							
Wryneck		25	86·8	80·5–94	25	31·8	23–40·5
Jynx torquilla							
Crested Lark		127	100·5	94–110	73	36·6	25·3–43
Galerida cristata							
Sand Martin	Spring	5	113·2	108–118	5	12·6	11·9–14·4
Riparia riparia	Autumn	762	104·9	95–117	600	14·3	10–20·5
Swallow		397	121·9	106–131	370	20·2	13–25
Hirundo rustica							
Red-rumped Swallow	Summer	16	119·2	112–126	15	20·1	18–23
Hirundo daurica							
House Martin	Summer	197	105·8	98–113	197	17·5	14–21
Delichon urbica							
Tree Pipit		22	87·7	80–92	21	22·5	17·4–28·3
Anthus trivialis							
Meadow Pipit		91	80·1	75–87	91	17·8	15·1–22
Anthus pratensis							
Red-throated Pipit		31	83·3	76–91	30	19·3	15–29·7
Anthus cervinus							
Water Pipit		9	83·9	79–90	7	21·6	17·4–23·4
Anthus spinoletta							
Black-headed Wagtail		21	80·6	76–84	21	17·9	14–21·2
Motacilla flava feldegg							

Species		Wing (mm)			Mass (g)		
		Sample	Mean	Range	Sample	Mean	Range
White Wagtail *Motacilla alba alba*		142	88·5	80–94	142	21·8	15·8–32
Wren *Troglodytes troglodytes*	Troodos	6	46·8	44·5–51	6	10·0	8–12·5
Robin *Erithacus rubecula*		394	72·1	65–78	348	17·1	13·1–21·2
Thrush Nightingale *Luscinia luscinia*	Spring	8	88·2	87–93	8	19·3	14·7–24
	Autumn	27	89·4	85–95	26	26·7	23·2–32
Nightingale *Luscinia megarhynchos*	Spring	114	84·9	78–91	111	20·4	12·3–26·8
	Autumn	2	85·5	82, 89	2	26·7	25·5, 28
Bluethroat *Luscinia svecica*	Males	15	73·6	67–77	15	18·0	15–21·1
	Females	16	70·7	69–72	16	16·3	14·3–21
Black Redstart *Phoenicurus ochruros*	Nov–Mar Males	6	85·1	79–89	4	16·5	16–17·1
	Nov–Mar Females	27	82·7	79·5–88	26	15·7	12–18
Redstart *Phoenicurus phoenicurus*	Spring Males	81	80·0	72–86	73	13·6	9·3–18
	Spring Females	85	77·1	70–82	80	12·9	9·8–19·2
	Autumn Males	61	80·0	73–83	58	16·8	12·1–22
	Autumn Females	54	78·4	72–83	52	17·0	12–21·1
Whinchat *Saxicola rubetra*	Spring	7	76·8	74–82	7	16·8	15·4–21
	Autumn	21	75·2	65–82	22	17·7	11–21
Stonechat *Saxicola torquata*	Males	79	65·6	61–70	71	14·9	12–17·8
	Females	45	64·4	61–69	39	14·4	10·7–17
Isabelline Wheatear *Oenanthe isabellina*	Spring	52	94·8	90–102	25	22·5	18·5–26·8
Northern Wheatear *Oenanthe oenanthe*	Spring Males	40	94·9	87–100	37	20·4	13·8–27·4
	Spring Females	13	92·5	86–99	11	19·6	14·4–28
Cyprus Pied Wheatear *Oenanthe cypriaca*	Males	57	82·3	79–91(92·5)	16	15·8	12–22·5
	Females	14	81·2	78–85	6	14·7	12–21
Blackbird *Turdus merula*	Males	43	128·4	120–138	34	91·4	77·5–108·4
	Females	36	124·3	116–132	33	90·0	72–132
Song Thrush *Turdus philomelos*		182	117·8	110–127	181	73·4	62–90
Cetti's Warbler *Cettia cetti*	Males	118	62·2	57–66(68)	118	13·4	10·0–17
	Females	123	56·0	51–61	123	10·6	9·1–15·3
Fan-tailed Warbler *Cisticola juncidis*		38	49·1	47–54	35	8·5	7·3–10
Savi's Warbler *Locustella luscinioides*	Spring	8	69·8	67–74	8	15·8	13·2–18·5
	Autumn	23	69·0	63–73	23	15·9	12·3–21·4
Moustached Warbler *Acrocephalus melanopogon*	Oct–Mar	22	59·7	57–61	21	11·3	9·7–14
Sedge Warbler *Acrocephalus schoenobaenus*	Spring	67	67·6	61–72(77)	65	11·6	9·2–15·6
	Autumn	183	66·6	61–71	181	12·9	8·4–18
Reed Warbler *Acrocephalus scirpaceus*		821	63·1	60–72	821	10·9	8·2–17·5
Great Reed Warbler *Acrocephalus arundinaceus*	Spring	24	96·5	92–102	21	32·4	25–40·3
	Autumn	26	95·4	87–103	26	32·5	25–38
Olivaceous Warbler *Hippolais pallida*		179	65·3	61–71	163	10·7	8–16
Spectacled Warbler *Sylvia conspicillata*		10	52·5	51–54	10	9·4	8·7–10

Species		Wing (mm)			Mass (g)		
		Sample	Mean	Range	Sample	Mean	Range
Subalpine Warbler	Spring Males	15	61·9	59–65	10	10·0	8·9–12
Sylvia cantillans	Spring Females	11	61·1	57–65	3	9·9	9·5–10·3
Sardinian Warbler	Males	96	58·5	55–63	93	13·3	8–17
Sylvia melanocephala	Females	84	58·5	52–61(67)	81	12·2	10–15·3
Cyprus Warbler	Males	68	59·7	55–65	61	11·2	9·4–13·7
Sylvia melanothorax	Females	48	58	54–61	42	11·5	9·5–13·8(15)
Ruppell's Warbler	Spring Males	48	68·6	61–74	23	12·6	9–16
Sylvia rueppelli	Spring Females	15	67·1	65–70	6	13·2	11·5–14·9
Orphean Warbler	Spring	167	78·2	71–85	166	19·9	14·8–28·2
Sylvia hortensis							
Lesser Whitethroat	Spring	846	64·7	56–71	664	11·1	6·8–18
Sylvia curruca	Autumn	95	65·3	56–71	80	14·0	10–19·5
Whitethroat	Spring	146	71·4	66–77	108	13·8	9–18
Sylvia communis	Autumn	11	73·0	71–75	11	16·0	14–18·5
Garden Warbler	Spring	28	81·2	77–85	28	16·6	13–20·2
Sylvia borin	Autumn	42	78·0	71–82	43	21·8	14–27·4
Blackcap	Spring	1625	75·3	64–83(87)	1518	16·7	8·5–25(29)
Sylvia atricapilla	Autumn	889	75·0	68–83(86,87)	810	22·8	14–31
	Dec–Feb	87	74·6	67–79	87	19·3	12–23·4 (25·8, 29 early Dec)
Bonelli's Warbler	Spring	57	65·6	62–71	52	8·3	6·5–10·2
Phylloscopus bonelli							
Wood Warbler	Spring	120	76·0	72–83	120	9·2	6–14
Phylloscopus sibilatrix	Autumn	3	73·1	71·5–74	3	10·1	6·5–12·2
Chiffchaff		1220	58·7	47–69	1186	7·2	4·1–12
Phylloscopus collybita							
Willow Warbler	Spring	134	67·3	60–74(76,77)	124	8·3	5·2–13
Phylloscopus trochilus	Autumn	1173	65·4	59–74(77,78)	1167	9·9	6·9–14
Spotted Flycatcher	Spring	51	88·0	78–93	42	14·6	9·8–18·8
Muscicapa striata	Autumn	107	87·8	84–96	103	16·6	11·7–21·5(28)
Red-breasted Flycatcher	Autumn Males	3	68·3	66–70	2	9·3	9·2–9·4
Ficedula parva							
Collared Flycatcher	Spring Males	37	82·3	79–90	37	12·9	9·2–16
Ficedula albicollis	Spring Females	18	81·5	76–85	19	12·5	10–14·2
Pied Flycatcher	Spring Males	40	81·1	78–84	40	12·2	9–18·2
Ficedula hypoleuca	Spring Females	50	79·6	76–85	50	12·2	9–16
Coal Tit	Troodos	15	60·9	57–65	7	9·4	8–10·4
Parus ater							
Great Tit		80	71·4	64–78	70	16·5	12·9–23
Parus major							
Short-toed Treecreeper	Troodos	22	62·0	58–65	19	8·5	7–9·5
Certhia brachydactyla							
Penduline Tit	Males	23	55·2	53–59·5	22	9·2	8·4–10·2
Remiz pendulinus	Females	18	55·4	53–59	18	9·4	8·8–10·4
Red-backed Shrike	Spring	46	89·7	81–96	38	21·9	17·5–27
Lanius collurio	Autumn	17	93·6	84–98(104)	16	32·7	26–41·2
Masked Shrike	Mar–Apr	16	89·2	87–93(81,84)	16	20·1	14·5–23·1(26)
Lanius nubicus							
House Sparrow	Males	209	80·0	73–92	116	28·0	22–35
Passer domesticus							

Species		Wing (mm)			Mass (g)		
		Sample	Mean	Range	Sample	Mean	Range
Spanish Sparrow	Males	69	79·7	73–84	68	27·2	23·3–30·8
Passer hispaniolensis							
Dead Sea Sparrow	Males	10	62·4	60–65	9	14·4	12·5–15·8
Passer moabiticus	Females	7	60·9	59–64	7	13·7	13–14·6
Chaffinch	Troodos Males	16	88·1	82–92	16	23·3	20–26
Fringilla coelebs	Troodos Females	39	83·1	77–89	36	20·7	17–26
	Low Ground:						
	Males	30	87·3	77–95(97)	19	22·0	20–26
	Females	200	83·2	74–92	157	21·2	16–26
Serin	Males	26	73·7	70–77	26	11·2	9–13
Serinus serinus	Females	33	71·9	68–75(78)	33	11·5	10·5–13
Greenfinch	Oct–Apr	73	84	79–90	72	22·5	19·4–28·5
Carduelis chloris	May–Sep	18	82·6	79–85	18	22·0	19·1–24·1
Goldfinch	Summer Males	63	78·3	73–81	59	15·1	13–21·5
Carduelis carduelis	Summer Females	39	76·5	72–80	35	14·8	13–19·2
Linnet	Summer Males	21	81·0	77–85	21	16·9	13·8–22·2
Carduelis cannabina	Summer Females	24	79·9	76–85	24	16·7	14·5–18·5
Reed Bunting	Thick-billed:						
Emberiza schoeniclus	Males	14	81·0	77–86·5	13	21·7	19–24·5
	Females	54	77·8	73–81	51	20·5	18·2–26
	Thin-billed:						
	Males	2	77·2	77–77·5	2	21·7	21·4–22
	Females	10	75·5	72·5–80	10	18·0	16·2–21·6
Corn Bunting	Males	15	99·2	88·5–104	4	45·2	38·4–50
Miliaria (= Emberiza)							
calandra	Females	23	90·2	88–92·5			

Notes

Numbers in brackets after wing or mass range are for individuals which fall outside the ranges quoted.

The above tables are primarily based upon data extracted from the files of the Ringing Office of the BTO Tring, England; from the unpublished records of S. Allen, W. F. Corris, V. S. A. Cozens, A. J. Crease, P. R. Flint, B. Hancock, M. G. Lobb and A. Smith and from Stewart (1968b). Some data were also taken from Machell & Rivers (1966), Stagg (1967), Stewart (1967), Hallchurch (1980), Horner & Hubbard (1982), Tourle (1986), Hjort *et al.* (1986) and Magnin (1987).

APPENDIX 4

SITES OF ORNITHOLOGICAL INTEREST IN CYPRUS

The following list of sites is intended mainly for visitors to the island, though it may also be of use to residents. Spellings of place names are taken from The Survey of Cyprus Administration and Road Map. Spellings may differ on other maps, notably those of the Cyprus Tourism Organisation, and some of these alternative spellings are given in brackets in the text. In writing the text we have assumed that visitors have an up-to-date road map and the use of a car. It is of course possible to get around the island by using a combination of public transport and taxis, and by walking. (An excellent guide for both walkers and car users is *Landscapes of Cyprus* by G. Daniel.) From late spring to autumn the sun is very hot in Cyprus and it may be advisable to wear a sun hat, and, if walking long distances, to carry a water bottle.

In general Cyprus is an excellent country for the visiting birdwatcher, the people are welcoming and hospitable and most of them speak good English. There are, however, many military camps, and when birdwatching near them extra care and common sense should be used. Signs prohibiting the use of cameras, which are taken by the military to include binoculars also, should be observed. Even in the absence of signs it is better to avoid the use of such equipment in potentially sensitive areas. The military also do not like people to be in possession of large scale maps near their camps.

The list of locations mentioned below is not comprehensive and many other areas are good for birdwatching, especially during the autumn, winter and spring. There are many small reservoirs we have not mentioned and all are worth a look if passing nearby. The various ports and harbours around the coast are all good for birds, especially in winter, when they hold some grebes and many gulls, and a search amongst the latter may reveal the occasional Mediterranean, Audouin's or Common Gull.

Both of the Cyprus Ornithological Societies welcome records from visiting bird-watchers. If submitting records of rarities, supporting descriptions should be enclosed. Descriptions of species seen out of season would also be appreciated by the societies.

Code of conduct for birdwatchers

Birdwatchers are a powerful force for nature conservation. The number of those of us interested in birds rises continually and it is vital that we take seriously our responsibility to avoid any harm to birds.

We must also present a responsible image to non-birdwatchers who may be affected by our activities and particularly those on whose sympathy and support the future of birds may rest.

There are ten points to bear in mind:

1. Whether your interest is birdwatching, ringing, photography or scientific study, the welfare of the bird must always come first.
2. Ensure that your activities do not damage the habitat.
3. Keep disturbance to a minimum, especially when birds are breeding and during adverse weather.
4. If you find a rare bird breeding it is generally best to keep the record secret in order to avoid disturbance.
5. Do not harass rare migrants.
6. Abide by the bird protection laws.
7. Respect the rights of landowners.
8. Respect the rights of other people in the countryside.

9. Make your records available to the local societies.
10. If you are a visitor to Cyprus, please behave as you would when birdwatching at home.

Limassol Area

Akrotiri Peninsula
One of the best areas for birds in Cyprus, with a variety of habitats ranging from citrus plantations, woodland and maquis to salt flats, salt lake, reed beds, sewage farm, gravel pits and coastal cliffs. It is also the most southerly point of the island and excellent for visible migration in autumn.

From Limassol the peninsula is best reached by driving west from the new port traffic lights and turning left in *c*. 1 km at a Petrolina station where a sign indicates Ladies Mile. Alternatively drive south from the new port traffic lights to a traffic roundabout at the entrance to the port. From here a road leads west, joining in *c*. 1 km with the road from the petrol station at some traffic lights. The road from the new port roundabout is bordered on the north side by a thin strip of reeds and seasonal pools where Great Reed Warbler usually sing in spring. Sadly this is all that remains of the formerly extensive **Zakaki Marshes**, which have now vanished beneath the new port area.

From the traffic lights the road continues west past some more reeds and pools to a bend to the left. Soon after the bend a track leads off to the right and continues along the north shore of the Salt Lake to Akrotiri reed beds and Phasouri. This track is not usually driveable all the way, but it may be walked. The original road continues on towards the sea. There is a wind-pump to the west, reed beds, a drainage channel and, nearer the sea, a football stadium. All these areas are good for grounded migrants. From this area two (usually driveable) tracks run south, the first runs behind Ladies Mile beach, where the sand/shingle bank between this track and the sea is worth checking for migrants. The beach itself sometimes has a few waders along the tide line, and shearwaters have been seen off the beach in autumn. To the west of this track are several areas of seasonal flooding, which usually hold good numbers of waders in spring. The second track lies to the west, running by an area of aerial masts, and passing through salt flats with *Salicornia* and *Suaeda* scrub which holds breeding Spectacled Warblers. In places other tracks (not always driveable) lead off through this scrub to and along the eastern edge of the salt lake. These salt flats sometimes briefly hold very large numbers of Yellow Wagtails in spring.

When full in winter the **Akrotiri Salt Lake** has a maximum area of 9·4 km^2 and a maximum depth of *c*. 1 m. When the lake is less than full the eastern and southern shores are especially attractive to many species of migrant waders, including Greater Sand Plover and Broad-billed Sandpiper and the occasional Terek Sandpiper. Kentish Plover nest around the lake, notably on the eastern and southern shores. In autumn, flocks of migrant cranes roost by the lake, particularly on the salt flats by the eastern and southeastern shores. Demoiselle Cranes occur mid August to early September and Common Cranes mainly mid October to early November. The salt lake is a very important site for Demoiselle Cranes, and is probably the best place in the Western Palaearctic to see them. Both species are easily disturbed, and once disturbed they normally continue on their migration to Africa, so please view them from a distance to give others an opportunity to see them as well.

In September and October the salt lake is an excellent area for raptor migration. In the early mornings some raptors rest on the salt flats, especially to the east and southeast of the lake, and it is sometimes possible to get good views from a car by driving up slowly – the species involved are mainly Honey Buzzards and Buzzards, but others also occur, including Saker. Later in the mornings many raptors glide

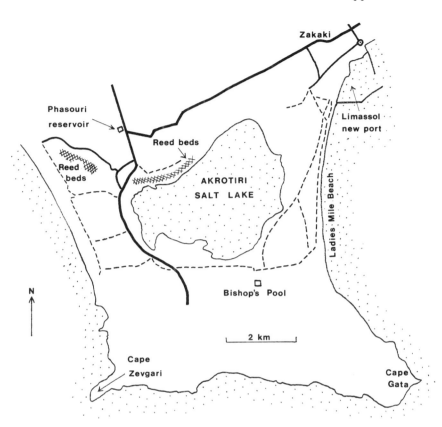

south across the lake and thermal up over the southern shore and good views of them can be had from the track there. These thermalling flocks are mainly buzzards, though many other species also pass overhead, including the occasional Lesser Spotted Eagle.

Near the southern end of the Ladies Mile track are two beach cafes from where tracks lead off to the right across the salt flats to meet the track which runs westward along the southern shore of the salt lake. This track initially passes through areas of high maquis which in autumn, winter and spring, often hold many migrants. Within this area a track to the right leads down past the southeast corner of the lake and back towards Zakaki. If this track is driveable it often gives excellent views of the lake edge.

South of the track along the south shore of the lake is a fenced area of vineyards and citrus plantations, this is another excellent area for migrants and also holds Cetti's Warbler. A gate in the fence is open during working hours and gives access to some of this area, but a new fence now prevents any access to Bishops Pool and the sewage farm. Anyone wishing to visit the Bishops Pool area should initially contact the Honorary Secretary of COS (1957) who may be able to assist them.

Returning to the track along the southern edge of the salt lake and travelling west, there are some small pools on the left where good views of waders can be obtained from the car, these pools have been good for Temminck's Stint and sometimes hold larger birds such as Glossy Ibis. Security along this southern shore has been greatly increased recently, and there are military checkpoints where visitors can expect to be stopped and questioned. The track continues up a slight rise to meet the main road into RAF Akrotiri; this is a good vantage point from which to overlook the whole lake and to view the wintering flock of up to 10,000 Greater Flamingo. RAF Akrotiri, which occupies the whole southerly part of the peninsula, is normally closed to visitors, though it may be possible to arrange visits escorted by service members of the Cyprus Ornithological Societies. Within the military base lie colonies of Eleonora's Falcon, and also the important migration watch point of Cape Gata, where raptors and other diurnal migrants concentrate to leave the island in autumn.

On reaching the main road turn right on to it and drive north along the west shore of the lake. If the water level is high the lake may come right up to the road, giving excellent close views of herons, egrets, Glossy Ibis, marsh terns and many species of wader. Nowadays the lake is more usually lower, and it is necessary to walk out through *salicornia* flats to view this western edge. This is well worth doing, especially in the evening, when the sun is behind the observer, as one can often get the best views of Flamingos, Black-winged Stilts and Slender-billed Gulls from this shore. In spring, any small islands along this side of the lake will hold breeding waders, so please keep off them.

Continue north on this road, pass aerial masts on the left, and *c.* 150 m before reaching the woods, turn off left and then left again onto a narrow metalled road which leads to **Phasouri reed beds**, which lie to the left of this road. Around the reed beds is an area of marsh and meadows and in spring the whole area is full of birds. Citrine Wagtail is now more or less regular there in spring, and Richard's Pipit is probably regular there in autumn. Black Francolin may also be heard calling. The narrow metalled road continues to a 'T' junction at where turn left on to a track which leads back south to an area with open scrub and pools. From here several tracks lead back to the main road, the one continuing south leading through the gravel pits where there are often gulls and waders.

Returning to the main road, where it curves left in the woods into Phasouri plantations, turn right on to a track which leads down through a eucalyptus forest to **Akrotiri reed beds**, an area of reed and tamarisk which extends along much of the northwestern shore of the lake. In this area breed Reed Warbler, Yellow Wagtail, Dead Sea Sparrow and frequently Black-winged Stilt, with Cetti's Warbler along the woodland margin. The Dead Sea Sparrows are not easy to find and are usually not present in any numbers until late April. In autumn the area is good for Savi's Warbler, Bluethroat and Kingfisher, with a huge hirundine roost in the reed beds. In winter it holds Moustached Warbler, Penduline and sometimes Bearded Tit, and Reed Buntings of the thick-billed races. Most of the above species also occur in the nearby Phasouri reed beds.

On returning to the main road, continue north through **Phasouri plantations**; pass the crossroads and on the left a farm shop lies back in a large clearing. Park here and walk round to **Phasouri reservoir** which lies behind the shop. Night Heron are regular here in spring, and the reservoir has held wintering Smyrna Kingfisher. Returning to the crossroads, the left turn leads back towards Limassol; along this road stop and listen for Serin which breed in the coniferous windbreaks throughout the plantations.

Episkopi Garrison Area
Continuing north out of Phasouri plantations, a left turn onto the M1 road leads towards Episkopi to join the main coast road. Turn left on to this and almost immediately left again onto a minor road which leads down to **Curium beach**, here and along the track to the south are open areas which attract many migrants. **Episkopi Bay**, which can be viewed from the beach, often holds large rafts of migrant duck in spring. Various rough tracks lead from here back towards the M1 or Phasouri, they pass through a rather barren area which is often good for raptors and Stone Curlew.

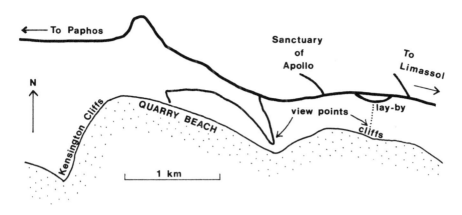

Security in the garrison area has been greatly increased recently and we do not advise visitors to visit Kensington Cliffs as directed in the first edition. Anyone wishing to visit within the garrison area should initially contact the Honorary Secretary of COS (1957) who may be able to assist in arranging an escorted visit. An alternative to Kensington Cliffs is **Quarry beach**, which is outside the military area. Coming from Limassol, a little west of Curium and almost opposite the track to the Sanctuary of Apollo, a track leads off to the left to the cliff edge. From here it is possible to walk along the cliff top or to drive down to the beach where quarrying takes place. The cliff and beach are good areas from which to see Eleonora's Falcon, Griffon Vulture and Alpine Swift. Looking across to the right, one can see the eastern face of Kensington Cliffs where some of them breed and where there are often Wallcreeper in winter. Visitors are warned that the cliffs here are high, crumbling and unsafe. On leaving the garrison area westward the main road drops down to the village of **Paramali**. From the village tracks lead through agricultural land to the beach, at the western end of which is the outflow of the Paramali river. The area attracts many spring migrants and breeding birds include Black Francolin and Black-headed Bunting. Rather similar habitat is to be found further to the west behind **Evdhimou beach** and **Pissouri beach**. To the west of **Pissouri beach** lies **Cape Aspro** where, and on the cliffs to the west of the cape, are the island's largest colonies of Eleonora's Falcon. These are not easily accessible, but may be reached by boat or on foot, either west from Pissouri beach or east from where the main road approaches the sea *c*. 2 km east of Petra tou Romiou (from this end it is possible to walk along the base of the cliffs).

East from Limassol

Close to Limassol is **Yermasoyia** (Germasogeia) **Dam**. Depending on the water level, the valley to the northeast of the dam may have a marsh and shallows (this valley is reached by walking down from the track to Phinikaria). The dam is reached by leaving Limassol on the Nicosia road and then turning left up the Yermasoyia valley and through the village of that name. Just north of Yermasoyia Dam, **Akrounda Creek** has been good for crakes, and for Moustached Warbler in winter. To reach it pass up the western side of Yermasoyia Dam and through Akrounda. Look for a football pitch on the left, a track runs down the north side of it towards the small Akrounda Dam, cross the stream at the north end of the pool and walk south along the west shore.

Moni beach, to the east of Limassol, is now rather built up, but still attracts migrants in spring, and has been good for Bimaculated Lark. To reach it drive east along the old Limassol/Nicosia road and on nearing Moni Power Station turn right down the road to the Meridien Hotel.

Returning to the old road and continuing towards Nicosia, a right turn in *c.* 18 km leads down to **Psematismenos** and **Maroni**. The valley here holds good numbers of migrants in spring and the area also has a good density of Cyprus Warbler. A track also runs along the coast from here towards Larnaca, crossing several river beds, and the whole area is worth exploring in spring.

Dhipotamos Dam is also accessible from the old Limassol/Nicosia road. Return to the old road from Moni and continue towards Nicosia for *c.* 5 km until the road crosses a bridge over a river bed (after the Skarinou turn off and before Kophinou). Take the track which leaves the south side of the bridge, this track curves down under the road, passes under the new motorway and leads up the valley towards the dam. Near the dam take the left track which passes along the west side of the reservoir. The dam has held good numbers of waterbirds in autumn, including White Pelican and Black Stork.

North from Limassol
A new road runs north from Limassol up the Garyllis river valley and on towards Troodos. A few km from Limassol the road passes immediately east of **Polemidhia Dam**, from where there have been many good records in the past.

Continuing on this road to Khalassa, a smaller road to the left (to Ypsonas) leads back south along the Kouris valley, in which lies the reservoir of the new **Kouris Dam**. This new dam is the largest in the island but as yet there are few records from it. (Access to the dam itself can be made from east of Erimi on the new highway west of Limassol.)

Continuing on towards Troodos from Khalassa, between Trimiklini and Moniatis, a smaller road to the left leads to **Perapedhi** and **Mandria**. The orchard areas on the Mandria side of Perapedhi are good for birds and have held Yellowhammers in some winters. From Mandria the road continues up through Platres to **Troodos**. In the Troodos forests may be found the endemic races of

Short-toed Treecreeper, Coal Tit, Crossbill and Jay; other breeding birds include Wren, Chaffinch and Spotted Flycatcher. Around Troodos village breed Pallid Swift and Crag Martin. Ravens gather in the Troodos/Amiandos area and may often be seen in aerial display. These high forests are also very attractive to migrant and wintering birds, and hold some species, such as Ring Ouzel and Hawfinch, more frequently than lower ground. It is possible to walk almost anywhere but the easiest access is along the recently laid out Nature Trails. Leaflets on these can be obtained from the Tourist Offices at the airports and in the towns (including Platres), and from dispensers by the trails. Trail No. 2 is recommended for most of the mountain species, the trees are well spaced giving excellent opportunities for observation; this trail starts from the southern end of Troodos main street. Trail No. 3, which follows the Kyros stream down to Caledonian Falls, is also excellent for birds. The area has breeding Spotted Flycatcher and possibly Grey Wagtail, and in autumn this perennial stream attracts many passerine migrants, especially warblers. This trail starts *c*. 1·5 km south of Troodos on the Platres road, opposite a sign indicating a Girl Guide camp. Another stream runs south from the Troodos Leave Centre, and eventually to some pools largely formed by an outflow from the RAF camp sewage works, the pools being quite productive at dawn and in the evening, particularly in summer, and Blackbirds probably now breed in this area. It is reached by taking the left hand road from the southern roundabout in Troodos village, there is parking just beyond the camp entrance and opposite the church. A track leads off through some old gates, and past another set of gates to the pools. Another good area, the Eagle's Baths and scout camp, is reached from the main Troodos/Nicosia road just above the Amiandos mine workings. A track on the right of the main road gives access to a picnic area from where it is possible to walk down to the scout camp. The reservoir near the road from Prodhromos to Troodos is also worth a visit. Some 6 km east of Troodos on the Nicosia road is the **Karvounas Pass**, used by many southbound migrants as they cross the Troodos range in autumn, and a good location to study visible migration.

Paphos (Pafos) Area

In the west of the island Black Francolin, Red-rumped Swallow, Cetti's and Cyprus Warblers, and Black-headed Bunting are all very numerous, and Paphos makes a good base from which to see them all.

During the migrations, **Paphos headland** is an excellent area, and for anyone staying in Paphos it is probably worth checking every early morning and evening. It is reached by taking the track to the right by the castle at the end of the harbour road, and various other roads also give access. Most of the headland is open ground which attracts many birds. The low sloping cliff around the headland can be very good after a fall of migrants, and the rocks by the sea should also be checked for waders resting there. There are a few areas of gardens and trees, and these and the archaeological sites there also hold migrants. The point of the cape is excellent for sea-watching, and duck, herons and egrets, gulls and waders, can be seen passing during the migrations. The rocks in the harbour itself often hold Kingfisher and occasionally other birds.

Southeast of Paphos

To the southeast of Paphos is a **cultivated coastal plain** crossed by several rivers, and much of this area is a permanent game reserve providing a haven for both migrant and resident birds. Some arable fields from Paphos down towards the airport and Mandria hold breeding Calandra Lark. The road down to the airport passes through a wood near to the sea, and this wood and the surrounding fields are worth checking.

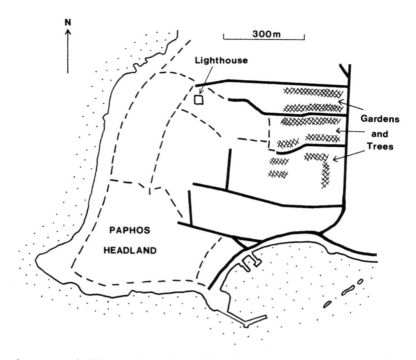

Further towards Limassol, and past Mandria, **Asprokremmos Dam** lies inland from the main road. If the river is flowing, the river bed between the dam and the main road will have birds, and has been good for Citrine Wagtail in spring. This area also holds breeding Spectacled Warbler. From the main road a track leads down the east side of the river to the sea, there are pools in the river bed and reeds by the river mouth. The reservoir can be viewed from the road which crosses the top of the dam, it is best in autumn and winter and is now used by overwintering Cormorant; raptors also occur over and around the dam, again mainly in autumn and winter. To view the reservoir towards its northern end leave the coast road at Timi, pass through Anarita, and just below Nata there is a disused water tank on a bank on the left hand side of the road, and almost immediately opposite this is a track to the right, which is difficult to see. (If you miss it, drive on 50 m to the Kholetria track, turn there and come back.) Follow this track down to the **Xeros Potamos** river, turn right and continue, past the deserted village of Phinikas, until the track runs into the water. There are good viewing points all along this track.

Returning to the main coast road, the next river to the east is the **Dhiarizos**, just before **Kouklia** (Paphos). Cross the bridge over the river and turn right on to the track which runs down the eastern side of the river bed to the sea. This is an excellent area, with reeds and tamarisk, attracting many migrants, and Stone Curlew flocks may be found here and by the Xeros Potamos, particularly on fallow ground. Returning to the main road, *c.* 1·5 km back on the road to Paphos, a right turn leads up the **Dhiarizos valley** through Nikoklia and Phasoula. This is a very pleasant drive, the valley road running close to the river where Black Francolin call, and the upper valley is now one of the few places where Griffon Vultures can often be seen.

North of Paphos

The narrow **coastal strip** from Paphos north to Lara attracts many migrants, particularly in spring, the most productive areas for birds being flat open rough

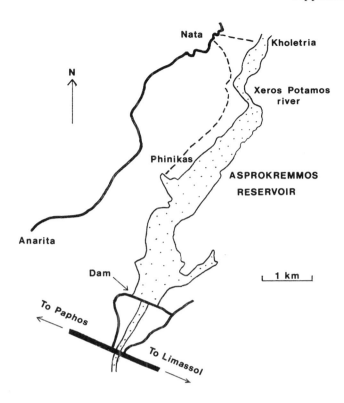

ground and newly ploughed fields near the sea. The various stream beds and valleys also attract many birds. **Mavrokolymbos Dam** (*c*. 10 km north of Paphos) and its valley should also be checked, and the narrow cultivated strip between the main road and the sea has been excellent for spring migrants. North from here the area running south from **Ayios Yeoryios** (Agios Georgios) to the cliffs north of Coral Bay often abounds with migrants in spring. It is probably best to check the rather rough area north of Coral Bay from that end, and then to return to Coral Bay and follow the metalled road round to Ayios Yeoryios, from where a track leads down the escarpment to **Cape Drepanum** (Drepanon). The bushes by the escarpment are sometimes full of migrant warblers in spring, and the flat open ground behind the cape holds many larks, wheatears etc., and has held Greater Sand Plover. The cape is a good site for sea-watching and **Yeronisos Island**, which lies offshore, has breeding Herring Gulls and often holds flocks of resting migrant herons and egrets. From the cape a track leads south through partly cultivated areas which hold many migrants in spring, Spanish Sparrows also breed in the windbreaks. **Lara**, another excellent coastal promontory, is reached by a very rough track which runs north from just before where the metalled road enters Ayios Yeoryios. It is worth driving at least some of the way towards Lara, as the coastal scrub holds many migrants, particularly shrikes. Avgas Gorge, *c*. 2 km along the track and on the right, can be of interest and may hold breeding Blackbirds.

A main road leads north from Paphos to Polis, **Evretou Dam** (map overleaf) lies in the hills to the east of this road, *c*. 26 km from Paphos. To view the reservoir turn west off the main road and towards Simou, where this road curves right near the top of a hill, take a narrow track left up a bank, follow this until a cliff overlooking the reservoir is reached, from where it is possible to walk in either direction. Continuing

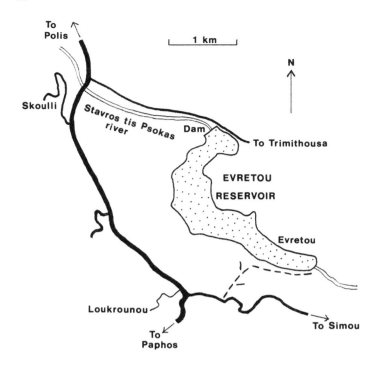

on the main road to Polis, drive north through the town and down to the sea shore to **Polis Camp Site** which is in a stand of eucalyptus by the river, here there is a marsh and reed beds which often hold migrants. From Polis a road runs west along the shore of **Khrysokhou Bay** to **Lachi** (Latsi) and **Baths of Aphrodite**. In autumn a very large movement of westward coasting waterbirds may be seen here, including many thousands of duck, with herons and egrets, waders and gulls. The narrow, partly cultivated, coastal strip is good for spring migrants.

From Baths of Aphrodite it is well worth walking the 8 km of coastal track to **Cape Arnaouti** (providing the area is not closed for military exercises). This is a very attractive area, with fine coastal views, and masses of wild flowers, including rock-rose, cyclamen and orchids. After *c*. 2·5 km the rocky track descends to an open grassy area with scattered trees and bushes, this area can hold very large concentrations of migrants and is worth searching thoroughly. The track continues on through rather denser scrub to the cape, from where diurnal migrants can be seen departing in spring, and the autumn flocks of coasting waterbirds watched as they round the Akamas peninsula.

Returning to the coast road and heading west from Lachi, a left fork leads to **Neokhorio** (Neon Chorion) from where a rough track leads up to the ridge to **Smyies**, where a stream and a wood attract birds throughout the year. Just below the wood the track passes Ayios Minas church, near which are excellent areas for orchids. From both Neokhorio and Smyies various walking tracks lead on to the Akamas.

The **Paphos Forest**, in the west of the Troodos range, is much larger and more isolated than the forests on Mt. Troodos. The roads within the forest are all unmetalled, and often narrow and steep, and plenty of time should be allowed for journeys. The forest is easily accessible from Paphos, which leave on the Polis road and turn right in *c*. 15 km to Polemi and Kannaviou. Some 2 km after Kannaviou the forest is reached, here leave the metalled road and follow the Ezousas river valley up through the forest to the deserted **Ayia Forest Station**. The forest along the valley is full of birds and it is worth spending some time here. With the exception of Crossbill, the forest contains all the resident species which breed on Troodos, and they are generally more numerous and more visible here. In early summer the valley is full of the song of many species, including Wren, Cetti's and Olivaceous Warblers, and Nightingale. Crag Martin also nest under the river bridges. Follow the forest road up to **Stavros Forest Station**, along the way keeping a lookout for Goshawk and Bonelli's Eagle, both of which occur within the forest. At Stavros there is a coffee shop where one can sit and watch Crag Martin and Red-rumped Swallow flying round the eaves. Accommodation at Stavros can be arranged through the Forest Department, Ministry of Agriculture and Natural Resources, Nicosia. At the crossroads above Stavros the forest road to the right leads past ridge tops with breeding Woodlark and on towards Kykko Monastery and Troodos. A detour south of this road leads behind Tripylos ridge to Cedar Valley. It is also possible to follow forest roads down to the north coast, returning to Paphos via Polis, and there are many other forest roads which can be followed.

Larnaca (Larnaka) Area

Larnaca seafront often holds gulls and terns, especially in winter. The best accessible areas are along the beach south of the marina, around the fishing shelter (*c.* 2 km south of the marina), and further south again off the Sandbeach Castle Hotel (where there are low rocks in the sea) and off the Constantina Beach Hotel (where there are groynes). These sites often have roosts among which may be found Sandwich Tern, and Mediterranean and Slender-billed Gull.

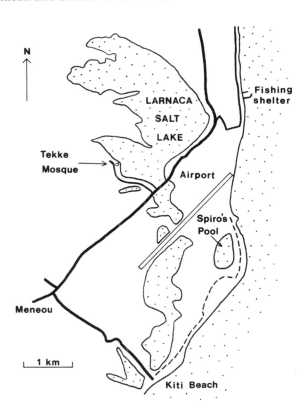

Immediately southwest of the town is **Larnaca Salt Lake**. The main lake is smaller than that at Akrotiri, and it is thus possible to get a closer view of the wintering Greater Flamingo flock. In winter and early spring the lake also usually holds many more gulls and waders than the Akrotiri lake does. Kentish Plover breed around the lake, with Spectacled Warbler in the low scrub and Calandra Lark in adjacent fields. The **Tekke Mosque** to the west of the main lake has a small area of woodland, reed and marsh and good views of the main lake can be obtained from here. There are also good viewing points on promontories to the north of the Mosque, though appearing above the skyline on them may attract attention from the National Guard camp opposite. Between the main road and the airport runway is a small lake which often holds interesting waders.

South of the runway is a larger lake which extends as far as the Meneou/Kiti Beach road, and there is another much smaller lake to the south of this road. A turn left off this road at Kiti Beach leads back northward, with the larger lake on the left and the sea on the right. The track follows a muddy and not always driveable diversion around Spiro's restaurant and a National Guard summer camp before returning to the beach and continuing on to **Spiro's Pool**. This is a fairly large pool with a surrounding marsh which attracts duck and sometimes geese in winter, it is also an excellent area for spring migrants.

Southwest of the salt lakes lies **Cape Kiti**, quite good for visible migration in both spring and autumn. Sea-watching here has produced Caspian Tern and shearwaters, and a coasting passage of waterbirds may be seen in spring. **Kiti Dam**, some 7 km inland from the cape, is also worth checking.

The recently constructed **Akhna** (Athna) **reservoir** lies some 20 km northeast of Larnaca. It is a shallow reservoir, well stocked with fish, and attracts a great number and variety of birds. It has been described as a super place to watch birds. Driving from Larnaca, the reservoir lies to the right of the Akhna by-pass, just beyond the end of the by-pass a metalled road goes off to the right and gives access to the dam and later to the southern end of the reservoir. Tracks also give access to other parts of the reservoir. At the southern end are some shallow pools good for waders. The village of Akhna is occupied by Turkish troops and there is a UN post and a National Guard camp to the north of the track on the north side of the lake. Soldiers from the National Guard may check to ensure that photographs are not being taken.

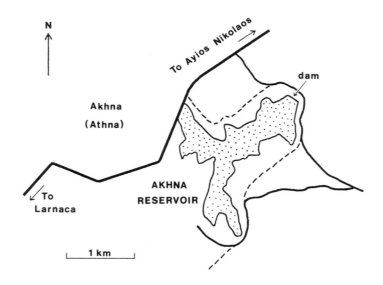

For a first visit at least it is probably best to arrange a guide through one of the COSs.

South of Akhna, on the coast, is **Ormidhia** fishing shelter, to the east of which is a small promontory which has a gull roost in winter. This roost has held many interesting gulls, including Slender-billed, and up to 4 *L. a. armenicus* 'Armenian' Gull. The site is adjacent to the main coast road, slightly west of where the road turns inland to Ormidhia village.

East from Larnaca, the scrub and cultivated land around **Paralimni** and up to **Cape Greco** attract large numbers of grounded migrants in spring and much larger numbers in autumn and early winter. The seasonal **Paralimni Lake**, to the west of Paralimni, has been the source of several unusual records recently. In winter the rocky ground on either side of the road from Ayia Napa to Cape Greco has Finsch's Wheatear. There is no access to the tip of Cape Greco, but the accessible parts of the cape, particularly the area below the cliffs, are very good for birds, Blue Rock Thrush often being seen there.

Ayios Nikolaos (formerly Akhyritou) **reservoir**, northwest of Paralimni, is bisected by the wire between the Sovereign Base Area and north Cyprus. The reservoir is disused but parts of the valley may flood in winter attracting wildfowl (including geese) and waders. **Potamos Liopetri** is a small inlet and fishing shelter on the coast south of Liopetri and west of Ayia Napa, Audouin's Gulls have occasionally been seen there. There are tracks along the coast in either direction which are worth checking, especially during the spring migration.

Athalassa Dam and Forest, just southeast of Nicosia, can be reached by turning right off the Limassol–Nicosia highway to the Experimental Farm at Athalassa. A track to the right beside the farm leads to the dam and forest. The reservoir attracts many migrant waterbirds, and Long-eared Owl may breed in the forest. Black-bellied Sandgrouse may occasionally be seen and heard flying over. Spectacled Warbler also breed in the cistus scrub around the reservoir.

Northern Cyprus

Although northern Cyprus has been greatly neglected ornithologically since 1974, it is in its own way at least as good as the south for birdwatching. As in the south the people are friendly and welcoming and most of them speak good English. In the north all place names are now signposted in Turkish only, and the maps available in the north also give only the Turkish names. A tourist map is widely available in the north but a much better map is published by K. Rustem & Brother, PO Box 239, Nicosia, Mersin 10 – Turkey. (A reprint of the Bannermans *Birds of Cyprus* is also available from the same publisher.) In the text below the anglicised Greek names are given in brackets after the Turkish names. There is a considerable military presence in the north, most obviously near the border. Visitors should avoid all such military areas, and should definitely not use cameras or binoculars near them. Apart from these obvious restrictions, 99% of north Cyprus is accessible to visiting birdwatchers. The main holiday centres in the north are Kyrenia and Famagusta/Salamis. In the text below the locations are listed from west to east.

Güzelyurt Körfezi (Morphou Bay) has coasting waterbirds in autumn, and large concentrations of duck offshore. The southern shore of the bay is best and has gulls in winter. On the eastern shore of the bay is **Yayla** (Syrianokhori) with its riverbed pools, marshes and reed beds and prior to 1974 the source of many records. North from here the forested sand dunes between **Akdeniz** (Ayia Irini) and the sea attract many migrant and wintering birds. Further north still **Koruçam Burnu** (Cape Kormakiti) is excellent for diurnal migration in spring and for the coasting passage in autumn. **Koruçam** (Kormakitis) **Forest**, several km inland from the cape, is good throughout the year. Northeast of **Çamlıbel** (Myrtou) the **Paleomylos** valley has Cetti's Warbler and abounds with migrants in spring. From the southern ridge of the valley Griffon Vultures could formerly be watched gliding across from Kornos Peak, though most if not all of the vultures have now been shot. Within the valley is the newly constructed **Geçitköy Dam**, which is visible and easily accessible from the main road north of Geçitköy (Panagra).

The **Kyrenia mountain range** has an unmetalled forest road along much of its length, from Kornos eastward to the Kyrenia pass, and again from near **Besparmak** (Pentadaktylos) eastward and on past Kantara. In places the road follows the mountain ridge, giving spectacular views south across the Mesaoria and north to the mountains of Turkey. Perhaps the best parts of the forest road are the stretch east past **Besparmak** to **Alevkaya** (Halevga) and the more easterly section around Kantara. Although the Kyrenia range lacks the montane endemics of the higher Troodos, it is possible to get good views of Crag Martin and Alpine Swift, and there is still a good chance of seeing interesting raptors. The mountain slopes contain good numbers of Cyprus Warbler and Cretzschmar's Bunting, while Black-headed Bunting are numerous especially in the lower eastern part of the range. The forests of the Kyrenia range are also very attractive to migrant and wintering birds. The castles along the range at **St. Hilarion, Buffavento** and **Kantara** are all good locations for birds. Blue Rock Thrush breed in their walls or nearby and the occasional Wallcreeper may be seen in winter. On the north coast at **Girne** (Kyrenia) in autumn, migrant waterbirds coast west offshore and buzzards can be seen gliding in over the sea from Turkey and then watched thermalling up to cross the mountains.

South of the Kyrenia range the shallow reservoirs north of **Lefkoşa** (Nicosia) near **Gönyeli** (Geunyeli) and **Kanlıköy** (Kanli) are excellent and often hold very large numbers of waterbirds. The former can be difficult to find, it is best reached by leaving Gönyeli northwards up a hill (past a Mercedes showroom on the right), at the crest of the hill fork right on to a narrow metalled road, turn left immediately then sharply back to the right on to a dirt track which leads around a hill (with a concrete water tank on top) and on and down to the dam wall. Kanlıköy reservoir is easily reached by taking a track north from Kanlıköy village. At the end of 1990 new reservoirs were brought into use near Değirmenlik and Serdarli, both to the northeast from Nicosia.

Further to the east is **Geçitkale** (Lefkoniko) reservoir, this is reached by leaving Geçitkale northward and turning left on to a wide dirt track *c*. 400 m before the right fork to Çinarli. The stony foothills in this area hold Finsch's Wheatear in winter. Northwards from here are two new reservoirs near **Yalı** and **Mersinlik**. The former is visible and accessible from the north coast road east of Yalı, the latter is reached by taking a track to the right off the coast road shortly before the right turn to Mersinlik is reached.

Köprülü (Kouklia) reservoir on the Mesaoria is now disused and usually dry but may hold water in spring after exceptionally wet winters when the reservoir and its surrounds become one of the best places in the island for migrants, attracting a large number and variety of birds. When dry the area is still good for migrant raptors, especially harriers, and has breeding Calandra and Short-toed Larks, a high density of Spectacled Warbler along the reservoir embankment and colonies of Spanish Sparrow.

The formerly excellent tidal mudflats at the southern end of **Gazimağusa** (Famagusta) harbour have been destroyed, and the area turned into a marina. The harbour itself is still very good for gulls but at the time of writing is not accessible. West of Gazimağusa is **Çanakkale** reservoir, which holds water in winter and spring when it attracts many waterbirds. It is reached by leaving the Monument roundabout on the Nicosia road and in *c*. 100–200 m forking left on to Bayraktar Yolu, which follow straight out to Çanakkale. The reservoir lies beyond the village and to the left.

To the north and south of **Salamis** several rivers flow into the sea and in winter and spring often flood areas between the coast road and the sea, attracting large numbers of duck, gulls and other waterbirds. Several roads and tracks lead eastward from the coast road giving good views over these flooded areas. Unfortunately these areas are now seriously threatened by tourist development. On the sand dunes at Salamis are plantations of *Pinus pinea* where Long-eared Owls have bred in several recent years. These plantations and the adjacent coastal scrub are excellent areas, often holding large numbers of migrant and wintering birds, as well as residents such as Cyprus, Cetti's and Spectacled Warblers.

Continuing north from Salamis, the coast road goes through Boğaz and passes south of Tuzluca (Patriki). Turn left off the main road towards **Tuzluca** and on the left before reaching the village are some small pools which are very attractive to waders in spring, and the surrounding area is also good for migrants. The main road continues on to Çayırova (Ayios Theodhoros), where a wide track to the right leads down through extensive carob open woodland to **Zeytin Burnu** (Cape Elea). The cape is ideal for watching the eastward coasting movement of waterbirds in spring, and the woodland behind the cape attracts many migrants.

Returning to the main road, a side road to the left after Çayırova leads to **Mehmetçik** (Galatia). On the left, immediately before the village, is a shallow seasonal lake. In a good year the lake has water from January to May and has held up to 1000 wildfowl and many species of wader. The main road continues on up the Karpas to Yenierenköy (Yialousa), from where a side road to the left leads down to **Yassı Burnu** (Cape Plakoti). The westward coasting passage of waterbirds may be observed from here in autumn, and the open stony ground at the cape is attractive to wheatears and other migrants. The main road continues northeastward to Dipkarpaz (Rizokarpaso), from where a side road to the left leads to **Ayios Philon** and then along the north coast to **Aphendrika**. This area of the north coast has much open woodland and is a first landfall for many autumn migrants. It is unfortunately extensively used by mistnetters who catch and kill the migrant birds.

The road along the Karpas finally leads to **Apostolos Andreas** Monastery, where it is necessary to produce for the police either one's passport or driving licence. From the monastery a dirt track continues on to **Zafer Burnu** (Cape Andreas). The cape is without doubt the finest location in the island for visible migration; there is some movement of birds there almost throughout the year, and during the main migration periods movement is always very apparent and often spectacular. The juniper scrub behind the cape has Black Francolin and Cetti's Warbler and often holds large concentrations of grounded nocturnal migrants. Coasting waterbirds pass northwards offshore in spring and sea-watching can be productive at any season. A considerable raptor passage also occurs at the cape in spring, the species involved are mainly falcons, harriers and buzzards, but small numbers of eagles, mainly Lesser Spotted, also occur. During the summer Audouin's Gulls breed on the largest island off the cape, and may occasionally be seen flying past. Outside the breeding season the Audouin's Gulls disperse around the coasts, especially those of the Karpas, where the shores, promontories and rocky islets should be checked for this and other species of gull.

The North Cyprus Society for the Protection of Birds would be pleased to receive records from birdwatchers visiting north Cyprus.

APPENDIX 5

BIRD PROTECTION LEGISLATION AND PROTECTED SPECIES
OF CYPRUS

This Appendix lists the bird protection legislation in the Republic of Cyprus (for brief details of the situation in north Cyprus, see the Postscript to the chapter on **Bird Killing and Conservation**).

Law No. 39 of 1974 contains all the hunting regulations. A full English translation is given by Magnin (1987). Paragraph 14(1) states that no wild bird shall be cooked, sold or served in any establishment. Paragraph 15(1) prohibits the use of search lights, hides, limesticks or any other trapping method, motor vehicles and driving or scaring, for the purpose of pursuing, taking or killing any wild bird. Paragraph 19 protects all eggs, except those of Crows and Sparrows. Appendix IV of Law No. 39 lists the protected species, they are:

1. All large wading and marsh birds such as Herons, Storks, Ibises, Spoonbills, Flamingos, Cranes, Pelicans, Cormorants and Shags, Avocet, Black-winged Stilts, *except* Geese and Ducks.
2. Gulls and Terns (all).
3. Diurnal birds of prey (all) such as Eagles, Hawks, Falcons and Vultures.
4. Owls (all).
5. Wren, Dipper, Cyprus Pied Wheatear, Great Tit, Coal Tit, Short-toed Treecreeper, Crossbill, Chaffinch, Cyprus Warbler, Black-bellied Sandgrouse, Hoopoe, Golden Oriole, Kingfisher. (In addition the Bee-eater was declared protected in 1984.)

The shooting of small song birds with shotguns was banned under the Council of Ministers Decision No. 25.261 of December 1984.

In addition to the above, the Republic of Cyprus is now also a Contracting Party to the Convention on the Conservation of European Wildlife and Natural Habitats (the Berne Convention). The Convention was published in the Gazette of the Republic No. 2309 on 18 March 1988. Accordingly all but 4 of the species listed in Appendix 2 of the Convention are also *strictly protected* in Cyprus. Of the species listed in Appendix 2, those which occur in Cyprus (and not already mentioned above) are:

Grebes: Red-necked, Slavonian and Little.
Petrels (all).
Shearwaters: Manx and Cory's.
Ducks: Shelduck and Ruddy Shelduck, Marbled Teal, Goldeneye, Smew and White-headed Duck.
Crakes: Spotted, Baillon's, Little; Corncrake and Purple Gallinule.
Bustards (all).
Plovers: Spur-winged, Ringed, Little Ringed, Kentish, Greater Sand.
Dotterel, Turnstone, Great Snipe and Slender-billed Curlew.
Sandpipers: Marsh, Green, Wood, Common, Terek, Curlew and Broad-billed; also Little and Temminck's Stints, Dunlin and Sanderling.
Phalaropes (all).
Stone Curlew and Cream-coloured Courser.
Pratincoles (all).
Great Spotted Cuckoo and Nightjar.
Swifts: Pallid and Alpine.
Roller and Wryneck.

Swallows and Martins (all).

Pipits and Wagtails (all).

Shrikes (all).

Waxwing and Dunnock.

Thrushes (*Turdinae*): Whinchat, Stonechat; Northern, Black-eared and Isabelline Wheatears; Rufous Bush Chat, Rock Thrush and Blue Rock Thrush, Redstart and Black Redstart, Robin, Nightingale and Thrush Nightingale, Bluethroat and Red-flanked Bluetail.

Warblers (*Sylviinae*) (all) *including* Blackcap and Lesser Whitethroat.

Flycatchers (all).

Tits (all) including Bearded Tit.

Buntings: Cinereous, Cretzschmar's, Reed, Black-headed and Yellowhammer.

Finches: Greenfinch, Goldfinch, Siskin, Linnet, Serin, Scarlet Rosefinch, Trumpeter Finch and Hawfinch.

Rock Sparrow and Rose-coloured Starling.

The 4 species given a lower level of protection are Short-toed, Lesser Short-toed and Calandra Larks, and Bee-eater.

The Berne Convention contains many other important provisions in addition to bird protection. They include the requirements to conserve both breeding habitats and the resting and feeding areas used by migratory species, to promote national policies for nature conservation, and to provide education and disseminate information on the need to conserve species of wild flora and fauna and their habitats.

APPENDIX 6

MIGRATION TABLE

This table shows when migratory species are likely to be seen. It includes passage migrants, migrant breeders and winter visitors. Migratory species, such as Greenfinch, which are also common residents, are excluded. Months are divided into equal thirds.

———— = Birds usually present in reasonable numbers and there is a good chance of seeing them.

– – – – = Birds usually or often present, in small or very small numbers, and there is a possibility of seeing them. Included in this category are some very scarce migrants, such as Terek Sandpiper and Yellow-browed Warbler, which we believe are more regular than their records suggest.

The divisions, especially between a broken line and no entry at all, are frequently arbitrary, and it is essential to consult the Systematic List if a detailed picture is required for a particular species.

The table shows an average year with reasonable water levels. Migration timing is influenced by the weather and varies from year to year. In the increasingly frequent dry years relatively few water-birds will be seen.

Migration is not uniform across the island. In spring some species are more numerous in the east, especially on the Karpas and at Cape Andreas. In autumn raptors are most numerous at Akrotiri where they concentrate to depart from the island. Also in autumn huge numbers of waterbirds pass around the north and northwest coasts but relatively few of them occur elsewhere.

Notes
1. Stone Curlew. The status shown includes the small resident population.
2. Chaffinch and Woodlark. In addition to the status shown, resident birds are present in the higher Troodos during the summer months.
3. In addition to the species in the migration table, the following are present and likely to be seen throughout the year:

Shag	Scops Owl	Jay
Griffon Vulture	Little Owl	Magpie
Kestrel	Calandra Lark	Jackdaw
Peregrine	Crested Lark	Hooded Crow
Chukar	Crag Martin	Raven
Black Francolin	Wren	House Sparrow
Quail	Blue Rock Thrush	Spanish Sparrow
Kentish Plover	Cetti's Warbler	Serin
Audouin's Gull	Fan-tailed Warbler	Greenfinch
Herring Gull	Spectacled Warbler	Goldfinch
Rock Dove	Cyprus Warbler	Linnet
Woodpigeon	Coal Tit	Crossbill
Collared Dove	Great Tit	Corn Bunting
Barn Owl	Short-toed Treecreeper	

4. The following species are present in small numbers throughout the year and may possibly be seen:

Goshawk	Bonelli's Eagle	Long-eared Owl
Imperial Eagle	Black-bellied	Dead Sea Sparrow
	Sandgrouse	(mainly Apr–Nov)

	Jan	Feb	Mar	Apr	May	Jun	Jul	Aug	Sep	Oct	Nov	Dec
Little Grebe												
Great Crested Grebe												
Black-necked Grebe												
Cory's Shearwater												
Manx Shearwater												
Cormorant												
White Pelican												
Bittern												
Little Bittern												
Night Heron												
Squacco Heron												
Cattle Egret												
Little Egret												
Great White Egret												
Grey Heron												
Purple Heron												
Black Stork												
White Stork												
Glossy Ibis												
Spoonbill												
Greater Flamingo												
White-fronted Goose												
Ruddy Shelduck												
Shelduck												
Wigeon												
Gadwall												
Teal												
Mallard												
Pintail												
Garganey												

	Jan	Feb	Mar	Apr	May	Jun	Jul	Aug	Sep	Oct	Nov	Dec
Shoveler												
Red-crested Pochard												
Pochard												
Ferruginous Duck												
Tufted Duck												
Red-breasted Merganser												
White-headed Duck												
Honey Buzzard												
Black Kite												
Egyptian Vulture												
Short-toed Eagle												
Marsh Harrier												
Hen Harrier												
Pallid Harrier												
Montagu's Harrier												
Sparrowhawk												
Common Buzzard												
Long-legged Buzzard												
Lesser Spotted Eagle												
Booted Eagle												
Osprey												
Lesser Kestrel												
Red-footed Falcon												
Merlin												
Hobby												
Eleonora's Falcon												
Saker												
Water Rail												
Spotted Crake												
Little Crake												

Months (columns): Jan | Feb | Mar | Apr | May | Jun | Jul | Aug | Sep | Oct | Nov | Dec

Species:

- Baillon's Crake
- Corncrake
- Moorhen
- Coot
- Common Crane
- Demoiselle Crane
- Oystercatcher
- Black-winged Stilt
- Avocet
- Stone Curlew
- Cream-coloured Courser
- Pratincole
- Black-winged Pratincole
- Little Ringed Plover
- Ringed Plover
- Greater Sand Plover
- Dotterel
- Golden Plover
- Grey Plover
- Spur-winged Plover
- White-tailed Plover
- Lapwing
- Sanderling
- Little Stint
- Temminck's Stint
- Curlew Sandpiper
- Dunlin
- Broad-billed Sandpiper
- Ruff
- Jack Snipe

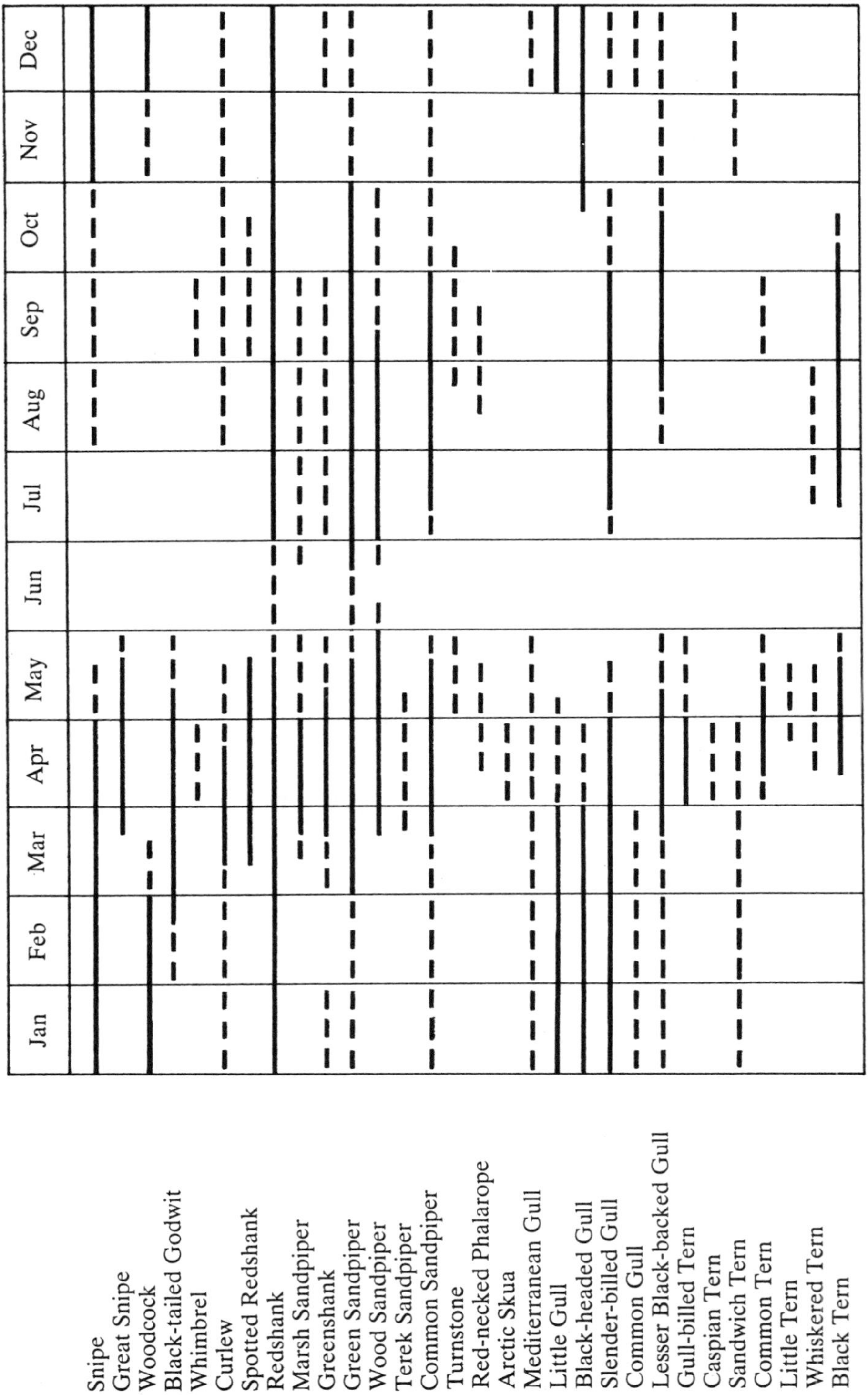
Jan
Feb
Mar
Apr
May
Jun
Jul
Aug
Sep
Oct
Nov
Dec
Snipe
Great Snipe
Woodcock
Black-tailed Godwit
Whimbrel
Curlew
Spotted Redshank
Redshank
Marsh Sandpiper
Greenshank
Green Sandpiper
Wood Sandpiper
Terek Sandpiper
Common Sandpiper
Turnstone
Red-necked Phalarope
Arctic Skua
Mediterranean Gull
Little Gull
Black-headed Gull
Slender-billed Gull
Common Gull
Lesser Black-backed Gull
Gull-billed Tern
Caspian Tern
Sandwich Tern
Common Tern
Little Tern
Whiskered Tern
Black Tern

	Jan	Feb	Mar	Apr	May	Jun	Jul	Aug	Sep	Oct	Nov	Dec

White-winged Black Tern
Stock Dove
Turtle Dove
Great Spotted Cuckoo
Cuckoo
Short-eared Owl
Nightjar
Swift
Pallid Swift
Alpine Swift
White-breasted Kingfisher
Kingfisher
Pied Kingfisher
Blue-cheeked Bee-eater
Bee-eater
Roller
Hoopoe
Wryneck
Bimaculated Lark
Short-toed Lark
Lesser Short-toed Lark
Woodlark
Skylark
Sand Martin
Swallow
Red-rumped Swallow
House Martin
Richard's Pipit
Tawny Pipit
Tree Pipit

214   Appendix 6

	Jan	Feb	Mar	Apr	May	Jun	Jul	Aug	Sep	Oct	Nov	Dec

Meadow Pipit
Red-throated Pipit
Water Pipit
Yellow Wagtail
Citrine Wagtail
Grey Wagtail
White Wagtail
Dunnock
Rufous Bush Chat
Robin
Thrush Nightingale
Nightingale
Bluethroat
Black Redstart
Redstart
Whinchat
Stonechat
Isabelline Wheatear
Northern Wheatear
Cyprus Pied Wheatear
Black-eared Wheatear
Desert Wheatear
Finsch's Wheatear
Rock Thrush
Ring Ouzel
Blackbird
Fieldfare
Song Thrush
Redwing
Mistle Thrush

	Jan	Feb	Mar	Apr	May	Jun	Jul	Aug	Sep	Oct	Nov	Dec
River Warbler												
Savi's Warbler												
Moustached Warbler												
Sedge Warbler												
Marsh Warbler												
Reed Warbler												
Great Reed Warbler												
Olivaceous Warbler												
Olive-tree Warbler												
Icterine Warbler												
Subalpine Warbler												
Sardinian Warbler												
Rüppell's Warbler												
Orphean Warbler												
Barred Warbler												
Lesser Whitethroat												
Whitethroat												
Garden Warbler												
Blackcap												
Yellow-browed Warbler												
Bonelli's Warbler												
Wood Warbler												
Chiffchaff												
Willow Warbler												
Goldcrest												
Spotted Flycatcher												
Red-breasted Flycatcher												
Semi-collared Flycatcher												
Collared Flycatcher												
Pied Flycatcher												

Dec | Nov | Oct | Sep | Aug | Jul | Jun | May | Apr | Mar | Feb | Jan

Bearded Tit
Wallcreeper
Penduline Tit
Golden Oriole
Red-backed Shrike
Lesser Grey Shrike
Woodchat Shrike
Masked Shrike
Rook
Starling
Rose-coloured Starling
Tree Sparrow
Chaffinch
Brambling
Siskin
Trumpeter Finch
Hawfinch
Yellowhammer
Cinereous Bunting
Ortolan Bunting
Cretzschmar's Bunting
Reed Bunting
Black-headed Bunting

USEFUL ADDRESSES

The Cyprus Ornithological Society (1957), PO Box 4319, Nicosia, Cyprus.
The Cyprus Ornithological Society (1970), 4 Kanaris Street, Strovolos 154, Cyprus.
Friends of the Earth (Cyprus), PO Box 3411, Limassol, Cyprus.
The Cyprus Wildlife Society, PO Box 4281, Nicosia, Cyprus.
The North Cyprus Society for the Protection of Birds, PO Box 634, Kyrenia, Mersin 10, Turkey.
The National Trust of Northern Cyprus, PO Box 583, Kyrenia, Mersin 10, Turkey.
The Green Peace Movement, Posta Sokak 23/1, Nicosia, Mersin 10, Turkey.
(Mersin 10, Turkey is the postal code for north Cyprus.)
Aktion Vogelschutz Nordzypern, Harry Sigg, Schulstrasse 16, D-W 5249 Birkenbeul, Germany.
The International Council for Bird Preservation, 32 Cambridge Road, Girton, Cambridge, England.
The Ornithological Society of the Middle East, c/o The Lodge, Sandy, Beds SG19 2DL, England.
The Royal Air Force Ornithological Society, c/o Ministry of Defence, Room B3/1 to B3/2, Leatherhead Road, Chessington, Surrey KT9 2LU, England.
The Army Ornithological Society, Candlewick Cottage, Avenue Road, Fleet, Hampshire GU13 8NG, England.

REFERENCES

ADAMS, D. W. H. 1962. Radar observations of bird migration in Cyprus. *Ibis* 104: 133–146.

ALLEN, S., CRABTREE, A. & CRABTREE, Y. 1980. Results of an expedition to Cyprus, spring 1980. Duplicated. Copy in RAF Orn. Soc. Library.

ALONEFTIS, B. D. 1985. The breeding cycle of the Masked Shrike. *COS (1957) Newsletter* 85/7: 5–6.

ASHTON-JOHNSON, J. F. R. 1961. Notes on the breeding birds of Cyprus. *Ool. Rec.* 35: 1–5, 17–22, 33–39, 49–55.

BACON, P. & BACON, E. 1986. Some notes on Cyprus Warbler territories. *COS (1970) Rep.* 13: 48–51.

BAIKIE, W. B. 1850. Migratory flights of birds observed on the north coast of Cyprus, during August and September 1849. *Zoologist* 8: 2654.

BANNERMAN, D. A. & BANNERMAN, W. M. 1958. *Birds of Cyprus.* Oliver & Boyd, Edinburgh & London.

————, ———— 1971. *Handbook of the Birds of Cyprus and Migrants of the Middle East.* Oliver & Boyd, Edinburgh.

BATE, D. M. A. 1903a. Field-notes on some of the birds of Cyprus. *Ibis* 1903: 571–581.

———— 1903b. *Anorthura cypriotes* n. sp. *Bull. Brit. Orn. Cl.* 13: 51–52.

BAXENDALE, F. R. S. 1913. Letter. *Ibis* 1913: 706–707.

———— 1915. Notes on the ornithology of Cyprus. *Ibis* 1915: 217–227.

BEAMAN, M. 1978. Systematic List. *Orn. Soc. Turkey Bird Rep.* 4: 12–209.

BELCHER, Sir Charles F. 1929. Something about Cyprus. *Ool. Rec.* 9: 49–52.

BELL, P. T. & SUMMERS, A. B. 1982. The ecology of the Chukar and Black Francolin in northwest Cyprus. *COS (1957) Rep.* 29: 67–79.

BELLAMY, C. V. & JUKES-BROWNE, A. J. 1905. *The Geology of Cyprus.* Plymouth.

BENSON, S. V. 1970. *Birds of Lebanon and the Jordan Area.* Internat. Council Bird Pres, London & New York.

BERGMANN, H. H. 1983. Some peculiarities of Cyprus bird voices. *COS (1970) Rep.* 8: 41–54.

BEST, J. 1986. Observations on breeding Spectacled Warblers on coastal flats east of Akrotiri Salt Lake. *COS (1970) Rep.* 13: 56–57.

BIANCHI, V. 1907. Catalogue of the species of Alaudidae. *Bull. Acad. Imp. Sci. St. Petersbourg* Ser. 5, 25(1906): 65.

BOURNE, W. R. P. 1959a. Notes on exceptional records affecting the status of birds on the Cyprus list. *COS (1957) Bull.* 6: 2–10.

———— 1959b. Notes on autumn migration in the Middle East. *Ibis* 101: 170–176.

———— 1960a. Migration through Cyprus. *Proc. XII Int. Orn. Congr. Helsinki:* 127–132.

———— 1960b. The status of the grey shrikes in the eastern Mediterranean. *Ibis* 102: 476.

———— 1963. Radar and moon-watching in the Mediterranean. *Bird Banding* 32: 162–165.

———— 1964. Annotated bibliography. *COS (1957) Bull.* 15: 39–44.

———— 1985. The breeding cycle of the Masked Shrike. *COS (1957) Newsletter* 85/10: 7.

BOURNE, W. R. P., GORE, M. E. J., NICHOLSON, J., SMITH, A. V., WALKER, F. J. & WILDASH, P. C. T. 1964. Check-list of the Birds of Cyprus. *COS (1957) Bull.* 15: 17–38.

BOYE, P. 1990. On the distribution and status of the Black Francolin in Cyprus. *Zoology in the Middle East* 4: 17–21.

BRANIGAN, J. J. & JARRETT, H. R. 1975. *The Mediterranean Lands.* 2nd Ed. MacDonald & Evans, London.

BRIDGMAN, C. J. 1962. Birds nesting in aircraft. *Brit. Birds* 55: 461–470.

'British Birds' List of Birds of the Western Palearctic. 1978. Macmillan Journals Ltd., Basingstoke.

BUCKNILL, J. A. 1909, 1910. On the ornithology of Cyprus. *Ibis* 1909: 569–613, 1910: 1–47, 385–435.

———— 1910. A list of the birds of Cyprus. *Cyprus Nat. Hist. Soc. Bull.* 2.

———— 1911. A further contribution to the ornithology of Cyprus. *Ibis* 1911: 632–656.

———— 1913a. A third contribution to the ornithology of Cyprus. *Ibis* 1913: 2–14.

———— 1913b. Chapter 'Birds' in *The Handbook of Cyprus:* 248–264. London.

BUNDY, G. 1976. *The Birds of Libya.* British Ornithologists' Union, London.

CASEMENT, M. B. 1966. Migration across the Mediterranean observed by radar. *Ibis* 108: 461–491.

CHAPMAN, E. F. 1949. *Cyprus Trees and Shrubs.* Govt. Printing Office, Nicosia.

CHRISTENSEN, S. J. 1967. Observationer af fugle og noter om fugletraek pa Cypern 1964–65. *Dansk Orn. Foren. Tidssk.* 61: 40–55.

————— 1974. Notes on the plumage of the female Cyprus Pied Wheatear. *Orn. Scand.* 5: 47–52.

CHRISTENSEN, S. J., LOU, O., MÜLLER, M. & WOHLMUTH, H. 1981. The spring migration of raptors in southern Israel and Sinai. *Sandgrouse* 3: 1–42.

CHRISTODOULOU, D. 1959. *The Evolution of the Rural Land Use Pattern in Cyprus.* The World Land Use Survey, Monograph 2: Cyprus. Geog. Publ., Bude, Cornwall.

CLARK, W. S. 1987. The dark morph of the Marsh Harrier. *Brit. Birds* 80: 61–72.

CLARKE, F. X. *et al.* 1967. Notes on Griffon Vultures. *COS (1957) Rep.* 14: 41–42.

COBHAM, C. D. 1908. *Excerpta Cypria.* Cambridge University Press.

COLE, L. R. 1972a. On the call of the Black Partridge *Francolinus francolinus. COS (1970) Rep.* 2: 104.

————— 1972b. Observations on the breeding of Black-winged Stilts in the Akrotiri salt lake game reserve. *COS (1970) Rep.* 2: 104–106.

————— 1972c. Male Bluethroat with an entirely blue plastron. *COS (1970) Rep.* 2: 111–112.

CRAMP, S. 1971a. Dead Sea Sparrow. *Birds of the World* 9: 2715–2716. IPC Magazines, London.

————— 1971b. The Dead Sea Sparrow: further breeding places in Iran and Turkey. *Ibis* 113: 244–245.

————— (Ed). 1985. 1988. *The Birds of the Western Palearctic.* Vols 4 & 5. Oxford University Press.

CRAMP, S. & SIMMONS, K. E. L. (Eds). 1977. 1980. 1982. *The Birds of the Western Palearctic.* Vols 1, 2 & 3. Oxford University Press.

CYPRUS AGRICULTURAL JOURNAL. Natural History Notes. 1910: 407–9, 1925: 147, 1926: 61, 1927: 28.

CYPRUS NATURAL HISTORY SOCIETY. 1908–1913. *Annals I–IV.* Nicosia.

CYPRUS ORNITHOLOGICAL SOCIETY (1957). 1957–1988. *Reports* 1–35.

————— 1957–1966. *Bulletins* 1–20.

————— 1970–1990. *Monthly Newsletters.*

CYPRUS ORNITHOLOGICAL SOCIETY (1970). 1971–1990. *Reports* 1–15 and 19 (*Reports* 16–18 not yet published), Nicosia.

————— 1972. *Check List of the Birds of Cyprus.* Nicosia.

DANIEL, G. 1986. *Landscapes of Cyprus.* Sunflower Books, London.

DAVIDSON, D. F. 1954. Questionnaire completed for the Bannermans' *Birds of Cyprus.* Deposited at Brit. Mus. (Nat. Hist.).

————— 1958. 'The Topography and Vegetation of Cyprus' in *Birds of Cyprus*: xli–xlv.

DEAN, A. R., FORTEY, J. E. & PHILLIPS, E. G. 1977. White-tailed Plover: new to Britain and Ireland. *Brit. Birds* 70: 465–471.

DEMENT'EV, G. P. & GLADKOV, N. A. (Eds). 1951–1954. *Birds of the Soviet Union.* Vols I–VI. (English Translation 1966–1970. Israel Program for Scientific Translations, Jerusalem.)

DRESSER, H. E. 1887. *Parus cypriotes.* sp. nov. *Proc. Zool. Soc. Lond.* 1887: 563.

ELLIOTT, G. & DUTTON, R. 1963. *Know your rocks: An Introduction to Geology in Cyprus.* Nicosia.

ETCHÉCOPAR, R. D. & HÜE, F. 1967. *The Birds of North Africa.* Oliver & Boyd, Edinburgh & London.

FERRIER, J. M. 1936. Sixteen days in Cyprus. *Ool. Rec.* 16: 53–59.

FIELD (THE). 1889. Birds of Cyprus. Letter from 'West Kent', 11 May 1889. No. 1898: 653. (See also letters in Nos. 1896–7 and 1899.)

FISHER, R. E. G. 1970. Black-winged Stilt colony at Akrotiri Salt Lake, 1969. *COS (1957) Rep.* 16: 49–50.

FLINT, P. R. 1971a. A reappraisal of the relative status of the Common Crane and Demoiselle Crane on autumn passage through Cyprus. *COS (1957) Rep.* 17: 102–109 and *COS (1970) Rep.* 1: 84–91.

FLINT, P. R. 1971b. Herring Gull attacking wheatear. *COS (1957) Rep.* 17: 55–56 and *COS (1970) Rep.* 1: 41.

———— 1972a. Observations of the autumn crane passage at Akrotiri. *COS (1970) Rep.* 2: 123–128.

———— 1972b. Observations of the Eleonora's Falcon colony at Akrotiri cliffs. *COS (1970) Rep.* 2: 102–103.

———— 1972c. Discussion on the status of the Slender-billed Gull. *COS (1970) Rep.* 2: 106–107.

———— 1972d. An examination of the sub-species of Reed Warbler breeding in Cyprus. *COS (1970) Rep.* 2: 109–110.

———— 1972e. Observations of diurnal migration at Cape Andreas and Cape Kormakiti – 1971. *COS (1970) Rep.* 2: 114–120.

———— 1972f. A census of the known Eleonora's Falcon breeding colonies in Cyprus. *COS (1970) Rep.* 2: 120–123.

———— 1980. Survey of breeding distribution and habitat 1979. *COS (1957) Rep.* 27: 95–100.

FLINT, P. R. & COLE, L. R. 1973. Reviews of *A Check List of the Birds of Cyprus 1971* and *Handbook of the Birds of Cyprus and Migrants of the Middle East. COS (1970) Rep.* 3: 81–84.

FLINT, V. E., BOEHME, R. L., KOSTIN, Y. V., KUZNETSOV, A. A. 1989. *A Field Guide to Birds of the USSR.* Princeton University Press.

FOERS, R. 1979. *Greater Flamingoes in Cyprus.* Duplicated. Privately circulated. Subsequently published in *COS (1957) Rep.* 27: 101–114 and (as a revised 1984 version) in *COS (1970) Rep.* 10: 46–57.

———— 1980. A record of Cyprus Ringing Recoveries up to 1978. Duplicated. Privately circulated. Subsequently published in *COS (1970) Rep.* 9: 50–81.

———— 1983. *Falco eleonorae* at Akrotiri Cliffs, 1978 study and census. *COS (1970) Rep.* 9: 82–85.

FRANCE, W. J. 1979. Spectacled Warblers at Nicosia Airfield, March 1979. *COS (1957) Newsletter* 88: 7–11.

GASS, I. G. 1980. The Troodos massif: Its role in the unravelling of the ophiolite problem and its significance in the understanding of constructive plate margin processes. *Proc. Internat. Ophiolite Symp. Cyprus 1979*: 23–35. Cyprus Geological Survey Department, Nicosia.

GHABBOUR, S. I. 1976. The ecology and pest status of sparrows (*Passer*) in Egypt. *International studies of sparrows.* Vol. 9, 1: 17–29. Warsaw.

GOODMAN, S. M. & MEININGER, P. L. (Eds). 1989. *The Birds of Egypt.* Oxford University Press, New York.

GRANT, P. J. 1986. *Gulls: a guide to identification.* (2nd edition). Poyser, Calton.

GRANT, P. R. 1965. Plumage and the evolution of birds on islands. *Systematic Zool.* 14: 47–52.

GRIFFITHS, W. A. C. 1975. *A Bibliography of the Avifauna of the Arabian Peninsula, the Levant and Mesopotamia.* Army Bird-Watching Society.

GUILLEMARD, F. H. H. 1888. Ornithological notes of a tour in Cyprus in 1887. *Ibis* 1888: 94–124.

———— 1889. Cyprus and its birds in 1888. *Ibis* 1889: 206–219.

HAIFA NATURALISTS CLUB BULLETIN. 1945. List of birds seen in Cyprus 26 July–5 Aug 1945. *Bull.* 1: 1. Duplicated.

HALLCHURCH, T. T. 1980. Report on the Army Bird-Watching Society Expedition to Cyprus 9–30 October 1980 (and amendments 1 & 2). Duplicated. Privately circulated.

———— 1984. Ringing activities in Cyprus. *COS (1957) Rep.* 31: 63–66.

HAMILTON, W. & PARKIN, T. 1946. Notes on birds seen during a visit to Cyprus, 23 June to 5 July 1946. *Jerusalem Nat. Club Bull.* 32: 5–6.

HARRISON, J. M. 1945. Three new Races of *Fringilla coelebs* Linnaeus from the Mediterranean Region. *Bull. Brit. Orn. Cl.* 66: 4–7.

HARTERT, E. 1903–1923. *Die vögel der paläarktischen Fauna.* Berlin.

———— 1904. (Description of *Certhia brachydactyla dorotheae*.) *Bull. Brit. Orn. Cl.* 14: 50–51.

———— 1917. *Alectoris graeca cypriotes* subsp. nov. *Novit. Zool.* 24: 278.

HJORT, C., JANSSON, R. & PETTERSSON, J. *In press.* The Ottenby ringing expedition to Cyprus 1985. *COS (1970).*

HOLLOM, P. A. D. 1959. Review of *Birds of Cyprus*. *Ibis* 101: 257.

HOLMBOE, J. 1914. *Studies on the vegetation of Cyprus*. Bergens Museums Skrifter. Ny Raekke. Bind 1. No. 2. Bergen.

HOMEYER, E. F. von. 1884. Beschreibung eines neuen steinschmätzers *Saxicola cypriaca*, nov. sp. *Zeitschrift für die gesammte Orn.* 1: 397.

HORNER, K. O. & HUBBARD, J. P. 1982. An analysis of birds limed in spring at Paralimni, Cyprus. *COS (1970) Rep.* 7: 54–104.

HORSBRUGH, C. B. 1951. Vultures, eagles and hawks in Cyprus. *Birdland* 6: 347–351.

HORVÁTH, L. 1959. Observations on the Potamic and Pelagic migrations of birds along the Danube and in the Levant. *Acta Zool.* 353–367.

HOURSTON, I. M. 1974. The song of the Black Francolin. *RAF Orn. Soc. Journ.* 9: 1–2.

HOVEL, H. 1987. *Check-list of the Birds of Israel*. Society for the Protection of Nature in Israel.

HUBBARD, J. 1967a. Additional observations. *COS (1957) Rep.* 14: 38–39.

————— 1967b. Species caught by limesticking. *COS (1957) Rep.* 14: 40.

————— 1968. Bird liming in Cyprus. *COS (1957) Rep.* 15: 23–26.

HÜE, F. & ETCHÉCOPAR, R. D. 1970. *Les Oiseaux du Proche et du Moyen Orient*. Boubée & Cie, Paris.

HURRELL, A. G. 1951. Ravens using thermals. *Brit. Birds* 44: 88–89.

IAPICHINO, C. & MASSA, B. 1989. *The Birds of Sicily*. British Ornithologists' Union, Tring.

INSKIPP, T. 1979. Recent west Palearctic records of Citrine Wagtail. *Brit. Birds* 72: 44.

JEAL, P. E. C. 1970. Spectacled Warbler breeding in Cyprus. *Bird Study* 17: 338–340.

JENKINS, P. G. 1986a. Note on Akrotiri Salt Lake colony of Dead Sea Sparrow. *COS (1970) Rep.* 13: 56.

————— 1986b. Observations of Great Crested Grebe breeding at Akrotiri Salt Lake. *COS (1970) Rep.* 13: 56.

JOHNSON, A. R. 1990. Taking a closer look at the Flamingos on Cyprus in winter. Unpublished report.

JOURDAIN, F. C. R. 1910a. (Letter about errors by Bucknill.) *Ibis* 1910: 216–217.

————— 1910b. (Brief notes on Cyprus birds eggs.) *Bull. Brit. Orn. Cl.* 27: 27–28.

————— 1913. (Brief notes on Cyprus birds eggs.) *Bull. Brit. Orn. Cl.* 33: 41–42, 84.

————— 1929a. Diary of a visit to Cyprus in spring 1929. Deposited at the Alexander Library, Edward Grey Institute, Oxford.

————— 1929b. The breeding birds of Cyprus. *J. Orn.* 1929: 33–40.

————— 1929c. On a visit to Cyprus. *Bull. Brit. Ool. Ass.* 2: 131–133.

————— 1930. Chapter 'Birds' in *The Handbook of Cyprus* (9th (Jubilee) Issue): 302–325. London.

————— 1931. Natural History Notes. Deposited at the Alexander Library, Edward Grey Institute, Oxford.

KEPHALAS, A. 1979. *Birds of Paralimni Lake and Phrenaros 1975–1979*. Privately published.

————— 1989. *Birds of Eastern Cyprus*. Privately published.

KLEINER, A. 1939. The Jackdaws of the Palaearctic region, with descriptions of three new races. *Bull. Brit. Orn. Cl.* 60: 11–14.

KNOX, A. G. 1975. 'Crossbill taxonomy' in NETHERSOLE-THOMPSON, D. *Pine Crossbills*: 191–201. Poyser, Berkhamsted.

KOURTELLARIDES, L. 1990. The nest of the Bonelli's Eagle. *COS (1970) Rep.* 19: 80–86.

LACK, D. 1969. The numbers of bird species on islands. *Bird Study* 16: 193–209.

LEONTIADES, L. I. 1977. *Report on Wetlands and Marine Parks in Cyprus*. Duplicated. Nicosia.

LICHTENSTEIN. 1823. Verzeichneiss der Doubletten des Zoolog. Museum der Konigl. Universitat zu Berlin: 85.

LILFORD, LORD. 1889. A list of the birds of Cyprus. *Ibis* 1889: 305–350

LOBB, M. G. 1981. Dead Sea Sparrow *Passer moabiticus*: a new breeding species for Cyprus. *RAF Orn. Soc. Journ.* 12: 25–27.

————— 1983. Didric Cuckoo in Cyprus. *Bull. Brit. Orn. Cl.* 103: 111.

LYNES, H. & WITHERBY, H. F. 1912. Field notes on a collection of birds from the Mediterranean. *Ibis* 1912: 121–187.

MACARTHUR, R. H. & WILSON, E. O. 1967. *The Theory of Island Biogeography*. Princeton University Press.

MACHELL, E. A. & RIVERS, G. F. 1966. RAFOS Cyprus Expedition. *COS (1957) Bull.* 20: Appendix.

MADARÁSZ, J. von. 1901. Description of two probably new European birds (*Scops cypria* and *Parus aphrodite*). *Természetrajzi Füzetek* 22: 272.

———— 1902. Der cyprische Heher (*Garrulus glaszneri* n. sp.). *Orn. Monatsb.* 10: 163.

———— 1903. Zwei neue cyprische Vögel. 1. *Loxia guillemardi* n. sp. 2. *Cinclus olympicus* n. sp. *Orn. Monatsb.* 11: 5–6.

———— 1904a. Über eine wahrscheinlich neue Form der Nebelkrähe: *Corone pallescens*. *Orn. Monatsb.* 12: 28–29.

———— 1904b. Über die Vögel Cyperns. *Ann. Mus. Nat. Hungarici* II. 1904: 499–561.

MAGNIN, G. 1987. *An account of the illegal catching and shooting of birds in Cyprus in 1986*. Internat. Council Bird Pres., Cambridge.

MARITI, G. 1769. *Travels in the Island of Cyprus*. (English Translation by C. D. Cobham, 1909. Cambridge University Press.)

MASON, R. L. 1980. A bird census of the Troodos/Mount Olympus area in Cyprus, April 1975 to January 1976. *RAF Orn. Soc. Journ.* unnumbered: no pagination.

MASSA, B. & CATALISANO, A. 1986. Considerations on the species richness detected along an ecological succession of Cyprus. *COS (1957) Rep.* 33: 61–64.

McCLURE, H. E. 1974. Migration and Survival of the Birds of Asia. Bangkok.

McNEILE, J. H. 1948, 1952, 1954, 1955. Diaries of studies of breeding birds. Typed, now in Royal Scottish Museum .

MEAD, C. 1974. *Bird Ringing*. British Trust for Ornithology, Tring.

MEINERTZHAGEN, R. 1954. *Birds of Arabia*. Oliver & Boyd, Edinburgh & London.

METEOROLOGICAL SERVICE NICOSIA. 1980. The Climate of Cyprus. Duplicated.

MOREAU, R. E. 1953. Migration in the Mediterranean area. *Ibis* 95: 329–364.

———— 1961. Problems of Mediterranean–Saharan Migration. *Ibis* 103a: 373–427, 580–623.

———— 1972. *The Palaearctic–African Bird Migration Systems*. Academic Press, London.

MORRIS, H. M. 1946a. Winter birds summering in Cyprus. *Jerusalem Nat. Club Bull.* 31: 5.

———— 1946b. Notes on bird migration at Nicosia, Cyprus. *Mid. East Biol. Scheme Special Bull.* 8 (2).

———— 1954. Questionnaire completed for the Bannermans' *Birds of Cyprus*. Deposited at Brit. Mus. (Nat. Hist.).

MÜLLER, A. 1879. Zur Ornithologie der Insel Cypern. *J. Orn.* 27: 385–393.

MUMFORD, S. 1982. Eleonora's Falcon at Akrotiri 1982. *COS (1957) Rep.* 29: 64–66.

MURRAY, R. 1985. The breeding cycle of the Masked Shrike. *COS (1957) Newsletter* 85/10:6.

———— 1987a. Migrating Common Cranes over Episkopi. *COS (1957) Newsletter* 87/9: 4.

———— 1987b. Association with man by an immature Masked Shrike. *COS (1957) Rep.* 34: 78–79.

———— 1987c. Feeding behaviour of a Great Reed Warbler. *COS (1957) Rep.* 34: 79.

———— 1987d. A census of *Larus audouinii* on the Klidhes Islands. *COS (1957) Rep.* 34: 80–86.

NIKOLAUS, G. 1981. Palaearctic migrants new to the North Sudan. *Scopus* 5: 121–124.

OREEL, G. J. 1986. Caspian Plover in Cyprus. *Dutch Birding* 8: 26–28.

———— 1987. Probable African Night Heron in Cyprus. *Dutch Birding* 9: 16–17.

ORLANDO, C. 1939. *Corvus corax cyprius* subsp. nov. *Riv. Ital. Ornit.* 9: 237.

OSBORN, D. 1983. Report on bird trapping and hunting by Cypriots. *COS (1970) Rep.* 14: 58–60.

PARAN, Y. 1980. Some notes on waterbirds observed in Egypt and North Sinai – 1978/79. *Orn. Soc. Mid. East Bull.* 4: 2–5.

PARAN, Y. & PAZ, U. 1978. Autumn migration of waterbirds on the north coast of Sinai. *XVII Congr. Internat. Orn.* Berlin, (West) Germany. Poster Presentation.

PARRACK, J. D. 1973. *The Naturalist in Majorca*. David & Charles.

PAYN, W. A. 1939. Notes on the birds of Cyprus. *Ibis* 1939: 735–742.

PAZ, U. 1987. *The Birds of Israel*. Christopher Helm, London.

PERRINS, C. M. 1973. Reviews of *Handbook of the birds of Cyprus and migrants of the Middle East* and *A check list of the birds of Cyprus 1971*. *Ibis* 115: 142, 145.

PETERSON, R. T., MOUNTFORT, G. & HOLLOM, P. A. D. 1965 (2nd edition), 1974 (3rd edition). *A Field Guide to the Birds of Britain and Europe*. Collins, London.

POLUNIN, O. & HUXLEY, A. 1978. *Flowers of the Mediterranean*. Chatto & Windus, London.

PRATER, A. J., MARCHANT, J. H. & VUORINEN, J. 1977. *Guide to the identification and ageing of Holarctic Waders*. British Trust for Ornithology, Tring.

PUBLIC INFORMATION OFFICE. 1980. *Cyprus in Brief*. Nicosia.

RAYNER, G. W. 1982. The breeding of the Night Heron 1982. *COS (1957) Rep.* 29: 62–63.

———— 1988. More on the Armenian Gull. *COS (1957) Newsletter* 88/2: 5.

RICARD, M. 1969. *The Mystery of Animal Migration*. (English translation by P. J. Whitehead.) Constable, London.

RIDDELL, W. H. 1927. On some birds of Cyprus in the spring. *Cyprus Agric. Journ.* 22: 94–98, 129–134.

RIVERS, G. F. & WALKER, F. J. 1974. Raptor migration at Cape Andreas 4–16 April 1973. *COS (1970) Rep.* 4: 69–71.

RUDOLF, T. 1990. Breeding record of the Goshawk for Cyprus. *COS (1970) Rep.* 19: 77–79.

RUSSELL, A. 1794. *The Natural History of Aleppo*. Vol. 2: 194–195 and plate facing 195. London.

RYDZEWSKI, W. 1958. "Avian Mail". *Ring* 2: 85–86.

———— 1960. Recoveries of ringed birds – Mediterranean Islands. *Riv. Ital. Ornit.* 30: 1–77.

SCHRADER, G. 1891. Ornithologische Beobachtung-en auf meinen Sammelreisen. II. Cypern. *Ornithol. Jahrbuch.* 2: 215–223.

SCLATER, P. L. 1904. On the birds of Sibthorp's *Fauna Graeca*. *Ibis* 1904: 222–227.

SEARLE, D. L. & PANAYIOTOU, A. 1980. Structural implications in the evolution of the Troodos massif, Cyprus. *Proc. Internat. Ophiolite Symp. Cyprus 1979*: 50–60. Cyprus Geological Survey Department, Nicosia.

SIBTHORP, J. 1787. Manuscript journal of a visit to Cyprus. Published in parts by Walpole (1818 and 1820) and complete by Cobham (1908).

SLUYS, R. & VAN DEN BERG, M. 1982. On the specific status of the Cyprus Pied Wheatear. *Orn. Scand.* 13: 123–128.

SMITH, A. V. 1960. Report on the expedition to the Klidhes Islands. *COS (1957) Bull.* 8.

STAGG, A. J. 1967. Spring Migration through Cyprus. *COS (1957) Rep.* 14: 24–27.

———— 1968. First breeding record of Long-eared Owl. *COS (1957) Rep.* 15: 21.

———— 1973. RAFOS Expedition to Cyprus – Spring 1972. *RAF Orn. Soc. Journ.* 8: 5–15.

———— 1974. RAFOS Expedition to Cyprus – Spring 1973. *RAF Orn. Soc. Journ.* 9: 17–38.

STEWART, P. F. 1967. Autumn Migration 1967. *COS (1957) Rep.* 14: 28–29.

———— 1968a. Bird Ringing Report for 1968. *COS (1957) Rep.* 15: 26–36.

———— 1968b. Individual wing and weight measurements of various species ringed during 1968. *COS (1957) Rep.* 15: 37–53.

STEWART, P. F. & CHRISTENSEN, S. J. 1971. *A Check List of the Birds of Cyprus 1971*. P. F. Stewart, Plymouth.

STRESEMANN, E. 1953. On a collection of birds made in Cyprus in 1820. *Ibis* 95: 549–550.

SULTANA, J. & GAUCI, C. 1982. *A new Guide to the Birds of Malta*. The Ornithological Society, Malta.

SUMMERS-SMITH, J. D. 1985. Notes on Dead Sea Sparrow colonies in Cyprus. *COS (1957) Rep.* 32: 83.

SVENSSON, L. 1984. *Identification Guide to European Passerines* (3rd revised edition). Natur-historiska Riksmuseet, Stockholm.

SWEENEY, L. 1979. Notes on observation of Griffon Vulture nesting sites at Episkopi from December 1978 to October 1979. *COS (1957) Rep.* 26: 62–68.

THIEDE, W. 1987. The Herring Gull complex in the Eastern Mediterranean. *COS (1957) Newsletter* 87/11: 4.

THOMAS, R. E. 1957. The Birds of Cyprus. (Typed systematic list of observations). Copy in the Alexander Library, Edward Grey Institute, Oxford.

TOOK, J. M. E. 1971a. Breeding Records 1971. *COS (1957) Rep.* 18: 40–49.

———— 1971b. Sexual dimorphism in the Cyprus Pied Wheatear. *COS (1957) Rep.* 18: 50–51.

———— 1973. *Common Birds of Cyprus.* J. M. E. Took, Nicosia.

TOURLE, M. J. (Ed). 1986. RAFOS Expedition to Cyprus March–May 1982. *COS (1970) Rep.* 13: 52–89.

TRISTRAM, H. B. 1872. On a new Sylviad from Palestine. *Ibis* 1872: 296–297.

UNGER, F. & KOTSCHY, T. 1865. *Die insel Cypern.* Vienna.

UNWIN, A. H. 1925. *The Forests of Cyprus.* Government Printing Office, Nicosia.

VAUGHAN, R. 1961. *Falco eleonorae. Ibis* 103: 114–128.

VAURIE, C. 1959, 1965. *The Birds of the Palearctic Fauna.* 2 vols. Witherby, London.

VITTERY, A., PORTER, R. F. & SQUIRE, J. E. (Eds). 1971. *Checklist of the birds of Turkey.* Orn. Soc. Turkey.

VITTERY, A. & SQUIRE, J. E. (Eds). 1972. Systematic List. *Orn. Soc. Turkey Bird Rep.* 2: 1–184.

VOOUS, K. H. 1960. *Atlas of European Birds.* Nelson, London.

———— 1977. *List of Recent Holarctic Bird Species.* British Ornithologists' Union, London.

WALKER, F. J. 1963. Distribution of Cyprus and Sardinian Warblers in Cyprus. *COS (1957) Bull.* 13.

WALPOLE, R. 1818. *Memoirs relating to European and Asiatic Turkey.* London.

———— 1820. *Travels in various countries in the East.* London.

WALTER, H. & FOERS, R. 1980. *Falco Eleonorae* on Cyprus: Population size and breeding success. *RAF Orn. Soc. Journ.* unnumbered: no pagination.

WATERER, R. R. 1954. Questionnaire completed for the Bannermans' *Birds of Cyprus.* With additional notes. Retained by P. F. Stewart.

WILLIAMSON, K. 1955. Migrational drift and the Yellow Wagtail complex. *Brit. Birds* 48: 382–403.

———— 1967, 1968. *Identification for Ringers.* (Revised). 3 vols. British Trust for Ornithology, Tring.

WILLIAMSON, M. 1981. *Island Populations.* Oxford University Press.

WILSON, G. F. 1925a. Decline and fall of the Cyprus Francolin. *Cyprus Agric. Journ.* 20: 33–34.

———— 1925b. Remarkable bird migrants, 1924–25. *Cyprus Agric. Journ.* 20: 71–72.

———— 1925c. The Spring Migration, 1925, as observed from Famagusta. *Cyprus Agric. Journ.* 20: 105–107.

———— 1928. The shooting and bird season 1927–28. *Cyprus Agric. Journ.* 23: 64–65.

———— 1945. Notes on bird migration in Cyprus in 1945. *Mid. East Biol. Scheme Special Bull.* (unnumbered).

———— 1946a. A checklist of the birds of Cyprus. *Mid. East Biol. Scheme Special Bull.* 8.

———— 1946b. Birds peculiar to Cyprus. *Mid. East Biol. Scheme Special Bull.* 11.

———— 1946c. With a gun in Cyprus. *Mid. East Biol. Scheme Special Bull.* 12.

———— 1954. Questionnaire completed for the Bannermans' *Birds of Cyprus.* Retained by P. F. Stewart.

WILSON, M. 1979. Further range expansion by Citrine Wagtail. *Brit. Birds* 72: 42–43.

WITHERBY, H. F., JOURDAIN, F. C. R., TICEHURST, N. F. & TUCKER, B. W. 1938–41. *The Handbook of British Birds.* 5 vols. Witherby, London.

WOLDHEK, S. 1980. *Bird Killing in the Mediterranean.* European Committee for the Prevention of Mass Destruction of Migratory Birds, Zeist/Netherlands.

INDEX OF SCIENTIFIC NAMES

(Page numbers in **bold** refer to the Systematic List)

INDEX OF ENGLISH NAMES

(Page numbers in **bold** refer to the Systematic List)